TALES FROM A BROAD

AN UNRELIABLE MEMOIR

FRAN LEBOWITZ

BANTAM
SYDNEY • AUCKLAND • TORONTO • NEW YORK • LONDON

The author can be emailed at fran@flebowitz.com

TALES FROM A BROAD
A BANTAM BOOK

First published in Australia and New Zealand in 2004
by Bantam

National Library of Australia
Cataloguing-in-publication entry

Lebowitz, Fran, 1963–.
Tales from a broad.

ISBN 1 86325 424 2.

1. Lebowitz, Fran, 1963–. 2. Americans – Foreign countries.
3. Travelers – Singapore. I. Title.

920.72

Transworld Publishers,
a division of Random House Australia Pty Ltd
20 Alfred Street, Milsons Point, NSW 2061
http://www.randomhouse.com.au

Random House New Zealand Limited
18 Poland Road, Glenfield, Auckland

Transworld Publishers,
a division of The Random House Group Ltd
61–63 Uxbridge Road, London W5 5SA

Random House Inc
1745 Broadway, New York, New York 10036

Typeset by Midland Typesetters, Maryborough, Victoria
Printed and bound by Griffin Press, Netley, South Australia

10 9 8 7 6 5 4 3 2 1

For whatsisname . . .

Pseudonyms have been used and other details altered to protect the identity of people and organisations in the book. Many incidents and characters are purely fictional.

'Waiter, hey you there, please come.'
'My dear, but your glass still has some.'
'Ah, the top is quite bare,
filled with just air,
so I must summon someone.'

Dear Mrs Lebowitz,
Fran said that she was too depressed to cut and paste today. I thought I should bring this to your attention . . .

Dear Mr and Mrs Lebowitz,
While we try to make our camp food as nutritious as possible, we are not able to produce the data Fran has requested on fat grams per servings . . .

Dear Mr and Mrs Lebowitz,
We regret to inform you that Fran has been suspended from school for initiating a small riot in the auditorium . . .

H. D. Rosen, Psychiatrist
File 109
Lebowitz, Fran
'No, please, they were great . . . very supportive. My mom told all of us that we were special! Gorgeous! Brilliant! My brother pushed her away, "Yeah, yeah, yeah." My sister hunched down, got embarrassed, "I am not." Me? Well, I *believed* her. "I am? You think? Yeah, I *am*!" And then, and *then*, I found out. She lied. This whole time, Mom lied. Just the other day, I was in a store with someone prettier . . .'

The Lancaster Herald Tribune:
Fran Lebowitz, sophomore at Franklin and Marshall College, was arrested last night for shoplifting at the 7-Eleven on Oak Street. When police questioned her about the package of bacon she had under her shirt, she responded, 'I was born this way . . . weird, huh . . . bacon grafted to my skin . . . That? Oh, it's my lucky cheese . . . carry it with me everywhere . . .'

Dear Mom and Dad,
When this gets to you, I'll already be in Mexico. I want to experience the real world . . . I have been asphyxiated by my middle-class upbringing . . . I promise to finish school next year . . . I have everything I need: my sleeping bag, a few clothes, pen and paper, some money I've saved, and your credit card, just in case . . .

Dear Bonnie,
Can you believe? He asked me to marry him! FINALLY! I mean, the guy could have buried himself a piece of coal when we met; it'd be a diamond by now . . . Mom nixed the idea of a white leather wedding gown and a barn dance. So it's ice carvings and pasta stations . . . After all the guys I've brought home, Mom and Dad don't even mind that he's not Jewish. He can read! He's a lawyer! That's sort of like being a Jew, no?

Dear Bonnie,
I thought it'd be a little different . . . a soulful, peaceful sort of thing. But Sadie, she just cries all the time. And I'm still fat. Tell me it gets better after the first week!

From the diary of Fran Rittman:
. . . Just when I needed him most, my dad died. He dropped dead on the tennis court. Two days after he retired. I had a bunch of things I needed to go over with him. The funeral was packed. People sent in the most gorgeous, abundant trays of food I've ever seen. I couldn't stop ploughing through it all: bagels, lox, cream cheese and sable, corned beef, roast beef, chicken salad and *challah*, lasagnas, casseroles, rotisserie chickens. By the time we got to the service, I could barely button my sombre but sexy miniskirt. How can I think of food? Turns out I'm pregnant!

Dear Bonnie,
The kids are fine. We miss you. I'm a little mixed up right now. (Don't say, so what's new?) Just made the biggest fuck-up to date at work and the client fired me. The insurance company is after me about the car. There's snow everywhere. I had to shovel the walk with Huxley on my back. Of course, Frank's away again. When do I get to go away . . . and do I have to come with me? I'm working on a plan, though . . . stay tuned.

Rut Radar

We are all born with a rut radar. Mine is finely wired, a little oversensitive maybe. Perhaps just a bit hyperactive. Twenty steady boyfriends before turning 16, a new best friend 12 times a year, switched college majors every time I met someone who seemed exactly like the sort of person I really, *really* wanted to be. I'm not fickle. I'm just never *there* yet. Whenever the pond of my life becomes still, I slip into the calm I so desperately crave. I lie on the rich, green banks and feel the sun shining, hear the birds chirping; a butterfly is . . . well, it's bugging me. A niggling sensation creeps in. This is not the perfect location; it's a little too hot/cold/wet/ dry/quiet/noisy and what is that smell and why the hell am I sitting on the mud next to a big puddle anyway? Give me the rapids, baby! Give me Niagara . . . Oh my God, is that my reflection? Why didn't anyone tell me about my hair? Next thing you know, I'm stirring those waters until the froth is as thick and heady and deceptive as the top of a pint of Guinness.

If I could change the old metronome, inhale-exhale, inhale-exhale, I would. I'd breathe sort of spirally. I'd take the thump-thump, thump-thump and give it a new beat . . .

until the next minute when I would question, once again, what exactly it is that I want. For some, this sort of agitation would lead to industrious results, scholarly pursuits, inventions that save the world. I am gifted only in how far I'll stretch to scratch an itch I can never reach.

One time, I made it clear across the globe and missed the forest and the trees but tripped over a surprising lesson. You're not supposed to keep scratching. I'm better now. I can see my glass is half full . . . but, of course, I did order a double.

When Sadie was two and Huxley nearly one, I was due my next personal crisis. I can't risk skipping one of those. (I still take great pride in having been, some 20 years ago, the first on my block to get anorexic.) So, when my father died and my biggest client stabbed me in the back, the door swung wide open.

I began passing countless evenings out on my freezing cold deck in Westchester County, in my puffy coat and hat (picture Taliban goes Gortex), chain smoking – or would have been if it wasn't such a struggle lighting up with mittens on – and drinking wine. I wanted to be a better mother. I wanted to be a luckier literary agent. I didn't want to be either. I couldn't believe I was smoking again. Thank God I could smoke again.

It wouldn't be fair to say my husband, Frank, ignored me. He'd wave now and then through the window as he walked to the kitchen to get another beer (so that'd be six waves on a weeknight and 12 on a weekend, which is more friendly than some marriages). Then, one evening, who knows why – maybe because my mitten had caught fire – Frank stepped outside and saw that I had been crying. 'Are you sad?' he asked. He's sensitive like that.

'Well,' I sniffed.

I'd gone too far. He got defensive. 'What's wrong now?' he asked. 'What'd I do?'

'No, no . . .'

'What didn't I do?'

'Nothing. Nothing.'

'Oh, great. This again. I do nothing.'

'No, it's not you. Really. I'm just a mess. That's all. It's stress, everything's too hard. I never see the kids. I'm missing out on everything they do. I need to connect with them. I need something. I don't know what I want to be when I grow up. I'm not good at anything . . . I want to get away.' I cried and thought of more things I wanted, needed, hated, but left it at that.

'Hmmm,' he said.

'Hmmm,' I said. 'You asked.'

'Want a beer?' he said.

'Nah, got some wine already.'

'Okay, I'm going in now. It's fucking freezing out here.' He ruffled my hair and went to his study and began working on a small miracle.

Two weeks later, we are on a 22-hour flight, heading 10,000 miles away into a 12-hour time difference, with two small kids. We are heading to Frank's Singapore office on an extended business trip. We fly up the front of the plane. We give each kid a lot more than the recommended dose of cough syrup. I display it with a wink-wink, nod-nod to the other passengers so they'll know we have their comfort in mind. The meds have the desired effect on Huxley. In fact, they work so beautifully that any time we see his eyes flutter – probably just REMing but who wants to take chances – I scream, '*Dose him!*' We might as well club the poor kid.

Unfortunately, but predictably, the cough syrup has the opposite effect on Sadie. She never goes to sleep. She never stops talking, except when she is simply yelling. Hundreds, thousands of times a minute she barks out something like 'I want to go on that plane!' or 'I'm going to Thingapore!' She rattles the back of her seat, jumps in her chair, runs up and down the aisle, up and down the stairs, in and out of the bathroom, dragging the toilet paper with her. We try to settle her down but lack the wit to do anything more creative than scream at her, spank her, hiss at her, threaten her, and toss her to each other saying, 'Your turn!'

She drives us crazy. I don't know about the other 30 people who paid $10,000 to fly themselves in style and comfort. It's entirely possible that they are a little annoyed. I don't ask. I don't want to disturb them.

All told, with the drive to the airport and the two hours waiting around, by the time we land we have been at it for about 27 hours. The very thought of fighting people in the baggage claim, juggling the kids as backpacks slide down my shoulder, elbowing my way into the taxi line, figuring it all out . . . I'm sure I don't have enough kick left to manage it. Frank has a serene look on his face. He's always fairly mellow, but this is something more. This is intense satisfaction; this is the look of a man in his finest moment. He is just so danged proud to be introducing us to his mistress, The Far East.

Lo and behold, our luggage practically leaps into our arms just as we get to the belt. But, of course, we still need to slog through Immigration and Customs. Slog? Wrong! In fact, Immigration and Customs wave happily to us. They give us candy. They are embarrassed to ask questions and demur about seeing our passports until Frank insists that we all want the stamp.

This is the single best airport in the world, bar none. I smile at Frank and he knows what I am thinking: We've really landed.

He smiles back: Baby needed a break? Baby got one. Just wait till I show you around.

My eyes flash trouble: Where is Sadie?

His mouth droops: I don't know.

My brows arch: What do you mean, you don't know?

His chin dips menacingly: Why is this my fault?

My neck goes forward: So you think you did your bit, huh, delivering me here, saving my soul, and now you're off duty so our kids can get stolen in this place crawling with heathens.

His body lurches. He catches Sadie, who was enjoying a bit of treadmill exercise on the luggage conveyer.

'Cute, *lah*,' says an airport worker, patting her head.

My smile at Frank: What softies these people are. Nice.

His smile: That's just one thing I'm gonna show you, baby.

Mere seconds later, we are in a pristine taxi, having waited in a line that was quiet, orderly and odour-free. I can tell you now, the line was purposely placed inside the airport building. Had we been waiting outside, as you do in most other places in the world, folks would have likely turned quite caustic, aggressive and rather smelly. Because in the true environment – the *outside* of Singapore – a freckle feels like an extra layer, the wind is an oven blast in a sauna. Tempers, certainly mine, tend to flare extravagantly in half a second over who knows what, something like having to tie the kids' shoes.

The taxi driver takes us on a road called the ECP. The sun is just coming up and I can make out the sea on one side between massive mango trees with twisted branches and roots that creep in and out of the earth like sea dragons.

There are palm trees and colourful lilac bushes, paths along the shore and inviting huts scattered here and there. The median strip contains carefully cultivated fronds and flower patches. We are home in five minutes.

Sadie has lost none of her energy. Huxley is choking on a candy. We haul our heavy bags into the lift lobby of block five, Fortune Gardens. It isn't yet 7 am. My clothes are damp; sweat slithers down my neck. Frank's hair is dripping and a dark blue stain is growing on the back of his shirt. We go into our apartment. I only notice the saturating starkness, the endless beige-ness of it all. I guess I was expecting something closer to a Hyatt than a Holiday Inn.

I close my eyes and ardently wish I could offload the kids and take a two-day nap. That might bring colour to my world. I hear a plop on the floor. It is the sound my sweat makes when it finishes hanging around my jaw. My thoughts move to the impossible heat. Through the haze and the beige, I spy lizards scrambling up the wall. Hey, I think, somewhat deliriously, they add a nice swatch of green. I look at the kitchen – no oven, only a stovetop and for that there is only a wok. I'm hearing myself thinking, 'Yeah, the glass is half full, but I ordered a double.'

Frank is beside himself with bust-a-gut joy. 'Hey, look at this! Ever eat off a wok?' He grabs Sadie to show her. 'Look on the ceiling. That's a gecko, honey, isn't it cool?' He takes the kids out on the balcony. 'See this view! Incredible!'

I take a shower but turn shy when I see a lizard sharing it with me. I try to ignore the dirt on the windowsill, the slick, black scum all over the tiles and the brownish water that never turns hot. By the time I get out, the aircon has kicked in. I let it chill me, get dressed and wander over to the family. I am shaved and clean and human. I have on a fresh pair of undies, a starchy T-shirt and shorts. I go out on the balcony, from where I see the gentle, rippling expanse of pale blue sea, the ships sitting in the near distance, waiting for their next command. I see the swimming pools, the playgrounds, the plaza of useful shops, the putting green. I see four pristine tennis courts equipped for night play. I see my happy husband and lovely children.

The pool at Fortune Gardens is as big as a reservoir. It's kidney-shaped and the water splashes over a sunken edge. There are six lap lanes that will take you 50 metres in one direction and another 50 to get back. The landscaping is glorious, with palm trees, hyacinths, blooming flowerbeds and well-tended bushes. Along the shores are enough tables and chairs and chaises and umbrellas to render it undeniably resort living. The kiddy pool is a replica of the adult pool. Several barbecue pits dot the perimeter, stopping at a turtle and fishpond. You only need to walk up a few steps to get to Fattys, the restaurant that overlooks the pool.

The pool calls out to me. It is to be our baptism, path, religion.

'We must go swimming!' I cheer.

I even know exactly where to find the swimsuits. Towels? Sunscreen? Who cares! I rally together the family, suit up the kids, down we go and over we trot, jolly as can be at the thought of swimming in March.

Three guards in uniform, who were just a second ago sound asleep with thoughts of betel-nut juice in their heads, sit bolt upright. A fat lady in the booking office – it looks like a movie theatre ticket booth – calls through her little cut-out hole, 'Where *caahd*?'

Frank, who has travelled all over the world and has spent a great deal of time right here in Singapore, uses his over-the-top-as-if-talking-to-a-hearing-impaired-retarded-person voice: 'WEEE JUSTTT ARRIIIIIVED HEEEERE. THE OFFICE, YOURRRRR PEEEEEOPLE, ARRRRRRE NOTTT OPENNN YETTT.' He adds pantomime just in case.

The lady of a thousand chins says, 'Cannot, cannot go into pool, *lah*, without caaahddd.'

We leave unbaptised. We head to the office, which is now just opening. Apparently we need all sorts of verification of our names, our lease, our entitlement to be here, pictures of just a certain size, laminated cards bearing these pictures and basically our raison d'être to get access to the goddamned pool. Frank gets on the phone to the real estate agent to get a copy of our lease. He then calls his office, the embassy, the ministry of this and department of that and scurries about getting the documentation. I stay in this little prefab, monochrome, overly airconditioned office with the kids. They have their swimsuits on. They expect to be in that pool. We're being denied something inalienable.

'Um, excuse me,' I say politely but sharply, 'do you think we came all the way from America just to swim in your pool?'

They look down at what they are doing, which appears to me to be making a paperclip chain. They turn inward at my formidable tone.

I speak up again: 'Look, we've come a long, long way. Can't you let us in for now and we'll settle up with you on all this paperwork really soon?' They open drawers to find more clips to organise. Sadie starts jumping on the furniture and Huxley starts wailing in his stroller. I mix up some formula for him and am careful to make a perfectly sizeable mess of powder on the rug. I tell Sadie that her jumping is really coming along nicely. I eyeball the crew of paperclip handlers. They are not derailed from their task; they do not speak.

I ask Sadie if she'd like to go out and feed the koi fish . . . some of these cough drops I found in my pocket. Huxley is wailing for his milk. I tell him, 'Don't worry, honey, we'll be in that pool in a few hours. Until then, you just cry your little heart out.' These people must have been trained by, I don't know, G. Gordon Liddy, or maybe they aren't even people. They simply will not be moved to pity or anger or intolerance, or even a mild dose of discombobulation.

Finally, Frank sweeps through the doors, waving damp papers and jingling keys. He walks to the desk. One person looks up. 'But you don't have the caaaahd,' she says.

He says, 'THESE ARE THE MAHTEEERIAHLS YOU REQUIRE FOR THE CARD. CAN WE GET INTO THE POOL NOW, PLEASE? WEEE ARE SORRRRY FOR ASKING YOU TO BEND THE ROOOOLSS.'

The supervisor rests her clip art and makes a call. She hangs up the phone and tells us that we can go to the pool now. Frank hasn't even shown her the papers he is clutching. She has randomly determined that she will let us have what we want. Much like the Wizard of Oz – a good man but a terrible wizard – it has always been in her powers, but that is beside the point.

Monday, Monday

It is the first day that Frank has to leave us and go into work. The kids are still not settled into the time zone and, therefore, no one is. Huxley's doing a lot of screaming – *a lot of screaming*. Therefore, we all are, though some of us put it to words. I guess we're just a family sharing a wavelength.

I have to get the kids back into a nap routine. If I can't, I don't know how I'm going to get any work done. Emails from clients have already averaged about 30 a day. And, to make matters worse, there's construction going on above us. The jackhammering begins the minute we get in the door, stops long enough for us to think it's safe to sleep, and starts the minute a head – any head – touches a pillow. It stops at 9 pm and then you're left with the ghost sounds buzzing in your brain.

On Sunday, yes, Sunday-gawd-gonna-smite-you-if-you-work-day, they were still at it. I went upstairs, found the apartment that was being renovated and stormed in. They were on a break. Huh? I just heard them . . . Oh, I get it, they stopped because I left the house. It's like when you're a kid and the minute you leave your room all your stuffed animals start dancing.

The workers were sitting on the floor eating saucy rice

with pincer fingers when I burst through the doors scream-ing, 'Can you possibly stop?' They stared. I felt stupid. I mean, I guess the answer was 'Yes, madam, we can stop. In fact, we have. Why don't you go back down to wherever it is that you came from and let us enjoy our tasty lunch. Say, have yourself some, too.'

Now it is Monday. And I am Frank-less. And I am in Singapore. By 10 am I have the kids bathed and fed and in their respective containers. Huxley is velcroed in his bouncy seat with a bottle and Sadie is in a high chair. She's a little old to be in one, but she likes it . . . I tell myself. A large component of my particular type of parenting has been finding a harness for all occasions. There's the car seat, the high chair, the double stroller, the bike cart, the bike seat, the backpack, the umbrella stroller, the snuggly playpen, crib and walker, and a host of floaty things that do require some adult supervision – or so the label would have you believe.

We managed to bring just about all of it. God forbid I'd be in a place where I can't have Huxley and Sadie hooked to a table, strapped to my back, hemmed in with some soft toys, clamped down for a walk to the store, roped in so I can ride my bike and get the extra cardio from lugging 15 kilos of baby behind me, or just plain kept safe from disasters while I take a shower.

What we *didn't* bring was a crib, because the realtor said she had a spare. She did. It looked like a bundle of firewood. When we cut the twine, we were left with a jumble of giant toothpicks and tongue depressors that we were supposed to hitch up log-cabin style without the necessity of a single nail, nut or screw. Our befuddled, jet-lagged minds couldn't figure out how to assemble it. After a few days, we came to the conclusion that there once *were* nails, nuts and screws and it wasn't us being daft. I mean, Frank can put together – after a night out drinking – an Ikea Igor Super Deluxe entertainment unit without ever referring to the instructions, ie, two line drawings: (a) how it looks now and (b) how it'll look later. As if to say, 'We won't insult your intelligence by walking you through the other 8,000 steps.' Perhaps it's just the Swedes being Swedish and not wanting to clutter the clean, white page.

Anyway, we washed our hands of the whole thing and Huxley has been sleeping on the floor surrounded by sofa cushions. Today I'll find something more suitable for him, which will make us all happier at night.

The phone rings. It's Frank.

'Hey, how's it going over there?' he asks, in such a sexy, deep Frank voice I suddenly feel needy and adrift, homesick. I want him with me.

'Great!' I decide to say, instead of, 'The minute you marched out the door on your way to a busy, eventful day, I looked around the room and saw a lot of dried-up egg yolk and cried inside the vacuum you left behind.'

I even go so far as to add a casually placed mundanity: 'That jelly you got, it's weird. It won't spread. Can you ask Serene if I'm supposed to nuke it or something?' I'm not getting into the role that well yet but it seems like a normal thing to say, a sign of domesticity, an indication that I am embracing the slower pace, appreciating this time spent away from the pecking of clients, instead focusing on small miracles, like jelly.

'Okay, hang on.' I figure that his interest in this is just as bogus as mine and he's rehearsing his role, too. The manly man bestowing upon me the leisure to ponder something we otherwise would ignore because it is dull – that is, unless we could find a way to get into a big fight about it. In the old days, it would have gone like this:

ME: Why did you buy this disgusting jelly?

16

FRANK: Sadie thought it was pretty.

ME: It's crap. Did you read the nutrition label?

FRANK: What's nutrish . . . nutrush . . . What was that word again?

I take the cordless over to the window and look down at the pool.

'Fran,' Frank gets back on. 'Serene says it's candy, sort of an Asian gummy bear. It's like you were breaking open a Reese's to make a peanut butter sandwich.' We both fake-laugh.

'That explains the individual wrapping,' I say. 'So, how's it going there?'

'Fine. I'm just hanging out with Sebastian.'

I snort. Sebastian Gok was fired from the Singapore office. Finding his successor is the reason we're here. This couldn't be fun for Frank.

'Actually, it's fine. He's great. He and Sylvia want to go out to dinner with us tonight. Can you try to find a babysitter?'

'I'll try. I definitely want to go out without the kids. I'll turn over every stone. Um, that didn't come out right. I'll call you at four and let you know.' I want to go out, get dressed up. This event, though, could be something strange: dinner with the guy Frank needs to find a replacement for. His wife, I'm told, is quiet. Moreover, I've never liked the Gok.

I hang up the phone and continue gazing down at the pool. The water is clear, crisp, inviting, the palm trees flutter in the sultry breeze, beckoning. The sea beyond is calm as it meets the clear, cloudless sky. So why is 'Monday' stamped all over the scene? We'd had such a great four days wandering around. We went to the Tiger Beer Brewery, Raffles Hotel, the zoo. When Frank said goodbye in his starched dress shirt and buffed shoes this morning, I just wanted to grab his ankles and make him stay and play, give our day some shape. Now, as I look down at the pool, enticing as it is, I still have that punch-in-the-gut Monday mood: blues mixed with anxiety. What can I do in three months that will change my life, anyway? Why are we doing this? The answers are not coming. All I want is a little clarity and what do I get? Monday. Monday is Monday, even if it's still Sunday in New York. Couldn't I have just gone without me this one time? Couldn't I have woken up like a puppy, without a doubt that the world is a great place?

I see some people arrive and set up at the pool. They're an abundance of beautiful, shapely blonde women and about 12 gorgeous towheaded kids. The moms take off their cover-ups and step into the pool. Preternaturally languid, their supple, tanned bodies marinate in the shallowest end of the kiddy pool, shoulders touching shoulders, long legs slowly scissoring in the water, conversation obviously flowing from thought to word without need or use of a filter. Easy friendship in the hot sun of a foreign place where their good and loving husbands have brought them to be happy. I imagine the kids playing an ongoing game of chase every single day and the moms, of course, discussing who will bring the juice and who will bring the snacks for tomorrow.

I have never had this. I had to be careful around all my friends – they were either neurotic or clients. I was a working, nervous wreck of a mother. Plus, I had frizzy dark hair and would have had a moustache if not for living in this century. Yes, I want in! I do! Especially if it makes me look that good.

I gather up our mountain of pool toys, shave my legs, get into my most expensive bathing suit and even put on lipstick. I have a sudden inspiration to put my very expensive sunglasses on my head (I can't see out of them – too dark – but they look real good up on my head). And . . . oh, wait! Some pool shoes, the heels I got in Italy for $400. Shit, what to wear as a cover-up? I pull out the dress my mother-in-law bought me in Florida. Yessss, I'm in, baby! I got the part! I'm the new girl, the New Yorker. I'll come in a little brash, full of Yankee spirit. I'll lay on the accent and drop in a few words these Barbies never heard before. I can't wait to get to the part where I tell them my husband is a lawyer in the music industry and I'm a literary agent. 'Oh, of course you don't know what an agent is . . . I forget . . . it's really a New York–London thing.' They'll love me.

After putting on more make-up and some self-tanning fluid (I wish I'd read the instructions first. Wouldn't you know it? It doesn't start to kick in for an hour. So, I'll be changing hue before their very eyes. How to explain that? Metabolic rate?), I go into the living room to gather the kids and change them into their swimsuits.

There are streaks of brown sludge all over the white marble floor. It stinks in there. Huxley's feet are encased in the same shit. And, shit it is. Sadie, who I had taken out of the high chair, had been running around bottomless because we're in toilet training. Apparently we're not there yet. She's taken a dump on the floor. Huxley is joyfully riding his walker back and forth, zigging and zagging it all over the place. We have miles of poo trails leading us through the living room.

I fill the bathtub with water and plop the kids in. While they play, I scrub the floor and soil my cover-up from Florida. There's a nasty spray of crap on my left heel and my fingernails can't help but harbour a little line way down deep that will diligently send up a subtle, foul reminder of where my hands have been. I get a chopstick and try to clean it out but the chopstick's too fat. I get a knife and start bleeding. I try soaking and scrubbing, but still the doody won't come out. Fuck it. The kids are prunes now.

I get them into their swimsuits, spread on a heavy layer of sunscreen and put them into the double stroller. Toys slung over my back in a knapsack, another bag full of really useful mom stuff like snacks and wipes dangling from the handles of the stroller, we all clatter into the elevator.

I push the heavy stroller up the hill toward the pool. When I pass the plaza of life-support stores, a woman suddenly appears before me. She's about four-foot-nothing, bowlegged, broad-shouldered, sturdy and stocky as a fire hydrant. Even though she's no spring chicken, I can tell she could beat the hell out of anyone. If you hit her with your car, pity the car, is what I'm saying. She looks Chinese with a mix of Malay, and her hair has a big, wide stripe of grey in the middle.

She smiles a toothy grin. All her teeth are exactly the same size and shape, as if designed by a rushed cartoonist. She hands me her card. It's more like a cut-out piece of paper but it has the card-like factoids: 'I am Pearl. I specialise in expat services. I can clean. I can babysit. Here are some of the ways to reach me.' There are three phone numbers, two fax numbers, a pager number, website and email addresses, home address, where she can be reached in case of emergency, and, if all else fails, just wish real hard, she'll pop round.

'Pearl!' I exclaim. 'This is great. Is there any chance you're free tonight?'

'Tonight, *lah*, can can.' She nods rapidly. 'What time you need me for?'

'How about sevenish?'

'Can can. Until what time?'

'I don't know.'

'I charge double after midnight. You pay taxi fare. Okay wich you, *lah*?'

'Fine, fine, fine.'

'How many kid you have?'

'Two.'

'I charge $12 an hour.'

'Fine, fine.'

'I like to clean when kids go to bed.'

'That's terrific. Th–'

'Okay, then I charge $13 an hour. There's a one-time charge of $6 for booking me under 24 hours' time notice.'

That last one stops me in my tracks – we pay her extra because otherwise she wouldn't have been working that night? Oh well, I am happy, grateful. This doesn't feel like Monday any more!

'Just come at seven, please. Thanks.'

I have a heck of a time getting the double stroller down the stairs to the pool. The guard sits there watching me bump it down step by step, all the while disturbing the fine alignment of my babies' skeletal systems. I turn the corner toward the kiddy pool and it dawns on me that I should have brought drinks to share.

Never mind. Because when I look up, I see there is no one to share with. Turns out that I missed the party. Everyone is gone. The pool is bereft of companionship.

Note to self: they go in for lunch at one.

I stay and play with the kids, endlessly sampling their 'soup', telling them to add more horseflies or take out the dragon pus. At last, when they seem to really need it, I finally bestow upon them the mark of good taste, rub my stomach and loudly beg for more. Then they come back with more buckets of soup. They must think that the reason I am focusing on them so much all of a sudden is because I really like this game. How would they know it's because I don't have a phone call to take or make or wish for or worry about, or a fax to write or send or read? The weather stays perfect, the water is warm and we are getting nut-brown.

Around three, a group of Singaporean mothers and their kids arrive. They sit quietly, somewhat sullenly, around the edge of the baby pool while the moms organise themselves. A few of the kids seem too old for a baby pool but don't look like swimmers either. They are a bespectacled, goofy lot for the most part. Their conservative bathing suits – hiked up too high on the boys and tugged down too low on the girls – don't spruce them up any. They watch us play, confused and perhaps embarrassed at how loud and expressive we are.

All of a sudden, they come to life. They lift their legs out of the pool and run. I figure they heard chip bags opening. But they're laughing and pointing. Jumping up and down, covering their mouths, pinching their noses. What? What?

Then I see it. Several hardy turds floating at various depths in the pool.

I don't need to dust for fingerprints. It was one of my kids.

Mondays. Shitty, aren't they?

Getting Goked

The first time I met Sebastian Gok was in Manhattan at the Rainbow Room, just Frank, Sebastian and I. We ordered champagne and tiers of nibblies. We watched Sebastian eat with gusto and noisily slake his thirst. We were toasting the opening of the Singapore office, which Sebastian, a Singaporean, had been hired to head. His and Frank's futures were intertwined. The evening had the trappings of a spit-in-your-palms-pact-making-all-for-one-united-we-stand sort of mood, except it never got to those great heights.

For one thing, Sebastian was an unbecoming man – barrel-chested and overweight, cursed with a porous, waxy complexion and a self-inflicted frosty perm. Oh, why stop there . . . He also had small, dim eyes, three hairs to call a moustache, and his lips seemed to be trying to dissociate themselves from the rest of his face as they hung down low, gelatinously.

Want more? Well, Frank and I were distracted by the regular, slurpy, phlegmatic sounds he issued. I'm no doctor, but I diagnosed Tourette's syndrome.

The night was not a total disaster because we wouldn't let it be. We wanted to believe. Struggling with English,

Sebastian tried to explain the company's good fortune. I briefly wondered why he was struggling with his native language. Soon enough, I realised he'd have just as tough a time with Chinese or French or pig Latin because his tongue was too thick, his mouth was too stuffed and his lips continued to try to make their getaway.

He wiped his mouth, popped the last teriyaki stick in, and told us the Singapore office was a brilliant move. Raids and audits were so ripe, the pirating thieves were just going to fall at the company's feet. They would have to pay! In settlement. In court. Justice would be served. Commissions would mount. He and Frank would be legends. As he made these pronouncements, his chubby, busy hands worked like a sewing-machine bobbin, stuffing mushrooms, beer-battered shrimp, spring rolls, crab puffs, peanuts, olives, ice cubes, limes and all six teriyaki sticks into his gob. These were the hands holding our fate. Maybe he was okay. Maybe I was just cranky.

'Waiter, we'll have another bottle of this and we'll try the smoked salmon pâté now,' he said, suddenly quite intelligibly. *We'll* try the smoked salmon pâté? Think I might get something to eat over here this time? He continued his chatter. Frank and I smiled with some effort and *tried* to believe.

The Singapore branch had been Frank's brainchild, but Frank's boss, Ken D—, had claimed paternity, leaving Frank in the role of kindly uncle. Nevertheless, the success of the office would be reflected in his bonus. It was his job to find candidates for the role of office head, get it going, create mandates, and oversee the day-to-day operations. Sebastian was on the B-list. His history had a few gaps. But he was cheaper than the lot Frank recommended, and apparently that counted for more than talent and experience. Was everyone too polite to comment on his grossness, or did they have a bout of 'The Emperor's New Clothes' syndrome?

('What a persistent cold he has, poor fellow.' – 'Oh, he's just a little, um, ravenous after the flight, the dear.')

For the first year he was head of the Singapore office, Sebastian Gok – doesn't it sound like a genus name for some type of swamp creature? – was laying the foundations for a huge anti-piracy campaign. He said that he was placing his pieces carefully, playing the game with a shrewdness born from an intimate knowledge of the players and their cultural codes.

'When's it gonna come down, Sebastian?' Frank would ask eagerly.

'Give it time,' he'd say. 'We're working on something big.'

By the second year, Frank was placing late-night calls to Sebastian and telling him he needed to produce.

'You must be patient,' hissed the Gok. 'We need to move cautiously in this part of the world.' He added, rather ominously, 'You can't make enemies here.'

By the third year, Frank was sick of the bullshit and Sebastian's inertia. The only time Sebastian seemed to put any effort into his communication was when he was whining about his dental plan or vacation time, or wondering whether he could stay at the Regent and have his massage covered. Frank warned him again and again that the boss needed action.

I'd sometimes bring Frank a beer and sit with him during his weekly late-night phone calls to Singapore, my stomach turning to knots as I heard him say once again: 'Write up a report, Sebastian.'

He absolutely spelled out to Sebastian what needed to be done, put together the precise m.o. and faxed it off. He went to Singapore a few times and conducted the raids and audits himself, allowing Sebastian as much involvement as was necessary to give him some esteem. As God is my witness, Frank tried to save Sebastian's hide.

But each time Frank returned from Singapore, he was disheartened and deflated. Trying to rev up Sebastian was like using a defibrillator on a stuffed moose. There was no response. Frank discovered files full of unopened mail – stuff he had sent to Sebastian – and car catalogues full of Post-its. It seemed that poor Sebastian could not really expand his focus much beyond being fed. He didn't even bother any more to deliver his teahouse wisdom about patience being rewarded and greed being a man's downfall. His mind was too addled with expense-account dinners and greasy *mee goreng* breakfasts.

We had him over for dinner with some company brass once when he was in New York. Had I not known from previous experience that he was just as delighted with fish heads and chicken feet, I'd have been somewhat pleased with his appreciation of all my hard work in the kitchen. Had this not been something of a business dinner, we all might have joined him, tucking a napkin into our collars, rolling up our sleeves and slurping away (I'd leave out the sweating), but the more he ate, the less anyone else felt like it.

He paid no heed to verbal expression. When we convened for coffee and conversation, his eyes darted to the desserts on the table, his discourse limited to, 'Is that savoury or sweet?' and 'This is cinnamon on top? I like cinnamon.'

In the end, Sebastian signed his own death warrant when he allowed himself to be quoted in a trade magazine. There was never any so obvious a trespass with Ken. It was strictly against company policy. Frank and I were astounded that Sebastian had anything to say on a work-related subject, but he did. 'We're planning some really big raids this year,' said Sebastian Gok of the music industry.

All the stars were now aligned. Sebastian was to be kicked out and Frank needed to sort it out. And I just wanted out. That's how we got our three months – enough time to see a new director through, too much time to leave the family behind.

Sebastian was dismissed with a generous package designed to mitigate any suffering. Our comfort poured forth: 'Anything you need, let us know.' Gosh, but he seemed to take it in his stride. He held nothing against Frank. Indeed, in the first few days of our being in Singapore, he chauffeured Frank around in the company car to help us set up home. He knew that Frank was his friend, that Frank had stretched himself so thin trying to keep everyone's head above water, that Frank had nothing to do with the decision. Sebastian was likely quite relieved to be out of the treacherous waters, tired of doggy-paddling from lie to lie, glad to go back to being a Gok, beached and bloated.

To hear him talk, he was flush with cash and prospects. He once let me know that when they were growing up he and his brothers were called 'The Sensational Gok Boys'. Apparently by the entire country. Obviously, he came from a family of standing and wealth. That explained his laziness and gluttony. What remained a mystery was how anyone would, without great irony, refer to him as a Sensational Gok Boy. Maybe it was Gok-boy, like Ape-man or Bird-man, something part 'gok' and part boy.

Now that we're to get together in Singapore for dinner with Sebastian and his wife, I'm just slightly concerned about the awkwardness. Obviously, I can't stand him, but I *do* want to go out. And I guess I'm a little depraved, a little compelled to poke around the body.

I dress in something new I picked up this afternoon. I'd taken the kids to the mall to look for Huxley's sleeping arrangements and found myself trying on clothes instead. The neat thing about shopping in Singapore is that stuff finally fits me. I can pop in anywhere and it's as easy as buying rice. I'm small. You wouldn't know it to hear me.

So here I am in a shiny little black top like a tropical sort of motorcycle jacket with silver zippers. Under that, I wear a black Harley tank top from the States, new black satin shorts and big, big shoes.

Frank and I leave early so we can have cocktails before dinner. Sebastian is a man given to ordering the food and drinks at once. I want happy hour. We stop in a place called Club Europa, which is downstairs from International Seafood, the restaurant Sebastian has insisted we eat at. Europa has nothing to do with International Seafood, but the phenomenon here is that eating and drinking establishments are all together in clusters. In fact, Club Europa is a disco, restaurant and bar attached to Wine Mine, a Thai place. All are adjacent to Big Splash Water Park, which has snack bars, burger joints, food trolleys and a coffee shop. Connected to the whole conglomeration are three outdoor restaurants – Indonesian, Italian and Chinese. From the obvious inactivity in most of the places, I believe the proprietors overestimated how hungry people would be after going down a big slide. It was certainly a lot of dining for one lame theme park attraction.

We had passed this world of food a few times already on our way into the city and thought it looked old and tacky. It had been repainted swimming-pool blue so many times, it looked slimy. Chunks of plaster had dropped off here and there. When Sebastian had suggested it, I'd said, 'It looks kinda yukky, Sebastian.' He said it was great; we'd love it.

Happy hour at Club Europa is fun. The bartender has watched that Tom Cruise movie *Cocktail* a thousand times, and does all the tricks. It's cute and I feel bad about ordering beer and wine. He looks forlorn with nothing to shake.

I take my last swig and my last puff and jump off the stool to go meet Sebastian and his wife, Sylvia. They're already in the foyer. Sebastian has on slacks, he looks clean, seems less mucousy. Sylvia is in a short-sleeved sweater, respectable skirt and flat, chewed-up shoes. She looks downright dowdy, which makes me look positively vampish. We embrace one another. It's a moment, all right.

Surprise, surprise, the place is a knockout. Behind the tired façade is an innovative restaurant buzzing with life. Upon arrival, we're given a number and, after a short spell, introduced to our personal shopper, Ms Chow. We take a supermarket trolley and follow her. First, she leads us to tanks inhabited by fresh exotic fish. On the wall, pictures depict how they can be prepared. Sebastian takes control and orders. A flopping fish is tossed into our trolley. Ms Chow speaks into her headset and leads us to the next station, the shellfish corner. Sebastian points, gets tête-à-tête with Ms Chow, obviously relating to her the precise way he wants the shellfish prepared, and a new bundle is hurled into our trolley. A similar pantomime occurs at the meat station, noodle counter, bakery. Then we come to the vegies, which are laid out like you'd find in a supermarket. Sebastian grabs two large, green bunches of something that looks a bit like celery cleaved to a cabbage head, tosses them into the cart, whispers to Ms Chow and leads us to the wine. Here, he allows Frank and me to have our say. There is a sommelier roaming about and we motion to him. He describes several of his favourites and we settle on three bottles of wine.

Ms Chow takes the trolley, talks into her headset and leads us to a table outside, overlooking the sea. Within moments, we're presented with the white wine and something called Drunken Prawns. The wine is fine but the prawns are still alive and twitching about in a covered bowl. Sebastian says, 'Okay, let's eat.'

I say squeamishly, 'Not for me just now.' Sebastian and Sylvia start to laugh. Oh, it was a joke. Sebastian and Sylvia are having a joke on us. That's cute. The shrimp are going to be cooked and dead when we eat them, but the custom is to show how they were once alive. Sebastian nods to the waiter and he removes the shrimp. But when they come back, their heads are still on. Part two of the joke?

We drink our wine and talk about Singapore. I'm doing most of the talking, yammering away about how wonderful it is here. I'm going on and on and I can't stop because no one is letting me. Frank is swirling his wine, Sebastian is attacking the garlic bread, and Sylvia doesn't know how to have a conversation. I'm just autopiloting, until I empty my head of all I know. I move to plan B: ask a question.

'Sylvia,' I say, 'I hear your father had a few wives.'

I wish I had asked about the Sensational Gok Boys because her tale is so depressing, I want to shoot myself. Her parents are Chinese. Her mother was her father's third wife. He was a mere farmer and there wasn't enough to go around. Her mother only bore girls so her father was displeased and didn't have much to do with them. But recently, when he got sick, he contacted her. They had a reunion of sorts, which cost her and Sebastian lots of money. It was incumbent upon them to get only the best care for this great daddy. The other wives and offspring were apparently too poor or too selfish or too bitter to part with a dime for his health. She and Sebastian have had to cut off her eight-year-old daughter's piano, ballet and tennis lessons for a year. And we all know the really happy ending . . . now her husband is out of work.

Suddenly, I wish I could take back everything I'd said about how thrilled we are here. I'm the one with Tourette's – tactless remarks jump out at regular intervals. I wish I'd recognised more fully that we were taking over their lives. I wish I could've embraced, or even endured, her husband's disgusting demeanour. Luckily we are all knocked out of an uncomfortable silence as the food arrives. With great pomp and circumstance, two waitresses come over. Placing each dish down, they ceremoniously state its name as if introducing us to Prime Minister 'Chilli Prawn' and his cabinet member 'Red Bean Garuper'. Along comes another waiter and another and another and another. 'Butter Lobster.' 'Beef Kway Teow.' 'Orange Chicken.' 'Baby Kai Lan.' 'Cuttlefish.'

Sebastian and Sylvia bend their heads down low as if to recite a prayer. Frank and I respectfully follow, but no 'Glory be to God who delivers' is uttered. This is merely the starting position. As soon as the staff say 'Enjoy', Sebastian and Sylvia commence scooping and passing and grabbing and plopping. It was the Singapore version of 'ready, set, go'. Are we on a timer? Is it going to be taken away?

At first I don't think I'm hungry. I usually eat much later after a lot more wine but, gee, if I'm gonna get any, I better start. One bite makes me feel like I've been hungry all my life. The fish is light and flaky, subtle; the toasted red beans on top, sweet and crunchy like a mild nut; the lobster fleshy, firm, rich and buttery; the *kway teow* a salty, slippery blend of broad rice noodles, stir-fried vegetables and strips of thinly sliced tenderloin. Everything is magical. Thousands of tastes in each divine bite.

I steal a look at Frank. He's finishing his wine, smoothing out his napkin and just about to tuck into his food: one slice of garlic bread, a nugget of lobster and a noodle cradling a small snow pea. I look down at my feed-the-village portion. I'm like Pinocchio as he gave in to Pleasure Island and morphed into a donkey – except I'm turning Gok. There's no going back now. I resume shovelling.

I don't care. Let Frank be a prissy eater. He has pretty much always been that way. I think my family disgust him as much as Sebastian does me. If you ever saw or read *Goodbye, Columbus*, that's us. The Lebowitzes exercise for hours on end; we are robust, handsome and fit and we eat ungodly portions thinking it's totally normal. No one just orders one main course! Our frenetic, vigorous activity also annoys Frank, who is capable of sitting and contentedly reading, or sitting and just whistling, or sitting and rooting around in his wallet studying old receipts.

During the summer, before kids, Frank and I would visit my folks in Baltimore some weekends. Days were spent playing tennis, swimming, jogging, playing *more* tennis. Afterwards, my dad would take us all to our favourite crab joint. It was always packed and we'd invariably have to wait at the bar. We'd get drinks, of course, and a bucket of steamers (steamed mussels). Once seated, we'd order pitchers of beer, two pizzas, soft-shell-crab sandwiches, two dozen crabs, crab fluffs (deep-fried crabs stuffed with crab cakes), and how about throwing in a few extra packages of saltine crackers. My dad would demonstrate, with terrific fanfare and flourish, his skill at opening a crab and getting the most out of it. With just one whack of the hammer and a perfectly placed knife, he was able to crack that sucker in such a way that all the meat was exposed and ready to be sucked up. He was like a master diamond cutter. He'd wave a big hunk of claw meat in front of us all, demanding our appreciation of his surgery. That's how it is in Baltimore crab joints. Everyone wants to show off how much they can extract from a single blow of the mallet. Total strangers lean over each other sharing tips, eager for acknowledgement. Indeed, in Baltimore, eating steamed crabs is a sacred rite.

Frank never even tried it. He nibbled a club sandwich, drank beer and worked hard at not offending my father when he beamed and shouted, 'Would you look at this! All this meat here!'

Nothing changes old Frank. At this table in Singapore, laden with amazing and exotic foods, he sticks to the familiar and keeps it real simple. I, on the other hand, can't help myself. I'm reaching and plucking and passing and drinking and scarfing and happy, happy, happy.

When nothing is left of the feast but bones, we start talking again. My neck is stiff from peering down for so long. I look Sebastian in the eye, finally understanding him, wipe my mouth and say, 'That was the best meal I've ever had.'

Frank pours another glass of wine and pushes his plate out in front of him. The snow pea remains.

The bill is handed to Frank. I find that strange. The waiter should ask, or place it in the middle of the table. Sebastian doesn't look at it. I take a gander. Whoa, $1,400. I see a brief smile pass between Sebastian and Sylvia. Frank tosses his card onto the table and doesn't show a single sign of shock or dismay. I look at him with a dumbfounded expression, but he just stays steadfast and cool. That's Frank.

We've been had but I surmise that I'm to remain insouciant. So, when we rise from the table I hug the Goks and tell them that I'd love to see them again soon. Of course, of course, we all agree. What a nice evening we all had. They stay with us while we wait for a taxi, despite our insistence that they don't need to. As we're sliding into the cab, Sebastian says, 'By the way, Mr Liao and his lawyers have, um, invited me to lunch to share some of my experiences in the old job. I think they have some questions about the raid you are planning on his record company. I'll be wanting to keep the car, of course, and anything else you can think of that might make me not remember certain things.'

My stomach drops. I squeeze Frank's hand. If only Sebastian had found this sort of gumption when he was working for Frank. Now, Frank is getting blackmailed. Frank smiles and shakes his head. He closes the cab door and we go home to pay the babysitter.

Pearl is a Gem

Okay, I know it's only going to be three months but these are the three months that are supposed to change my life. I need some structure. Right now, I'm just sort of pacing, head full of steam, no good place to blow it off. Not having an itinerary to my day is like not changing my underwear. I feel pretty icky. Right, make a list. There are three things I need to do . . . well, maybe four or five: I need an exercise regime to get me upbeat, I need to get work done so I don't get fired, I need to be a good mom because . . . I haven't been and I need to be, I need to have fun because I want to be more cheerful, I need to open up the goddamned stack of books on things to do in Singapore and do some of them because I will have fun, dammit, and grow more cheerful from the experience. The end result, I just know, will be a serene but lighthearted completeness that will last for the rest of my life.

First, to gird me for the long, hot days of my friend-empty, plan-bereft, daycare-free, long vacation of sorts, I need to get on with some exercise. It's always been part of my life. I've known since I was 14 that if I don't do something vigorous, I am doomed to be full of unnamed dread and anxiety. Sure, sure, running can be a bitch and, yes, I know they make this stuff called Prozac now so I could stay clean and dry while also remaining relatively sane. But I happen to love a good run almost as much as sex. Like sex, there are often times I don't think I'm interested until I'm into it. Unlike sex, I do have to get out of bed and into the elements.

I hate leaving bed. Every morning at reveille I come up with excuses to my inner drill sergeant: 'Ummmm, you know how it is, Sarg, Frank needs a cuddle.'

'Tie up your shoes, soldier!'

'Frank, do something, dammit!' If Frank were to grab me and pull me back under the covers, I'd settle for a dishonourable discharge, but he is fast asleep, hugging a pillow. Frank loves sleeping so much, he even yawns in his sleep because he's dreaming about going to sleep.

Post-exercise, I'm singing, 'I am so glad I did that!' Of course, about five minutes later, something unfortunate will happen to me, because I have a black cloud for a pet. I might close the car door on the end of my raincoat and not be able to open it again because the keys have fallen into the lining in the very corner that is on the other side of the locked door. I might do it again the next week. This is a typical start to a normal day in Franland.

But it'd all be worse if I didn't run.

Exercise is the highest priority. I wouldn't leave my kids alone in the house to go out for a run . . . but I *would* strap them to my ankles and get a better workout. The only time I didn't exercise was during both pregnancies. My body made a good argument when it wouldn't fit into the shorts.

Now in Singapore, a full week has gone by and I haven't done anything about finding my exercise routine. It is beyond my ken, running in this heat. The air is so thick, the sun so broiling, the locals are guided by one survival code: *go to the mall*. This way they can enjoy someone else's air-conditioning and get their exercise by finding just the perfect place to eat. I can't blame them. If you lived in a steam room, would you want to go out and play?

The pool doesn't open until Frank leaves for work. I dismiss the idea of doing laps while the kids bob up and down in their floaty things. I mean, they'd invariably blow over into someone else's lane (unless I tethered them to the railing . . . nah, couldn't . . . could I?). They'd also get pretty fried and by the second minute of my workout they'd just be screaming and crying and taking turns at having to go to the bathroom.

I have to find a regular babysitter. I look everywhere for Pearl's card-shaped piece of paper and finally find it, a tight little laundered ball in my shorts pocket, the writing obliterated. I step out with the kids to get a newspaper and see if there are any leads. We sit on the steps to the shops. I buy Sadie a breakfast ice-cream cone that almost immediately collapses into a muddy river flowing between her thumb and forefinger. Huxley is happy with his cookie. Only, I didn't bring him a cookie. Either he stole it off a shelf in the store or it's been waiting for him in the folds of his stroller since America.

The problem with finding help in Singapore is that it's pretty much a live-in-maid-only world – expats, locals, people in public housing, even maids have maids. Because having a maid is as commonplace and cheap as owning a coffee maker, there just isn't much call for part-time work.

We go back home and I write up a notice. I shove it in my bag, gather up the kids again and go to stick it on the grocery store bulletin board.

A voice behind me says, 'I can, *lah*. Few hours a day. No problem.'

'Pearl, I was just thinking about you. I was just going to put up a –'

'No need, no need, *lah*. Can can.' She unwads a sheet of

paper. It looks like my notice. 'Few hours a day, *lah*, some evenings, *lah*. Where Jane and Michael?'

'Sadie and Huxley, actually,' I correct her. 'I have to tell you, though, you know I was taken aback when we came home the other night to find a stranger's kid on our sofa.'

'Don't worry. I don't charge extra. First playdate is free.'

'My kids don't have playdates at night, and anyway, they tend to have less fun with their friends while they sleep.'

'Next time, you pay dollar more.'

'Please, just don't bring other kids into the house.'

'Why you so like that? Okay, okay, Jane and Michael go to Anastasia's house.'

'Sadie and Huxley! No, you babysit my kids alone. That's it.' And, remembering some lesson from responsible parenting, I ask for references.

'Oh, I don't believe in references.'

What the heck, I don't mess with people's beliefs. 'You know, we're only here –'

'For three months' time,' she interrupts.

'Yeah. Can you –'

'Can can.'

'– start today?' I decide to finish the sentence even though she is already pushing the kids back to the apartment.

Once inside, I head to my bedroom, calling out behind me, 'If you're all okay, I'll just get into my bathing suit.' No response. The kids are glued to Pearl, watching as she pulls things out of her bag, amazed at what she can fit in such a modest compartment. When I leave, Pearl is giving the kids something yummy on a spoon.

At the pool, I find myself intensely moved – almost doubting reality – by the change in my circumstances. A week ago,

I was using my coat sleeve for a tissue and I didn't care. It was more absorbent than paper anyway. A week ago, I was stomping my feet while waiting for the train. I was standing on the corner of Fifth and 57th in the company of 900 other people waiting to cross at the lights. I was sizing up a large and determined group on the opposite side who wanted to switch turf. It didn't seem possible to accomplish this in the few seconds allowed, without stampeding each other to death. My team, the Heading Downtowners, looked ready and well trained, but I could see the Travelling Uptowners had some talent too, a few peddlers wheeling pretzel carts for instance. Damn, why didn't we think of that, guys? Those things'll just flatten you. All we had going for us were some suits, heavy briefcases and high heels. The walk sign came on and we were off . . . I survived to tell the tale, obviously.

I dip my toe into the water and watch the palm trees bristle dreamily, gracefully, in the barely there breeze. The few occupied chaises hold content, coconut-scented people reading books or magazines, sipping odd drinks, like Calypsos soda, Grass Jelly Tea, Pocara Sweat. No one is swimming. Not even a soul in the baby pool. I put on my goggles and slide in. The water has magically found some way to both refresh and soothe. I feel the sun pressing big, heavy hands on my back and shoulders, undoing knots, unleashing joy, turning me brown.

The last time I really had a power swim was at the municipal pool on 50th and First. The heater had been busted all day, but no one told me. I jumped in. It was frigid. I couldn't think straight. I was demented, and determined to get my workout in. I swam my 50 lengths, losing all feeling in my face, arms and legs. They didn't allow hair dryers at this place – but they did allow homeless people to bathe and wash out their belongings. It was pretty dismal, really. The showers, a line of rusty faucets along one green mossy wall, also served as a spacious drawing room for several sorry bag ladies who could often be found entertaining invisible guests. I generally got out of the pool, into warm clothing and took the bus to my apartment. But, this one fateful night, the bus didn't come, the temperature was below freezing, my hat was somewhere at home or left in last night's bar or on a subway, anywhere but with me. As I waited, my hair froze into a winter wonderland of dreadlocks. Hairsicles clinked against each other, lashing at my face and neck. Unable to have rational thoughts, I wound up walking 30 blocks home, fell in the door stiffly and said, 'Cccooolld. I had a sssspott of bad luck, Frank.' As I sipped my Baileys in coffee and Frank took a break from chastising me, I said, 'It'd be worse if I hadn't exercised.' We laughed.

Pulling arms, breathing harder, I kick and turn, shoulders crashing, breaking the silence, strengthening, toning, challenging my triceps, my pecs. My legs force me through the water as my hands grab an invisible rope, pulling me from one end of the pool to the other faster than I've ever swum before. And, once in rhythm, I figure out my response to a letter, write a pitch for a proposal and invent a recipe for chilli shrimp.

Man, that was an hour well spent. I hoist myself up next to a woman who is standing at the edge of the pool tucking her short curls into a swimming cap. She is smiling and talking to herself, as if she's offering herself encouragement. I nod non-committally and look for my towel and cover-up. I feel guilty about being away from the kids. The woman shouts enthusiastically, 'Hi Fran!' How do I know her? I don't know her.

She goes on, 'Ya looked good in there. Forty-seven seconds a lap.' She grins, showing nice white teeth and two deep dimples.

'Thanks. It felt good. Too bad I'm only here for a little while.'

'Well, three months for now . . . who knows later? Okay, gotta do it.' And with that, she jumps in, still smiling, and strokes away.

I find the kids flying kites on the lawn. Somehow I wind up paying for the kites, the sweets and the second hour, which we are all of one minute and 40 seconds into. Plus, I am asked for an advance against Pearl's services later that day (I have asked her to come back so I can get some work done).

But first we are going to meet the baby-pool crowd. I take the kids back to the apartment to change them into their swimsuits and we're back at the pool in no time flat. The group is larger than I'd seen before, not all blonde this time. Still not a single Asian. Perhaps they're at home teaching their kids something more useful.

There are even a few 'plain' women in attendance (a coarser sort, a cattier person, not me, might toss out the phrase 'butt ugly'). Hmmm, take a look at *this* one, would you? Now, she could be American . . . or maybe British. How in the world did her grandmother preserve that bathing suit so well? It's a little dress down to mid-thigh, green with small blue flowers, and she wears a matching hat and shoes. *Now* I'm thinking British. Very white. Looks like someone who'd enjoy cream teas and blue Stilton on digestives. I see two kids – a boy and girl about my kids' ages struggling toward the pool, shackled with arm floats and ankle floats, and each wearing an inflatable vest and an inner tube around their waist. What isn't covered with life-preserving garments is hidden beneath a plastering of sunscreen. I think you could even call it sun-repellent. I wait around to see who the mother is. Maybe she'll pull out blow-up hats or something. You know, in case everything else pops and the kids just start sputtering away. Yep, there she comes. She sticks little plugs of silly putty into each of their ears and goes over to sit in the shade with a book. Occasionally she looks up to say, 'Jason, don't splash' or 'Zooey, put them back in'. She has a sweet face, curls, freckles. American.

There are four other women – three golden blondes and a strawberry blonde, all of whom I've seen before. I throw Sadie and Huxley's toys into the middle of the pool, hoping to entice some of the other kids. No one is attracted to our garbage. The others have watering cans and super soakers, boats and swimmer Dans. We have margarine containers and shoe liners (I thought they'd float and Barbie could pretend she was on a raft). Undefeated, I cautiously inch closer to the crowd and lob a universal icebreaker: 'Where can you get a Diet Coke around here?' The general opinion is: 'I dunno' and 'Never thought about it'. Thick ice. But the lady with the book bolts up and offers, 'Prestons has them cold and Liberty has them warm. Either way, you'll need to go early on Friday.' I sidle over to her and tell her my stats: 'from New York, here for three months'. She lounges back, turns a page of her book and says, 'We all thought we were here for three months.' A moment or two later, she calls over to me, 'I'm Caroline. Do you want a Diet Coke?'

'Sure,' I answer.

'Okay.' She pulls out a little keep-cold bag and gives me her only can, then goes back to her book, after shouting, 'Jason, don't you dare run.'

Around 11, Jennifer, from Australia, a truly Olivia Newton-John fresh, minty beauty, pulls out a splendid array of homemade cookies and coffee cake. Yenna, from Sweden, with thick rings of blonde hair, high cheekbones and a gorgeous bustline, lays out a dozen cups and produces some tea. Tess, from South Africa, with silky, shimmering blonde hair and an impossibly flat stomach, pops open soft drinks. My compatriot has a Tupperware container of devilled eggs (no doubt a real crowd pleaser in the searing mid-morning

41

heat). I offer up Cheez-It crackers and no one objects or even notices. At noon, the kids are called out of the pool and the eating begins.

I don't feel quite invited and a few cheesy crackers that have flown from America probably don't amount to admission.

'Well, nice meeting you all.'

Nothing.

'We're off to do some sightseeing,' I say, walking away but still facing them.

'Have fun,' someone says and a few others giggle.

I add, 'Then I have to come back and *work*. Yeah, can you believe? I've kept my job. I'm a literary agent . . . Yeah . . . okay . . . well, see you tomorrow.'

I'm humiliated. I stop in the ladies room to change Sadie's and Huxley's diapers. When I look in the mirror, I see myself at 13 losing David Satosky to Paula Levin. I also see that my eyes have deep rims around them in the exact shape of my goggles – dreaded goggle eyes – and my forehead is beet-red. I look butt ugly.

But, it would have been worse if I hadn't exercised.

Bugging Out

While the kids and I were out conquering the world, making friends, sightseeing and absorbing the culture, Frank was ducking into doorways, talking into his shoephone and drawing down the cone of silence. Level-headed Frank was taking the whole Sebastiantrigue pretty hard. He was hurt and he was angry. No one was beyond suspicion now. He still had a job to do and a new director to hire on top of everything else. I didn't know where he was finding the time. He was making late-night calls to New York City and frantically bashing out follow-up emails. He was busy debugging his life – serious pest control. Nothing was straightforward any more; everything had an angle, no matter how bizarre. He rarely greeted me. I was afraid to say much to him. One conversation was aborted because, well, I *tend* to think it was one of God's creatures, but . . .

'Oh, you think that's a spider, do you, Fran? And I suppose that's a web, too? Haven't you heard of *fiber optics, Fran?*'

Then there was the time I was clumsy and careless when I asked, 'How are you?' I actually spoke before all the windows were shut and the television volume cranked up to 11.

'Frank, aren't you getting carried away?' I asked as he hacked at the butter and peeked under the bread . . . just in case.

'Are you fucking blind, Fran? You act like you don't want me to make a go of it here. You want me to fall on my face, is that it? You want four years of work to go down the fucking toilet? Why don't I just walk under a goddamned bus, Fran? You'd like that, huh? Get all that insurance money and find yourself a nice Jewish boy. Why don't you just go, go out that door, 'cause I don't want you, I don't want you any more. After all I've given . . .'

I banged out loudly, taking Sadie and Huxley with me. I took them off to the playground while they still had a few good years left. With a manic mother and paranoid father, I could see their shameful lives pass before me. First, they'd be picked last for all teams because no one had taught them how to catch: the roundness of a ball depressed Mom, and Dad thought the ball was out to git 'em. In a few years, they'd be making powerful little bombs in the basement – Mom loves big noises and Dad believes our zip code needs its own arsenal. Or, worse, they'd get into scouting.

Before long, I wasn't mad any more. More to the point, I found myself sort of wanting to hear the next riveting instalment. Last night, I learned that besides the car, Sebastian is now demanding a ton of cash and a letter of recommendation. He told Frank that he already had one lunch with the defendant's counsel, at which he only said they must wait. It sounds a lot like his stint at Frank's company: 'Be patient . . . I have the goods . . . *Feed me.*'

I should mention that owning a car in Singapore is as expensive as owning a house in Singapore. First, you have to purchase a document saying you have the right to own a car, and that costs about 150 per cent of the car's worth, then, the base price of the most modest set of wheels is about

$80,000. After ten years, you have to give it up because there is a no-clunker law. In fact, you could get a ticket here for driving a vehicle that has a couple of mud stains. What Sebastian was driving was worth $130,000 plus.

'Come on, Frank, call his bluff,' I whispered. 'I could use some wheels 'cause tomorrow we're going . . .'

Frank's eyes darted from side to side. He took up a pen and paper and wrote: *Shhh.*

I laughed.

He didn't.

He furiously scrawled: *He might tell them who we're targeting and blow the raid!*

'What a sexy business you're in, Frank. Raids, bugs – what's next?' I leaned closer and asked in a low voice. 'Fly swatters? Why not put a nibble of cheese out for him?

'I'll tell you why not,' Frank said, shoving me into the safe room, which happens to be in the stairwell, in another apartment building, 'but then, I'll have to kill you.'

I can make fun of Frank all day, for sure, but the truth is he finally has my attention. I mean, the whole time Frank and I have been together, we've talked about me. Certainly in all work-related discussions. Really, honestly, by and large, most of our other discussions have had a way of revolving around me too, but work-talk in particular has always been me, me, me. It was ever thus. I'm the more entertaining, engaging one, undeniably, and my job provides better stories. If I let him, Frank could be really boring.

I knew where he worked and his title, but any time he tried to tell me more, I'd wave my hands, like, 'Oh, I just couldn't . . .', as if I were being offered a second scone. 'Too full from all that stuff about Lexington Avenue and some cross street in midtown . . . A VP, did you say? Do you make good money?'

Now, all of a sudden, I'm listening. Frank is full of energy. The stress is revving him up, taking him a few crayons away from his place among the pointy-headed beige set. I believe he is starting to feel burnt-umberish.

There is also a tacit understanding that we are here because of me. I folded from the vicissitudes of life; I let everything get to me. I prayed for time to get in touch and slow down. To start breathlessly bemoaning the day's events on the job while wearing a wet bathing suit, arms and legs bronzed and shapely, would have really been like a picnic at the beach where you never actually get out of the car, like leaving the wrapper on the sofa, like seeing the glass as I tend to see it. A reason for Frank to say, for the bazillionth time, 'You are never happy.' At which point I usually start bawling and say, 'I am too!'

Plus, starting every tale of office drama with 'I just got an email . . .' quite lacks the same punch as the sort of stuff I used to bring home, eg 'You'll never guess who hung up on me today' or 'Fucking so and so just fired me' (at which point we'd open a bottle of something yummy we'd been saving and toast good riddance to bad rubbish, and *then* I'd start to bawl).

But, I'll tell you, listening, well, that's an art form. It's hard.

'I hate to interrupt,' I say one night when I am truly starving for the sound of my own voice.

'Sure, sure,' Frank responds magnanimously.

'Do you know that they don't have shakes at the McDonald's here?'

'No.'

Enough for me. 'Yeah,' I say, getting excited about the chance to spin a yarn. 'And when we ordered the Happy Meal, it was like a Monty Python sketch. I said to the lady at the register . . . and they aren't pimply high-school losers in the place, either, they're prim old ladies who have found a way to be useful in society . . . they *respect* this job. I think they were all recruited at some church function where Ronald

McDonald snuck in and waved a fry around. Now, they *believe*. They got McJesus in their hearts and grease in their souls. Anyway, I get to the register . . . and let me tell you, the way people around here line up . . . if your nose isn't touching the back of a head, you just aren't in line. Someone will come between that half inch and claim a space.'

Frank interjects, 'That's a very ingrained Chinese incentive: if you aren't first, you're last.' He says the motto in Chinese, *kiasu*.

'Whatever. And, when I get up there, they ask, "Meals for you?" Like, "Cripes, I don't know. I just found myself waiting in line with two small, starving kids because I wanted to get close to you. *Kiss me, you fool*. No? Okay, then I'll order something. I want a hamburger Happy Meal, a fish burger, fries and a toy. But instead of Coke, I want milk."

'Madame barks at me as if I need to learn my catechism. "Cheeseburger Happy Meals. No toy with fish. Large fries for one dollar more." Softening, she asks, "Super Guzzler today?" I say, "I don't want a cheeseburger, just a plain hamburger, and I'll buy the toy. Regular fries and I'll pay extra for the milk." She repeats: "Cheeseburger Happy Meal, no fish Happy Meal. McFlurry for you?" I repeat louder, "Why don't you just grab a hamburger instead of the cheeseburger and let me know what I owe you for an extra toy. Give me a side order of milk." The manager appears and they go into a conference. Meanwhile, the kids have pushed down on the straw dispenser enough times to splice together a hollow plastic bridge from here to Timbuktu. After a bit, she calls into the mike, "Cheeseburger without the cheese." She puts the fish, fries, drinks and toy on a tray – it was the exact same Ronald-McDonald-in-his-spaceship toy I had when I was a kid hooked on Happy Meals. "Where's the burger?" I asked. "Gone already." Frank, they didn't *have* hamburgers in stock after all that!' Hoo whee, I'm cracking myself up.

47

'Frank,' I look up. 'Frrraaannk,' I shout. He's slinking out of the room. 'I got more . . . Haw Par Villa, we went there, too.'

But he's somewhere else, morse-coding messages to the home office.

I spend another morning swimming, being the invisible lady at the baby pool, and the afternoon pushing the double stroller through another sightseeing mission. I wish the book had a page or ten that said 'Stay home'.

For today's sojourn, I pick the Crocodilarium, which has over 1,000 crocodiles and alligators from all over the world. Kids and crocs go together like peanut butter and jelly, no? Also, it's down East Coast Park, which is right across from Fortune Gardens. I can take Sadie and Huxley out in the stroller and make a day of it. We can play on the beach and get lunch at any number of places and ice-creams on the way back. If anyone has to go to the bathroom, there are several clean facilities available at regular clips.

The story of East Coast Park is that of much of Singapore's park and recreational growth: massive land reclamation. They are so good at it, so addicted to it, that Singapore has probably tripled its birth weight in the past 40 years. Reclamation is responsible for turning the East Coast into an 8.5-kilometre palm-fringed park along a sandy beach. Designated trails cater to cyclists who generally rent bikes at kiosks in the park. There are very few places to practise riding in Singapore and, as such, many locals are not especially good riders. Add to that the endearing tendency of many – blame it on the heat – to invite collision in any activity that offers promise. Just try getting out of a lift here if others are waiting to get in. I don't believe it's an act of aggression when you're walked into and pushed back into the lift. No, in fact, once over the sheer surprise that people were already in there – how'd it happen? Magic? – apologies come forth with embarrassing sincerity.

The cyclists, young and old, ride in curvy lines and stop in the middle of the path whenever the heck the urge hits them to do so, oblivious to the possibility that someone might be surging full speed behind them. Imagine you are driving down the highway and suddenly brake to a stop just because you feel like it. Bang. Boom. Crash.

My dad actually taught me and my brother and sister this lesson one day, though it wasn't the lesson he was intending. It happened on a summer vacation, the day he came through with the promise, 'I'm going to stop this damn car if . . .' The ifs varied from 'if you don't stop fighting' to 'if you don't stop singing' and a few times we were threatened with being stuck in an unmoving, cramped, smelling-like-orange-peel car instead of a *moving*, cramped, smelling-like-orange-peel car, because we were making fun of Dad.

This time, we were on a treacherous mountain path in Wyoming where you couldn't see what was ahead. We weren't fighting or being particularly bratty, but my sister – sweet-sweet Bonnie as we called her because she never did anything mean to anyone – had the gall to busy herself with hook-rugging instead of looking out the window at the view. We'd have been safe if she'd just proffered a line or two in response to Dad's poetic enthusiasm at the big tree. Unaware, happily involved, she continued working on the ladybug's shaggy wing. Dad screeched to a stop in the middle of the road, on a steep hill where my thumping heart told me a camper van was going to barrel into us. We couldn't believe Dad was risking our lives because Bonnie wanted to do a craft. He yanked her door open, ripped the hook rug out of sweet-sweet Bonnie's hands and hurled it over the side of the mountain. He started the car half a second before a pig truck flew into the rearview mirror. We weren't hit but the close call had us glued to the windows and thanking Dad repeatedly for showing us these awesome things. Bonnie especially found a million ways to say 'Wow'.

Aside from the bicycle paths, the park has large, open grassy spaces ideal for kite-flying, picnicking, frisbee, soccer; clumps of wild, dense bird sanctuaries with lily ponds fringed with pink frangipani, periwinkle and yellow allamanda; and an array of forests, some with evergreen and Binjai trees, others with palm varieties.

All is well for the first half hour, not that it isn't arduous. Manoeuvring a double stroller with two plump passengers – plus the must-have bag – along sidewalks hugging the equator takes its toll. When Sadie asks me for the fourth time to pick up an egg – which is really a young, green mango, rampant on the ground at this time of year – I get irritable and angry. I tell her they are all full of bugs. That shuts her up. She gets worried for Daddy. *Bugs. Safe room. Sebastian's out to git 'em.* I tell her I didn't mean that sort.

She unworries quickly when we turn into the California Dog for lunch. After that I ask the kids if they want to play on the beach. Of course they do. I buy sand toys at a stall and put them in their swimsuits. From the path, the beach looks groomed and inviting. Up close, I realise an AA meeting must have just broken up, cigarette butts and coffee cups everywhere. The next curve of beach is a little better, fewer cigarettes, more chip bags. I clear a nice little square for us and we make sand castles. We hunt for shells, have races along the beach and swim in the water. It's oily, tarry, carrying all manner of man's and ship's waste, but I don't let on, try not to think about it. The kids are having fun. Freighters, tankers and other vessels anchor so close to the shore, you can see the barnacles. It's the shipping industry that has made Singapore a wealthy nation. It is also what deprives it of a glorious beach. We'll take a 20-cent shower at one of the bathroom stations. For now, it's good. We're a mom and her kids being silly and carefree. I smile to myself. I can do this.

The Crocodilarium is farther away than I thought. The kids are getting uncomfortable in the heat and I am becoming drained. My arms are sore and complaining, spasming at times from the effort. I haven't brought enough water and everyone is parched. Sadie wants to go home and watch a video. I stop the stroller mid-path and berate her for not appreciating the scenery. I throw her egg collection overboard.

At last we get to the Crocodilarium. I read the sign: 'Due to new management, we have discontinued crocodile wrestling as the new management feels it is an abuse of animals.' The next paragraph says: 'Shop open from 10 to 4, crocodile shoes, wallets, purses all big discount. We take all credit cards.' Fighting? Not nice. Skinning? Okay.

There are three tour buses in the parking lot, their passengers milling around the shop. They fit the stereotype of the Japanese – short, skinny, good clothes, faces behind cameras. Do Japanese get two lives? One to photograph and one to watch? There is also a janitor-type in a sarong that seems to be made from a patchwork of teatowels. Tucked into this is a fresh, bright red Lacoste shirt. He pushes along a cart made of spare parts – bamboo for the handles, old signs for the bottoms and sides, bike tires – and he speaks on his cell phone. I wish the kids could appreciate the irony.

I pay $15 admission and buy two Yakult yogurt drinks for another five dollars. We stay ten minutes.

The crocs are in cesspools according to their type – the North American, the Asian, etc. To our eyes, they are separated by size and heaped together with nothing to do or look at. They seem in a stupor, flopped over one another with wide-open mouths, like the orgy is just winding down.

Even the kids feel repulsed. The promise of ice-cream and a video back home help cleanse the mind's palate.

I don't have the heart to tell them that tomorrow, we're going to the Bird Park.

I come home beat. My work is piling up and I have to attend to it instead of tuning in to the Frank show. But like clock-work, as soon as I hunker down and get myself all set up, he comes out onto the balcony with nothing of his own to do, watching as I attack my emails. He hovers around all hangdog, like I picked someone else for the prom, just because I continue to tap, tap, tap away. He takes my working at night as an affront and a rejection. Indeed, he is becoming dangerously hooked on attention. Resigned, I shut down the computer.

'Okay, talk. But I'm timing you. You only have three months. Then we go home and this has to stop.'

'What if we have more than three months?' he asks.

'What do you mean?'

'Nothing.'

'Why did you say that?'

'I don't know.'

'Well, it's a strange thing to say.'

'Stop grilling me. Get off my back.'

Okay, you are a witness or perhaps even a friend – exactly where in this exchange did I cross the line and start badg-ering? Was I not minding my own business when he came out and tossed over an odd little morsel worth sniffing?

Ordinarily I'd let myself feel the rage, I'd admire its colour, swirl it around, take a sniff, take a sip, let it linger on my tongue, swallow it slowly, and only then breathe fire. But now I am a muted dependant and I need a bunch of money to keep up with the tour book. So, instead of exploding, I get up and make him his favourite dinner: pretzels in a bowl. I should have known – been through it before, haven't I? In his peculiar little mind – not all the time, but some of the time – feeding Frank means I'm trying to 'control' him. I might as well bring him stuffed garbage cans, unpaid bills, wrinkled shirts, broken toys and a soiled wok. It all screams: Fran wants me to do something. It all triggers the same reaction: *I don't hafta if I don't wanna. She's not the boss of me!* He is convinced – some of the time – that anything I suggest smacks of puppeteering. Some of the time, when I suggest we play tennis, he's sure what I'm really saying is that I think he's fat and lazy.

'What about a movie?'

'Oh, right, drag Fatty off to the movies?'

'No, no, tell me what you want to do.'

'I don't have to tell you anything.'

'Well, I'm not doing a good job guessing.'

'Why do we have to do anything? You always have to do something.'

'I can't do nothing. It's impossible. Especially if I'm in the same room with someone who is also doing nothing!' Now I'm screaming.

'You're never, ever happy, Fran.'

Though these conversations are regular, they're random. They only happen some of the time. Months and months go by and I forget, because this man just finished dancing with all my girlfriends when no one else would. He stayed up all night fixing the printer. He organised my closet when it appeared that I had no intention of picking things up off the floor. When Frank is good he is very, very good. And when he is bad, it is a surprise all over again.

I have learned how to stop the fight before it starts *and* give us something to do: a blowjob. He never bothers interpreting fellatio. He never isn't a changed man afterwards.

I finish wiping my mouth with the back of my hand and slink toward his chest. I take a moment to look at him, kiss him, lay my head on his shoulder. His eyes are closed and he wears a light smile.

'Enjoy that?'

'Hmmm.'

'Me too.'

'Hmmm.'

'Frank?'

'Hmmm?'

'What did you mean when you said something about being here longer?'

Silence. Dread. I didn't wait long enough. I picked the wrong time. His eyes fly open. He turns his head to me. But instead of being irritated, he takes me in his arms and, full of sex, murmurs into my ear. 'Let's go out tonight. We'll play some tennis, get some dinner.' He kisses me on the top of my head, gives me a final squeeze and gets up to read the kids a story.

Pearl happens to be available and is, funnily enough standing at our elevator bank. She is expensive but the kids look forward to her visits, so I tell myself she is guilt-free. She brings dry, awful cookies and gummy candy shaped like American food – hot dogs, pizza, burgers. She also cooks them heaped helpings of 'Frat Rat' which, if we use proper diction, is fried rice. She understands that she can't bring in other wards but her husband, Bert, is okay. When she comes through the door, Sadie waddles over to her, takes the bag of sweets and tells Pearl she's her favourite person.

Tennis under lights is strange at first, a little too soft and unreal. But we get into it soon enough. We can hear the laughter and screams of children in the playgrounds nearby, see couples strolling along the path and joggers bounding by. After about 20 minutes, we're playing extremely well together, smashing the balls, making terrific shots, offering up 'Too good' when an impossible point is won. We are living, breathing fountains of salt water. Eight at night and the weather is relentless. I'm sloshing through puddles that come from me. We towel off every ten minutes, but still the racket slips in my hands. Places I had no idea held sweat glands – ankles, thumbs – are raining. After an hour, we rinse off, change and charge into the pool.

At night, the grounds are lit up by lanterns; submerged globes make the pool luminescent, the colour of blue ice. The moon appears with uninhibited visibility, a crisp, full circle, large and close, tucked into a thick, black, endless sky embroidered with stars. The stillness and calm, the homeostasis that slowly blankets us as families return home and kids quieten down, reminds me of something I keep shooing away: happiness, peace, excitement poised on the horizon ready to be experienced later when I can actually feel, for the first time in years, rested and rejuvenated. We cool down and swim, smooch and caress, splash and frolic and decide it's high time for a beer.

We trudge off to our locker rooms, shower and change. I'm beat. I just can't get up. The locker-room lady comes in and starts the whole deep-throat hocking cleansing ritual that so many people here seem to think is just so damned appropriate to do any time, anywhere. She motivates me to get out.

Frank has been waiting for me for quite some time. He's whistling the sixth song in the Beatles *White Album*. He whistles an album in the correct order.

'Sorry. Where to?' I ask.
'Let me show you Boat Quay.'

We get a table right on the riverbank. Postcard romantic. People stroll, look at menus offered from the village of restaurants and pubs. The weather has cooled off enough to make sitting outside peaceful and comfortable. It's a put-your-feet-up, the-day-is-over, take-stock night. A bumboat passes by, an ancient fisherman steering her quietly through the water, pensively. Heading where? How much has he seen of the world? What can you make doing that sort of thing? Ah, who cares. Where the fuck is the waitress, is what I want to know. I start flapping my arms. She comes over and we order a jug of Tiger and a vodka grapefruit.

'Grapefruit, is it?' asks the waitress.
'Yeah, grapefruit juice.'
'Uh, yeah, let me check for you.'
A while later, she returns.
'We don't have that juice.'
'Okay, I'll have cranberry.'
'Cranberry, is it?'
'Yeah, cranberry juice.'
'Okay, let me see.'
A while later she returns.
'We don't have cranberry.'
'I guess you didn't look at what else you have in the way of mixers on either of those trips –' I begin.
'I go check for you.'
'– *Because then we might actually get down to having a drink!*' I finish, shouting after her. People are staring. I can't help it, I'm getting hypoglycaemic because this idiot is standing between me and my cocktail.

'Let's go,' I say to Frank.

'We can't,' he says. 'My jug's here.' He sits back with extreme satisfaction. His jug, his Singapore, his new role as a world-famous spy chaser and copyright superhero, and his girl (in that order?).

The manager comes out and asks me if he can help. I glare at him, menacingly, challengingly, and tell him that if he can get me a large vodka tonic in ten seconds flat, then, yes, he can help me.

Once we – including *me* – are all settled in, Frank leans forward. I figure he's going to whisper something about you-know-who.

'Do you like Singapore?' he asks.

'Yeah, it's wonderful, isn't it? I'm really happy we came.' And because he's my husband, he knows it's true.

'Here's to three more years, then.' He raises his mug.

'You mean months,' I say, holding my glass (drained already) aloft.

'Years.' He stretches over, taps my tumbler and says, 'I hired the only man I can trust.' A beat. 'Me.' Clink.

He smiles.

Expat Like Me

My head is playing scenes from last night. It was filmed like the De Beers commercial – Ring silver bells, da da da da, calling away, for Christmas Day . . . da dada daaa da da da da da da . . . merry merry merry Christmas . . . merry merry merry Christmas . . . but targeted to the more diamond-chip-buying types.

Here we are popping the champagne at Boat Quay; here we are toasting each other with glasses the size of Huxley's head at the Marina Mandarin; here we are sucking on straws out of a ceramic alien skull at . . . at . . . some place where they have this sort of thing. Here's Frank on his cell phone. Huh? Here I am doing a mazurka on the table at Esmirada's, throwing dishes on the floor. Oh, look at us dancing . . . no, that's not us . . . okay, there we are . . . I'm on the bar and Frank is chatting up a 14-year-old China Girl. Wow, look at how I land like a cat from that bar . . . Oops, steady on those heels, kitty. There he is again on his cell phone . . . Ah, I remember this one, kissing naked on our balcony, knocking over a litre of Tiger Beer.

The first scene is at Boat Quay as Frank tells me the news about his job. He had negotiated an arrangement.

There is a scrap of trouble when 'had' sinks in. It is past tense.

'So, Ken *had* me make out a budget and I *recommended* . . .'

'Frank, you're talking past tense.'

'Huh? Yeah, so anyway, I *sent* a memo to the Board of Directors . . .'

Past tense. It means that I *had* better be delighted for Frank to *have had already* accepted the position he *had generously offered* himself while my back was turned.

'So you've sent it?' I double check.

'Yes, and it was approved.'

'Already, huh? What about checking with me?' I start in on a 'How dare you?' harangue but, frankly, even with all the good ammo in my bunker, my heart isn't into it like my head is. I am much too enchanted by the evening to let a colossal little shift of events ruin it. I vaguely remember praying for such a colossal shift. The drinks are good and they keep me busy, what with the stirring and the reordering and the cigarettes and the peanuts. Frank is looking awfully handsome here in the dark. And he's doing a manly job convincing me he knows me better than I know myself. It is high time I lightened my load. Let him carry the weight of the world. Hallelujah, praise be. Except this means I'll have to leave my job.

'Aw, that? You don't want it,' Frank responds.

'But I like it.'

'Oh, right? Nah, you don't. Take my word for it. You complain all the time. You could probably find a way to do a little here and there if you get bored. There's always work at the American Club or The American Women's Association.'

'Come to Singapore and hang out with Americans,' I answer dryly.

'I don't know, talk to some of your friends. What do they do?'

'I don't have any friends. Maybe I won't do anything,' I moan, but it doesn't seem to touch Frank's teflon of good cheer.

'Sure, sure, that'd be great. Can't imagine it, but I'd love it if you stayed home and took care of us. You can enjoy the kids, plan trips. Slow down for once.'

'Oh, back to you again, is it? What you'd love!' I turn up the burner. 'This is *your* thing. Not *my* thing. I don't want to do *some* thing. I had a *thing*. It was a *good* thing. I always had *lots* of *things*. I can find *new* things but . . . see . . . oh, what's my point, Frank? I lost the thread. Oh lookee here, my drink's empty. Can you order me something, *anything*, I got to go pee.'

Clearly, the sober moment, suitable for discussing and making life-changing decisions, has already passed. But that's never been the moment when we make them, only the moment when we regret them. I look at myself in the mirror of the ladies room and I like what I see. I like the shorts and tank top. I like my well-rested face. My hair is a little too responsive to the humidity, but it'll calm down. Mostly, I just feel alive and excited by life. This is a good thing, yeah? Right, back inside, let's party like it's . . . what is it, anyway? March? April? All the damn months are the same here, same sunrise, same sunset, same temperature. Damn, I look good!

After Boat Quay, we wander to Chinatown and into a kara-oke club. The place is pretty deserted except for one other couple and a man by himself. There are tiers of booths done in plush black leather, black marble floors and tables, dim lighting. We are given a great big bowl of party mix – dried peas, chilli crackers, palm-oil-glazed nuts, toasted broad beans – and a loose-leaf binder.

'Look, Frank,' I say, 'homework!' I take out my pen and

draw a heart on the front of the binder. 'Frank loves Poon Tang.' Ha ha ha.

'Fran, jeez, what are you doing? You don't write on other people's property, especially in Singapore. This is the songbook, see it's got about 12,000 tunes.'

'Well, you're a real model citizen now, aren't you, Mr Flank. You'd have laughed yester –'

All of a sudden, a lonely man a few levels behind us starts singing a song in Chinese. I don't know what the words are but pain is in the room. The tune alone would make anyone jump on his sword.

I wished he had a good song. I wished he had a style. But I had to see him and listen for a while. And there he was this fat guy, a strange look in his eye. Singing his song in a loud voice, full of whiskey and beer. Killing my straight face with his song, killing it softly with his . . . belting it out, sweat pouring down his sideburns, thin hair matting down, he croons out the final chorus with a Go-tell-it-on-the-mountain self-righteousness that absolutely sends me over the edge into hysterics.

'Tell her, baby! Sing them blues away . . . go tell it to the mountain . . .'

Frank yanks me up and out the door.

'You do not laugh at karaoke,' he says firmly.

'Aw, why you so like that. Why you never laugh no more?'

'Fran, they take it very seriously.'

'Now maybe someone knows he shouldn't,' I toss. 'Where to next?'

As we wander around, I see ornate red and gold little cabinets, like birdhouses, tucked here and there on a front porch or a vendor's countertop. On them joss sticks burn alongside oranges and little mounds of rice. Every now and then, I see piles of charred paper. These are all offerings for dead relatives. The paper is supposed to be money for the ghosts, and the rice and oranges are provided just in case the deceased would rather dine there.

We come to Duxton Hill, a curvy side street that stands out from the old neighbourhood, shouting, 'They took centuries off my life! I have been revitalised! It's a miracle!' The signage is doing its best to say, 'This ain't your uncle's old Chinatown.' We go into The Elvis Lounge first. There is a guy by himself at the bar and a couple behind us. The waitress gives us peanuts in the shell. A picture of Elvis hangs over the register and an Elvis lamp stands behind the whiskey bottles. We order from the bartender. Someone turns on a Chinese heartbreak song. A few minutes later, a girl approaches Frank and asks him if he needs anything else. He says he's okay for now.

'I could use another one of these,' I tell her loudly, pointing to my glass.

But her back is already to me and she's walking away.

Frank whispers, 'She's not a waitress.'

'Ohhh,' I say, all wide-eyed. My first encounter with a China Girl.

We go on to the next place, Bongo Surf Bar. There's a couple at the bar and a man by himself at the other end. The bartender smiles, happy to see us, and we order. We get a bowl of chilli crackers with our drinks. The room is painted brown and decorated with business cards and a poster of a koi fish. I yell over the music, which is a Chinese heartbreak song, 'See, it's a fish. That's where we get the surf theme, Frank.'

Next door is Brew Ha Ha. We go in and the bartender tells us about the wine promotion. We leave because they don't have any beer at Brew Ha Ha and we don't like the look of the toasted broad bean snack. The other three people in the pub seem to be enjoying themselves, though.

From Wild Pat's Party Pad to The Dixie Chicken Bar, it is as if this street was built the second before we got there. The 'boy are you gonna wish you weren't hurting so bad tomorrow after all the fun you had last night in crazy, wild Chinatown' pub names were likely picked out of a hat by the town fathers. The patrons are the same three people, out-of-work actors I presume, who just go round the back to the next bar and settle in before we get there.

That's the way things are done in Singapore. Come up with the slogan and then go out to lunch. Folks just don't notice or care that they are living in a façade. Take the national emblem, the Merlion, a half fish, half lion mythical mascot, for example. Merlions can be seen all over the place here, on T-shirts, paperweights, cookies, shiny new statues situated in key tourist spots. But buying a Merlion souvenir isn't like taking home an Empire State Building thermostat or a ceramic moo cow that squirts milk, or a hat with Mickey Mouse ears. The Merlion merchandise isn't a response to years of public enthusiasm. The Merlion didn't bubble up from history; it didn't prove itself over the decades to be a defining element of culture. The Singapore Tourist Promotions Board was given the mandate to come up with an icon whose unique and attractive design would become the nucleus of a successful souvenir industry. Basically, a 'Grandma went to Singapore and all I got was this Merlion'. The Merlion is nothing more than a concept, like a pet rock or a smiley face. Maybe there was a contest on the back of instant noodle packets: Draw something we can make into T-shirts and key chains, mould into cookies, make into chess-pieces, and the one who comes up with the best design gets a free buffet at the Goodwood Park Hotel. The Merlion is not unattractive, it's just missing any possible shred of real meaning.

Now the stores are left with quite an overstock of Merlion hats, socks, key chains, snow globes (who's the genius behind selling snow globes in a place that has never and will never see snow?) and cookies. There really should be a contest for the person who can offload all this crap.

The last place we go in this district is finally iconoclastic. We walk through an indoor waterfall, everything is blue, I am blue, Frank is blue, the drinks are blue. The place is called Reds (just kidding). Anyway, it's a gay bar. They tell us we'd be more comfortable in the back room.

'No, we wouldn't!' I bellow. 'We're from New York. I'm in publishing, for God's sake.'

Frank turns me to face him and says, 'It's against the law to be gay in Singapore. Give them a break, for Christ's sake.' He leads us out the door, but the night goes on and on.

At Mushafah Dan's, the owner says, 'Stop! Stop! No one has ever had three Mushies!'

'That may be true,' I declare, 'but tonight, I will make history!'

Perhaps, one day, I'll remember the rest of the evening, but for now, the little school marm in my biology is making me remember to pay. I have this condition called blepharitis. Not only is this an unsuitably named affliction for a sexy tart like me, but the symptoms insidiously undermine my perfection. Why couldn't I have something called panther, meaning I'm always so cool. I have *blepharitis*. It's when your eyes . . . oh, I'm so embarrassed to talk about it . . . but they get hideously sticky and incredibly painful. It feels like conjunctivitis only it hurts worse, lasts longer and you sometimes have to tell people to please focus on your lips and forget about the ooze-making machine under your brows. It comes out after bouts of bad diet and, okay Marm, bouts of drinking.

I simply cannot open my eyes. Apparently, while I stupidly thought all face parts were having fun, my eyes came up with a plan to punish me. They invented a blephar-itic adhesive so advanced, so insoluble, it is stronger than superglue. I am in misery.

The first time I got it, I was about six. (Obviously, it wasn't from too many cocktails.) I was naturally rather panicked. Until then, the worst experiences of my life had been coming second at Pammy Diener's dress-up party, missing the school bus and getting yelled at by my dad for crying when he yelled at me about something else in the first place. (Dad could yell logarithmically.)

I called out for my mom. 'Mom! Help! Help!' I waited for her to come charging into the room, as I knew she would, like the time I bit down on the thermometer, or when I got a nailfile stuck in my teeth or couldn't get Barbie's head off my thumb. She never even let a minute pass if the television picture went bad. But she sure was taking her time now. Maybe she was desensitised from all the times I cried, 'I fell in the toilet,' legs and arms pointing at the ceiling. Maybe she should have gotten me a special seat. Maybe she wasn't such a swell mom.

I knew that blind people had great ears and I'd have heard her galloping toward me even if she were across the road at Aunt Lois's, which she wasn't. And how did I know? Because I could *smell* her. I called out louder, more plaintively. Nothing. Blind and motherless, I turned to God, promising I would fess up to the hole in the wall I blamed on the house-keeper, I'd stop talking during Hebrew school (he'd like that one), I wouldn't throw my apple away at lunch, please, just let me see again.

Along with the supersonic hearing and genius nose, blind people are also more spiritual. Before – when I was whole – I only told God what I wanted and he silently took notes. Now, all of a sudden, he was handing out tests. Letting me know I was special. I thanked him and politely told him I would prefer to be especially pretty instead.

I needed help. It wasn't coming to me so I felt my way around the room, sliding my palms along the walls, bumping into furniture, loudly, slowly, painfully, making my way to the kitchen . . . seven paces from the bed to the door . . . nine paces from the door to the corner of the hallway . . . six steps down to the foyer. When the linoleum ended, I was there. I'd made it. And without a dog!

Mom had closed the kitchen door so she and Dad wouldn't wake us up. I bumped into it and heard Mom telling Dad that she was sorry she broke the egg yolk and would fry him up a new egg. Dad was still pissed off that the one he had been counting on, had already buttered his toast for, had tucked the paper napkin into his dress-shirt collar in anticipation of, was, in fact, not fit for human consumption.

'Just look at it, Eunice,' I heard him say. I imagined the microscopic droplet of yellow that was pale and chalky instead of incredibly, unexpurgatedly sunny. He scraped his chair back (a bloody cacophonous sound for me now that my other senses were making up for the one that died so young). 'Forget it. I'm not hungry,' he said through a mouthful of toast.

Dad read egg yolks like the *I Ching*. 'Puncture in upper quadrant: bad day for signing contracts . . . Heavy layer of albumen: best not to schedule important meetings . . .' It wasn't just eggs, sometimes it was the fat on a lamb chop, plain as day, forecasting this or that, or the temperature of the bread or the meaning lurking within a lemon slice, as opposed to the preferred wedge, with his Chivas.

He thundered out and encountered me.

'Hello baby doll,' he said as he kissed me on my forehead.

'Father? Father? Is that you?' I asked, placing my hands on his face to 'see' his expression.

'What the hell are you doing?' he asked.

Mom's slippered feet, her morning scent. 'Harvey, don't use that language. Frannie, what *are* you doing?'

'I can't open my eyes, Mommy.' I started to cry and then, a second later, I could open them and see through some spiderwebs. I felt the urge to rub and soon enough I had balls of gunk all over my cheeks and hands but my sight was restored. Either I was no longer special or I was forgiven.

Oh, to be six years old again. It's not that I remember loving being six, but I'm sure I didn't have hangovers. So far, I've only discussed the upper tenth of my body. But, down to my digits, the cellular me was protesting. My throat was parched, my stomach was angry and my feet throbbed out a warning of what they'd do if I ever wore those shoes again.

I'm sure we came home because that's Frank's shoulder I'm drooling on and these feel like my sheets. I'm sure we paid Pearl because she'd still be here ratcheting up the total if we hadn't. Frank enfolds me in his arms and pulls me close, settling in, safe and warm. He sighs.

'*Frank!*' I shove him.

'Whaa . . .'

'You have *got* to turn your head the other way or just stop breathing altogether,' I say.

We both get up; I follow the sounds of his bare feet. We wash, brush and gargle. My eyes are burning and still fastened shut.

We lurch back to the bed. Frank nuzzles again, a salve, a tonic, a shrine, a lily pad on a warm, gentle pond. I start to slip back into sleep and that can only mean one thing: yes siree, the kids are up and the demanding has begun. Not in a 'when you get a minute' kind of way, rather in a series of *now* sounds. Hoarse crying from Huxley's room. *Now!* The banging on our door of Sadie's small, determined fist. *Now!* Rattling crib wall. *Now!*

Frank doesn't move a single, solitary molecule in his body.

He's relaxed as a marshmallow. I'm blind and I'm angry. Furious that this is not an 'up for grabs' chore. This is *my* chore. Because *he* is working and soon I will not be. Because *he* is the *man*. Because that is what expat life is like. Because I better get used to it. I crawl out of bed but take the long way, over his body, traversing his midsection, my elbows and knees not missing a trick.

'Ow, oof, wha's that about?'

'Well, Frank, the knees were because, gee, you're still here and the elbows were because, hmmm, because I hate you.'

He whips the covers off and now we're racing out the door, a war on the horizon. See, he wants me to think that getting up was never a big deal to him, can't imagine why I continue to make such a hullabaloo over every little thing . . . *I mean, shoot, Fran, don't you love the kids? I know I do, can't wait to see their fresh morning faces* . . . Okay, that's what he wants everyone to think and most everyone falls for it. He's a master at turning the situation over onto its flip side and gaslighting me. I'm supposed to think I'm a nut, that I make all this up. I can hear my mother saying, 'Frannie, just go and apologise to Frank. He's a good man.' As if I would never interest anyone else and should thank my lucky stars. Maybe in your day, Ma, you had to break a few eggs but I know what's going on. He kept the job and I didn't.

We both grab at Sadie.

'Hello, sweetie!' she hears in stereo.

'How's my best girl?' says Frank in a 'can you possibly top that?' tone.

I'm afraid I can, Mister: 'Sadie, do you want me to make you waffles for breakfast?' Frank doesn't know we have them . . . hee hee.

'How about you come to work with me and we'll have breakfast at the coffee shop. Just me and you. A Daddy–Sadie day.' He smiles at me with his big blue eyes crinkling, brimming over with tears, for God's sake. Like Sadie's going to know how to handle *that*!

Disgusted, I run to Huxley's room.

'My, precious, mmmmmm, kiss kiss.' Oh, he is so stinky. I wish I'd won in the first round because now I have to change his diaper. But I can't really; I can hardly see. Though my eyelids have started to peel open, my vision is rather viscous and my eyes hurt so much I have to cry.

'Fran, it's okay, I'm not mad,' Frank says at Huxley's door, then walks to the changing table.

'Oh, imagine my fucking relief!' I shout.

'I was going to say, "But why are *you*?"' He punctuates it with a little pat of hurt.

'Fuck you,' I say, rubbing my eyes.

'Hey, I thought we had a great night, celebrating our success. I'll be making a shitload of money, we get to stay here and you get to quit working.'

'*Our* success? How is any of it *my* success? I get to quit working. That sounds a little like the opposite of success. And now that I'm not working, you're treating me like shit.'

'What? When?'

'Just now, when you left it up to me to get the kids.'

'Jeez, I always do that. I thought you wanted the kids to see you first.'

I did.

I do.

'You better tell me now if you don't want to take this gig,' he says.

When I first got here, it felt like a farm stay or something. I didn't think I'd wind up a farmer. Now, it turns out, I'm not just playing Expat Like Me. This isn't research. This isn't a break. I am no longer a literary agent. I am no longer a New Yorker. Say it after me. It's a classic case of 'be careful what you wish for'. I wanted an escape, but did I want a total rebirth? On the other hand, three more years of fun in the sun. But three years is a long time. Who's even going to recognise me? I'm looking more like tree bark every day with all this fun in the sun. Shut up, Fran. You are going to live abroad. Who gets this chance? Be an expat. Be a real mother, for God's sake. Do it well. Frank heard me wail and moan and beat myself up. He remembers what it was like. Maybe I've forgotten already. We wanted life to be simpler and easier and much less bumpy. Oh, my God, I will have fuck all to say to anyone after a month. Shut up, Fran. See, maybe even sooner.

Striking an accord, we (six sides of me, one husband and two children) sit at the breakfast table. Over my mug of coffee, I start to get myself really riled now, not because events have swept me away but because Frank hasn't even noticed my exaggerated wincing every minute and a half. Dabbing at my poor eyes, I see him gingerly push away his barely eaten wok-fried omelette.

'Why aren't you eating that?'

'I guess I'm not that hungry.'

'Is it bad?'

'No, it's great. I'm just full from last night.'

'We ate last night?'

'Actually, I have no idea.'

'Me neither. So eat your omelette.'

'Christ, Fran, I don't want it. Look. You didn't line up the edges when you flipped it. It's ruined.'

'So let me make you another one.'

'Forget it. It's not important!'

I don't want to cry. I say to myself I am happy, I *am* happy. Call me Happy. Happy is me. I'm H–A–P–P–Y, I'm H–A–P–P–Y. I make my way out onto the bedroom balcony where I have been drying out the clothes.

I open the sliding glass door and am hit by an intense

acrid smell. The sky and the sea are the same shade of dull grey; the ships have completely vanished. My eyes start to burn so badly, I almost fall over from the pain. They feel like they're getting pulled back into my head.

'Frank! I think there's a fire!'

'Yeah, in Indonesia,' he calls from the dining room.

Apparently Indonesia shares its smoke with us even though we don't do any of the forest-burning. As the haze hunkers down, the government tells you when it's safe to play outside by issuing a 'haze index'. The heavy air captures all of Singapore's stench: the mosquito spray, the fertilisers and the durian (a type of fruit that smells like Frank's feet would if he dipped them in cheese and then died for a few days).

I hope it's better down at the pool. I unclip a towel. I have to be careful or it might break. It's a giant saltine. That's what happens when you line dry. How am I supposed to fold this into the swim bag? I hear the doorbell ring. I unclip Sadie's stiff little bathing suit and once-fluffy robe. The bell rings again. 'I'm 'a'comin',' I say. I scuffle in carrying the weight of my oppression.

'I'll be gettin' that, Massur Frank. I knows how you aren't up to no good in the mornin'.'

'Hmmm?' Frank says, turning a page of the paper.

'Neva you mind.'

I look through the peephole.

'It's Pearl,' I stage whisper. 'Did we forget to pay her last night?'

'Well, I started out with $800.' Frank digs into his wallet and looks at the receipts. 'Two hundred at The Captain's Table for three vodka tonics, three beers, one bottle of wine, cash. We charged The Town Crier Karaoke and everything in Chinatown . . . Five hundred at Banana Leaf – three Singapore Slings, one beer, pappadums, samosas, potato roti,

71

chicken tikka, chicken murg, rice, fish curry, butter naan, cheese naan, vegetable jalfrezi, beef vindaloo . . .'

'Please tell me we packed it all up for starving Indians,' I say.

'. . . lamb masala, vegetable biryani, bottle of wine, jug of beer . . .'

'Okay, okay, so we gave her $100?'

'Ten dollars cash at Swensons for an ice-cream.'

There's a Swensons here?

'Fifteen dollars for the taxi.'

'Okay, so we gave her $75. Should be enough.'

'Thirty dollars at Our Place karaoke club.'

'Did I sing, Frank?'

'Oh yes, "Country Road, Take Me Home". Like you never have before. And then you sang "Cotton Fields Back Home" and bought a round of drinks for everyone. That was $300, which I charged.'

'This leaves nothing for Pearl.'

'I went to the bank machine while you were sleeping in the car.' He laughs.

'Okay, okay, so it's safe to answer then.' I open the door. 'Pearl! What brings you here?'

She steps inside, grins and waves at the kids. Sadie rushes over and hugs her knees.

She reaches into her bag and pulls out two lollies for the kids and a dark bottle with Chinese symbols on the label for me.

'Here. Use this.' She hands it to me. 'Spread this over your eyes and eat a ginger root. Eyes clear up. I found apartment for you.'

'But we have an apartment,' I say.

She waves me off. 'You pay too much, no hot water, bad view . . . The man in 14–56, his daughter get a divorce. He move near her now. His wife, she no good, *lah*, she get

72

cancer next year. I can lock in your rate for the next three years. No commission.' She flips out a new card: 'Pearl The Finder, specialising in short-term rentals, babysitting, cleaning, ironing.' The usual list of contact possibilities.

'No commission? Then what's this?' I say, pointing to the final line on her card: '10% Fee'.

'Finder fee, no commission.'

'It's even higher than a realtor's . . .'

'Can't trust a realtor, money on their mind all the time, *lah*.' She yanks the card out of my hand. 'Fifty dollars for the medicine.'

'Maybe we'll take a look at it another day.' I don't want her to be insulted.

'Gone already.' She walks out the door.

'Are you sure you're going to be all right?' Frank asks, standing by the elevator, dressed for work.

'Yeah, this stuff Pearl got me is working great. We'll just go to the pool and take it easy.'

'Okay, sweetie. Love you.'

I don't answer. I still don't know how I wound up jobless. Yes I do. I begged.

I go to my computer and write a difficult email to the office. I tell them that we have decided to stay in Singapore for three more years and while it seems best for the family, I will certainly miss the job and working with them.

I send it and we set off for the pool.

When I get there, I see Tilda retreating. Tilda's a British pixie with a mod haircut and intelligent, animated face. I've seen her gather a crowd and have them all laughing as she recounts some escapade or another. She points to the sign: 'Due to haze index, the pool is closed.'

'So now what are we supposed to do?' I say, rhetorically of course. But she thinks for a moment.

'Fancy coming round mine for a tea? Might as well get to know you since you're staying.'

'How'd you know?' I ask.

'Oh, when you've been here as long as I have, you know who got a great shag last night. Anyway, three months is always as good as three years. Plus, Pearl told me.' She laughs.

'I never told Pearl. I just found out yesterday.'

'Pearl Popiah knows when the wind's changing direction. She's already on to the family that just got here from Texas, so don't count on her for long. Never mind.' She screws up her nose at the haze and the stench, looks back at me and says, 'Forget tea, let's make up a batch of fog cutters.'

I like this Tilda.

After a few hours of cog futters and great conversation, watching our four kids playing happily, increasingly glad that the haze has given us an excuse to stay inside and get loopy, I leave to go make dinner.

I give Huxley his cream-pea dinner and Sadie her chicken nuggets and check my emails. There's one from my boss. She says they don't want me to quit. I've been doing fine from here. If my clients are happy, that's what matters. What amazing people I work for. I was sure the only reason I got the job in the first place was because my mom called my boss and told her I had cancer and to be nice to me, that she'd pay my wages. But after ten years and no sign of malignancy, I had to reckon that they were decent and I wasn't horrible.

I hear the door open.

'Helloo!' Frank booms.

I rush into the foyer. 'Frank, guess what? I can keep my job!'

'That's great.' He kisses me. 'Are you sure you want to?'

'Yes, definitely. Thinking I lost it proved it more. And this will be perfect. I can do it and be home with the kids and it's only three more years . . . not like forever . . .'

'Good for you.' He kisses me again. 'Hey, here's *my* news.' A two-pound *Straits Times* lands on my lap. I see a picture of Sebastian. The headline: 'Singaporean on trial for helping CD Pirates'.

'Frank, when did this happen?'

'Last night.'

'You were with me last night, you couldn't have . . .'

He raises his eyebrows and shrugs. 'You were having such a good time, Fran.'

I read the article . . .

Sebastian Gok, entrusted to enforce the copyright law . . . is accused of accepting bribes from pirates in return for warning them of impending raids. He is also alleged to have borrowed $10,000 from one of the illegal CD sellers . . . If convicted, he faces a fine of $100,000 and up to five years' jail . . .

No quotes from Frank.

'Holy shit, Frank.'

Dum da da dum. Dum da da dum. Merry, merry, merry Christmas . . .

Hey! Hey! We're Malaysian

With all that was happening in the office, Frank thought it best to shut down for a while, lay low, make the pirates, thieves and lawyers think he'd closed shop for good. I couldn't have agreed more – not that I understood what he was talking about. But I did understand that we'd have a few weeks to hang out and then go to the US to make the necessary arrangements for moving overseas for so long. When I called the owner of our apartment in Fortune Gardens to tell him we'd like to extend the lease, he sadly informed me that he had just rented it out to a family from Texas. Their agent seemed to know me, he said. 'At least she knew you were looking for a bigger apartment,' he said. 'Strange,' I said.

Frank suggested we take a trip, visit a neighbour. He'd heard about this fine little getaway in the highlands of Malaysia. It would be perfect for an outdoorsy experience. Quick flight, a road trip and sweaters at night.

So, off we go to take our first trek in the jungle . . . with kids.

First thing I notice, because we do have these kids along and they have certain predictable needs, is that there's absolutely no milk in the Malaysian highlands. I can't rough it without milk. Another thing I notice – I'm sorry to say – is that they pray too much. That just doesn't leave enough time for other stuff, like chores, education, driving lessons, farming, picking out drapes . . .

On our first day, after hours of tooling around in a rented 'car' (Fred Flintstone should be so lucky), we find what looks to be a well-lit, well-stocked, generic sort of mini-mart. So, in we go, as a family, because, indeed, this is our first family vacation on this part of the planet and we want to do everything together, as a family. The first aisle is filled with several hundred different kinds of potato chips. The kids go wild. We smile and let them fill up a basket with enough flavours to simulate a well-balanced meal – vegie-flavoured, chicken-flavoured, roast-beef-flavoured and mutton-satay-flavoured.

The next aisle has more snacks, but apparently someone finally lost steam on what else could be done to the potato. They started on something called tapioca crisps and a crunchy extrusion sort of thing made from dahl flour. The packaging is a little more homemade-looking, some stapled shut at odd angles, some just taped closed. The next aisle has peanuts and dried noodle soup, and the last one has car supplies and candy. There are beer and smokes at the checkout.

For lunch, Frank has the beer, I have the cigarettes, and Sadie and Huxley rip through some bags of chips.

The women, all in proper, serious Muslim dress, just can't get enough of Sadie and Huxley. Every time we're spotted, we feel like the Beatles coming to America. They do this running ululation and kiss and pull and hug them. My kids are freaked; if the ladies' noses weren't covered, I'm sure Huxley would bite one.

We get ourselves into the car despite the throng and start the longest, windiest ride on earth. The roads become more and more narrow, the tarmac turns to rubble, which then disappears entirely until we're driving on grass and dirt. Every turn is just a matter of luck, or out of luck, because if another car were to come by, it'd be us or them over the side of the mountain. Huxley pukes. It isn't just the wild ride; it's also my fault. I never did learn that not all cries are for food and I kept stuffing him with more and more. We have to drive a while before finding room to pull over and clean up.

Oh, we are so happy when we see the lush, green fields and rolling mountains of Frasier's Hill come into view. It looks just like the picture in the brochure. There's what appears to be a tidy, quaint village, an extremely inviting-looking pub, a horse stable and, perched up on a small, sunny mound, an outdoor restaurant.

Then we get a little closer.

I can't take away the fact that it *is* hilly and it *is* green and the weather does feel finer than Singapore's. Other than that, the village is mostly defunct – broken windows, empty stores, trash flying, flies flying, mosquitoes munching on my children. The pub – hallelujah – is *not* closed and from the outside it does still look inviting and old and cosy. Walking in, it's a different story. You can't get all that comfy without, I dunno, chairs? Never mind, we say, let's check out the restaurant we saw up on the hill. It's called The Satay Shack. There are swarms of things darting through the air and landing on mounds of dirty dishes, but we are determined not to get totally pissy, for the sake of the children and for the fact that this is a family vacation. Frank goes up to the service counter and says, 'Some satays, please.'

'We don't sell satays.'

Course you don't at The Satay Shack!

Back to the pub. The proprietor couldn't be more delighted to see us return. He brings out a few folding chairs and tells us about his brother in America. Do we know him?

We get some cold drinks and look at the menu. There are about four things on it. None of them will ever make it past the kids' lips but I don't want to disappoint the owner who, in his way, takes pride in his establishment. It dawns on me that Frasier's Hill has seen better times and is simply tired and poor and ignored. I am still going to murder the person who had the nerve to recommend it as a vacation spot.

Our *nasi lemak* and samosas come with a hot dog frankfurt on the side. The kids are in luck after all. Frank and I, on the other hand, are not so lucky. We are cursed with the problem of how not to insult the owner and still not eat. Whatever is slipping around on our plates, it is absurd to call it food. It's fatty, oily, greasy, smelly and ugly, and I think even hairy, too. We cover the plates with a napkin. Then, a butterfly truly the size of an ample rear end comes through the window and alights on our table. I knew the area was world-renowned for its butterflies but I agreed to come anyway. In other words, I pretty much couldn't give a shit about colourful moths. They are bugs to me. Still, this one is cool because it is so big. Obscenely so, actually.

Off we canter back to the car to find the house we rented. The directions Frank received from the travel agent don't seem to work. I ask some tourists with butterfly nets for help and that doesn't work. (But Frank and I do feel so much better about everything after we laugh at them. 'Just shoot me if I ever look like that,' we say.) Then a helpful old codger motions for us to follow him and for some reason, we don't take a moment to think 'Why not?' He leads us up and up and round and round to a gigantic flat house surrounded by a big iron fence. He climbs under the gate – a bit peculiar, that. He motions for us to wait and then disappears around the back. At last the gate opens and we go in. The remains of a recent party – smouldering butts, chip crumbs, dirty cups – decorate the living room. We are dumbfounded, but move through the hall to the bedrooms to put down our bags. The first one is occupied, or at least the lump in the bed seems pretty organic. We're nudged along to another door leading to an unoccupied room. The old man nods his head.

I didn't know it was coming, but rage takes over and I start screaming at everyone. I am incredibly fed up with my intrepid husband who 'planned' this trip apparently during that one moment when he became an idiot. This is a backwards garbage dump of a place, not just the house, the past 50 million miles. Plus, I still have the smell of vomit in my olfactory memory. I wave my hand under the old man's nose. 'See?' To top it off, I saw a butterfly that was too big to be pretty. I'm pinching my wrist in an effort to shut up, cap it there. *You've said enough. Stop, stop. You are ruining the vacation and scaring the kids.* That just isn't reason enough to actually calm down. But when the man laughs his veiny little bald head off, I stop and laugh, too. It turns out he thought we needed a place to sleep; he thought he was rescuing us. He doesn't know where the hell 6 Orchid Lane is. This is 2 Crescent Close. He is obliging enough to direct us back to the centre of town.

'We're so stupid. Why don't we just call the house and tell them to come get us?' I say. Why in the world didn't we think of this sooner?

Well, according to a shrinking Frank, the place we are to stay with two small children in a foreign and strange land *has no phone*. I better pray a few times in the right direction that our cell phones work up here if we need them.

I huff away and light a cigarette. I see a police station. '*Frank!*' I shout. 'They'll know how to get there.'

Frank gets all shy about this because it hits two large nerves: one, that he's asking for directions and two, it's the *police* (oooohhh, like they're aware of Frank's high-school drug use). I march in. I take pen in hand and ask them to draw me a map. I ask for street names and landmarks and I repeat the directions to them eight times. I motion for us all to get back into the car. I let Frank drive so he can feel a little less castrated.

About five minutes later, there we are at 6 Orchid Lane. The bungalow is large and situated on a little, cultivated plateau overlooking the valley with a grand view of the mountains. The garden is brilliantly in bloom, full of exotic flowers. Unfortunately, the smell of rotting garbage robs the setting of its glory.

Our caretaker, 'T', and his family live behind our bungalow in a home of equal size and dimension, only theirs looks newer. I'm sure they switched accommodations on us. In ours, each bathroom is worse than the last. The first has a toilet and rusty tin shower. The second has a toilet and sink and the third just has a squatter. The bed sheets are made of Kleenex and, instead of a kitchen, T has brought in a bucket with a few ice cubes. I can hear his kids laughing at a show on their cable television. We don't have a radio. But the place is roomy. No doubt it would have been less so with the introduction of furniture.

Never mind, this is a family vacation and all of these oddball events are what make it memorable. Let's all go out and sit at the picnic table and dig into some bags of roti chips. 'Huxley,' I say, 'I want you to eat all your spinach-flavoured crisps before you start on those chocolate ones.'

Later, we tuck the kids in bed and have a good story and a good laugh. They're snug in their squeaky cots. We make up a one-act play with their stuffed animals, do a few shadow pictures on the wall. We eat them up, 'Love you', 'Love you', 'Love you too', and we retreat with haste out the door to start our happy hour. I uncork the wine, we find some light by rigging a lamp just outside the front door, and we begin to read aloud from the short story book we're on.

When we get peckish, we make a stew of peanuts, chips and dahl flour extrusions. We finish reading and discussing the goodness of our future and go to bed. Seemingly, moments later, there is clatter and confusion in the house. T is delivering us our breakfast. I know I didn't tell him to.

We are all mad at T for waking us up unannounced, but when the meal arrives, it seems the kids are ready. There is buttery toast and instant coffee and one hot dog frankfurt on every plate. When I ask for milk, T is only too happy to oblige and returns with packets of non-dairy creamer. Maybe the kids could eat it like some sort of nutritious 'Lickemaide'. T lurks about, presumably to fetch whatever else we need. I'm too bushed to try to get an egg out of him. Besides, his family is probably having ours right now on English muffins with hollandaise sauce.

Even after I've nodded and smiled and done my best to indicate that we are all set, things are swell, you can go now . . . really . . . you can . . . T hangs around. He leaves eventually, but only to appear unannounced at other times, walking in whenever he pleases, trying to learn a little more about America, like how we look when we're naked and other practical things. 'How many citizens are in a town of New York?' 'What car was cost?' If we had furniture, I would have been able to duck out of the way at least. Instead, I run from him and shout out misinformation because I'm not sure myself. I'm angrier with him for taking the better house than I am with him for catching me off guard.

Our morning activity is a walk to a nice waterfall in the area. I've read that it's a short walk along a paved path and down some steps to the falls. Sadly, we discover that they have found a way to make it anything but a sight to behold. First, wherever nature intended there to be rocks, there is cement – behind the falls, in front of the falls, even the 'beach' is a cement slab. The park service thought to supply trash cans but then forgot to assign someone the job of emptying them.

In short, it's depressing. We head back to the car. Frank elbows me. 'Eleven o'clock,' he whispers. 'Do me a favour and just kill me if I ever look like that.' I locate the subjects. Oh, mood soaring, they are perfect. Just about the pastiest couple on earth, in their 50s or 60s – or 30s for that matter. Who can tell? Clearly British. They proudly wear their various butterfly nets in special carriers, like soldiers, and their binoculars and water canteen at a predetermined angle, for quick access. They have matching khaki outfits and their trouser legs are stuffed into their thick, woolly socks. Wow, do we ever feel better after that laugh.

We get into the car and drive to a hotel that was written up as being a landmark, full of antiques and history. It is a lovely place, even up close. It's amply furnished and the only sign of the downturn in the tourist trade is the carpet, which is thread-bare, but not sad. It adds character. It bespeaks decades of elegant, leisure-class expats journeying here to escape the heat and drink tea or scotch. As Frank waits for the hostess, I go off to the bathroom and who should I spy having a cuppa but the same British couple who made our day. They are now in matchy-matchy tea-drinking costumes.

'Hi,' I say to them. 'I think we just saw you out by the waterfall.'

'Oh yes, we were so disappointed,' the woman says.

'Rather,' says the man (or maybe I just assumed he would say that and didn't really listen).

'Yeah, it was like travelling for miles to visit the sewer,' I say.

'You mean the waterfall?' she asks. 'We felt the same way, didn't we, when we first came here.'

'I should say so,' says the man (or at least he *should* have).

'You've been here before?' I ask.

'Oh yes, we make it a point to come when there's a chance to see the magubericks. They eat the cinderberry pistula near the waterfall.'

'Indeed,' the man probably doesn't say.

'What are magubericks?' I ask.

'Oh, they are rare butterflies who grow to enormous dimensions,' she says.

'Wingspan of an eagle,' he says and gulps down the remainder of his scotch.

'Gee, I wonder if that thing we saw in the pub was one?' I muse.

They lean forward in their chairs, eager for news. I describe the bug I saw. They press me to think hard, try harder – *you aren't trying hard enough* – to remember the exact time I saw it.

'Cheer up, Nick,' says the lady. 'We have two more weeks to finally track it down.'

'Very well,' I say for Nick.

It seems the couple have been coming over from Surrey for the past 20 years. Frank near busts a gut when I get to the part about them staying for two weeks.

We sit outside, surrounded by a glorious garden and a moody view of the mountains. From here, they look carpeted in curly green brush, half shrouded in clouds, wrapped around them like a shawl. I am dying to run wild over them. The weather is perfect and the kids are enjoying themselves on the swinging porch seat. We take lots of pictures and then horse around in the soft, cool grass. Sadie orders 'bubble and squeak' based on its name, I order the salmon salad, Frank, the cottage pie, and we get Huxley an omelette. The beers are nice and cold. The kids slurp up their apple juice – no milk again today. Our lunches come out together, which is extremely rare in Asia because either they think you are all sharing everything . . . or, they don't care, you'll take it when it's ready . . . or, it's just a coincidence you're all sitting at the same table. The food looks wholesome and delicious; even the hot dog frankfurt curved on the rim of each plate seems plump with good health. I think a hot dog frankfurt is their garnish, like a parsley sprig. I wonder what happens when you order a hot dog.

As Frank says, 'Vacations with you are like boot camp.' After lunch, I have assigned us a big trek through the jungle on a path leading to the 'Vicar's Cottage'. My literature says it is 'superb' and the journey is suitable for young and old. Somebody edited out the line 'for the first ten minutes'. At the beginning, the trail is nicely dug out and follows the edge of the mountain so that we can sense our altitude and enjoy the cool shade of the jungle vegetation. We see monkeys and are on the constant lookout for tigers. We stop to watch a six-pound centipede, and we pluck and dissect several types of berries and fruits. But that all grows stale as the troops grow cranky, hot and exhausted. The kids are thirsty. I've run out of water. The monkeys become menacing, hissing and lurking too nearby, scaring Sadie and enticing Huxley. But I make it perfectly clear to the family: we are not quitters. We *will* reach 'Vicar's Cottage' and we *will* work as a team. The kids break the whine barrier as their mosquito bites inflame to the size of human heads. The path becomes narrower and overgrown, difficult to decipher. The markers aren't presenting themselves as they once were. Are we still on a path?

Just when I'm about to cave, feeling great embarrassment and remorse, just when Frank is hurling another 'Way to go, Columbus' insult over to me, there's a sign: 'This way to Vicar's Cottage – .02 kilometres.'

Hooray!

Tragically, that .02 kilometres is entirely straight up a slippery mud slope with far and few handholds. Frank and I are each balancing a kid on our back by now. Frank is good and mad. He tells me he hates me.

Glory be, we get to the top. We round the bend and there's the 'Vicar's Cottage'. It's a heap of stones covered in graffiti and sprinkled with broken beer bottles. There's a soiled mattress in the corner. Naughty vicar!

The retreat is quicker than the one we made at the falls. We're getting good at this turning-on-our-heels-in-disappointment-and-disgust thing. I try to make it all happy by singing a song but no one joins in. Oh, except when Frank starts singing a song, then the kids scream 'Bravo' and ask for an encore. But once the trail levels and becomes well defined, there's a bit of jocularity, and it's okay that it's all at my expense. Long as they're happy again. Frank has Sadie on his shoulders and is leading the way. I have Huxley on mine. I spy a big old mud blob on Frank's calf. I bend down and flick it off. 'Just a little mud, honey, I got it off.' But blood starts spurting out. It's dripping onto his socks and dribbling down over his nice new hiking boots. He keeps walking. He doesn't know he's bleeding. He doesn't know he's been leeched. I am faced with quite a dilemma: do I tell him? Do I let him bleed to death (he was pretty nasty back there) and save myself the lecture? Should I watch it for a while for something to do?

I decide on not telling him, *and* watching. After a few hours, the wound has finally coagulated. Back at our bungalow I gather the dirty laundry as fast as I can and he never even knows he lost a bucket of blood. My only problem is how I am going to convince him to wear long pants tucked into his socks for tomorrow's hike.

Three More Years

What if you woke up one day and checked your 'Dumb things I gotta do' notepad to find this list:

Rent out Westchester house
Pack Westchester house as follows –
    Ship
    Store
    Suitcase
    FedEx
    Hide at mother-in-law's
Get daycare
Go to job
Make out will
Meet financial advisor
Meet realtor
Clean house for viewings, per realtor's instruction
Get house painted, per realtor's instruction
Shampoo carpets, per realtor's instruction
Call snowplough guy per realtor's instruction
Call gardener per realtor's instruction
Take car to Baltimore

Take train home
Say goodbye to everyone
Work for a living
Cook breakfast (hmmm, what can you do with bread
   crumbs and candy corn)
Cook dinner (damn, I used all the candy)
Go to supermarket.

One minute, my biggest worry is sitting on a plane again for 24 hours with nothing to do and the next, I'm back in New York with a staggering amount of organisational activities swirling in my head like a snow globe. We need to come back in order to leave again for the long haul. We need to . . . oh, I already mentioned the list. But I can't get the flakes of 'to do' to settle. It feels like a blizzard, a haphazard series of words. The caterwauling duet of Sadie and Huxley is accompanied by ringing phones, incoming faxes, lawn mowers, leaf blowers . . . It's really just Daily Life, but I can't live with Daily Life now that Big Picture has landed on the doorstep with a steamer trunk.

On any given day, I am confounded by logistics. How am I supposed to exercise, bathe, dress, brush three sets of teeth, clothe, feed, pack the necessity bag, find a parking spot, buy a paper and make the train all in the space of two hours when it takes me an entire hour just to drink my coffee?

Frank tiptoes around waiting for me to fall apart.

I don't let him down. Within a couple of days or so, I am paralysed. I became a human pinball, bumping into things to do and careening back into things undone, zinging around, then staring into space in the gutter.

At eight o'clock at night, Frank is dutifully, efficiently, logically wrapping and boxing, and writing comprehensive notes in a manifest. A blur of industriousness, he is labelling everything according to some Franky-decimal system. He waves and smiles at me through the glass doors as I take up my familiar position on the deck and he travels that well-trodden path to another beer. Sometimes I see him stop suddenly, jerk the pen from behind his ear and scribble away. Still, I sit huddled in layers of outerwear, smoking, drinking, and thinking. Occasionally, I perform a little pantomime for Frank indicating I'm just 'on a break'. I stridently stub out my cigarette and move toward the door as if I were equally eager – compelled! – to resume the same such busy-ness. When he's out of view again, I just sit back down.

Sometimes Frank slides open the door and puts his head through, asking in an amiable tone something like: 'Do you think you're going to want to take the crystal?' Automatically I say 'No', because if it was 'Yes' then one might wonder why I didn't pack it myself. I try to convey during the one-millionth of a second it takes to say 'No' that I have given it a lot of thought and, in the end, determined it best to leave it here. I just haven't had the time to tell him . . . busy, busy, busy. The truth really is that, yes, I do want my crystal and now it's too late and the tenants are going to get in a big fight and smash my goblets against the walls and floors.

Before the week is over Frank has finished the packing, despite having gone into work every day well groomed, despite being fuelled by a handful of pepper for dinner. He is also loving and playful with the kids, bathing them, dressing them and taking them to daycare (which I lined up, thank you).

My pace at work is a different story. There, I am frenetic. First of all, I sit in the office and swivel in a chair. I watch Jason, my assistant, make sounds to me. I pick up the phone and speak to grown-ups who call themselves clients. I write pages of notes that only look like doodles to the naked eye.

Eventually, though, as the house gets tidy and I warm up to this being back in the office instead of in a bathing suit, I do actually get my act together. I arrange a party for a celebrity client (famous, mostly, for being insane, but why should that stop us from throwing a party?) and schedule meetings for a book fair in Germany where I will be making a huge amount of licensing deals for an upcoming movie. Everyone is positively kissing my ass because I have a hot property, I have two books on *The New York Times* bestseller list, and my clients' royalty statements are going through the roof. I am finding myself getting juiced, feeling like 'the man', loving the pressure, 'on the phone'.

There are two problems: I don't want to go back to Singapore any more, and we haven't found a renter yet. Perhaps that is one problem and one solution? Not a chance. I have to go. Frank has to go. We're a family. He never would have made this decision had I not complained so. How was he to know that when I said 'My job is killing me; I never see the kids' I meant, 'Oh, wait a second, I'm alive again. What's to see? They're kids.'

And anyway, they've already lined up a new agent to take my office.

My heart tightens as I imagine tenants in our living room, sitting by the fire where, after putting the kids to bed, Frank and I would play Trivial Pursuit and eat Chee Whiz on crackers and body parts. Suddenly the house symbolises my life and I know I don't want to leave. I mean, what the hell was I thinking when I decided to stay on in Singapore? I'm a New York literary agent. This is my home.

Our house is on the edge of a nature preserve. The deck where I constantly seek refuge is just off the living room and looks out over a large forest. Before we moved in, there was just one tiny window in the corner of the room. We knocked out a wall, put in huge sliding doors, built the deck and made a fantastic place to watch the seasons change, from inside and out. (Which reminds me, there are no seasons in Singapore. They think they have two – rainy and not so rainy – but they don't. They are lying.)

There is a catwalk library off the master bedroom, which also has a great view of the trees. I set up a desk there and used to look at the woods as I worked. The built-in shelves were lined with all the books I loved and those I couldn't wait to read. We had two fireplaces. The problems with the house became fewer as we poured thought, money and man-hours into it. We had a cool house and in it we brought new people to the planet.

George Groves is the best realtor on the face of the earth. We found him when I was pregnant and we decided to move to Westchester. He showed us – literally – 200 houses. He was never vague. He was never fatigued. He never seemed annoyed that we just didn't get it: we were too poor to be rich. He never tried to sell. He would point out the good, the bad, the fixable, the 'whys' and 'why nots'. He didn't just drive us to a site and drone, 'Here's the bedroom . . . Here's the kitchen.' Not our George. He saw me get larger and larger with Sadie, and I heard all about his life. My mother-in-law joined me on many of these house hunts and he responded to her challenging questions with unwavering calm and educated answers. When we finally bought our house, he remembered – from almost a year before – that we had said we wanted 'funky'. He also thought to comment, 'You realise you are 500 yards from your mother-in-law?'

So when George says, 'Don't worry, we'll get you a renter,' I know I shouldn't be so nervous. The clock is ticking, but just as the alarm is about to go off, a wonderful grown-up family fall for the place, the deck, the nature, the kitchen and library.

I like her, the wife, in particular. She's warm and effusive. She doesn't ask things like, 'How old is the drier?' Instead, she asks, 'What will it be like for your kids in Singapore?' She tells me all about her kids and her sister's kids, and unabashedly gushes over things I did to the house.

I guess that's why I choose to ignore the, um, import of all those 'must do's' right there on her personage. She has buttons missing, resident stains on her slacks and a way-past-due-date on her roots. She's the sort of person who would marvel at a crater in the ceiling of her own bedroom *if* she noticed it at all, and, if it rained, she'd just put a hand over her head. But she would love our forest.

The deal is signed. The tenants move in, the kids and I move over to the in-laws. Frank goes to Singapore to get stuff sorted out. I go to daycare, work, and the grocery store. By eight at night, I have the kids in bed. Sometimes Frank and I talk on the phone, but, given the fact that one of us is just waking up and one of us is ensconced in happy hour, we're forever struggling to find a common mood. Emails are safer.

When it is time for me to go to the book fair in Germany, Frank returns to New York victorious. We have a fantastic apartment ready and waiting back in Fortune Gardens – two floors, a sea view from every window, the works. He swings me around the room. Thrilled for me.

I hand over the diaper bag and head off to Frankfurt. For the first time in a long time, I am without kids, doing my job, being on, partying without my husband. I am getting a great workout from kicking myself about the whole Singapore situation. I don't want to go. I belong here. (Well, not exactly here in Germany, oy . . .) But then I lose the videotape. The one that has the words 'DO NOT LET OUT OF YOUR

SIGHT' written all over it. The one that, if ever seen by anyone but authorised individuals in a secure environment, will mean thousands of lives at risk – or at least a couple of people out of a job. I have no idea where I left the almost final edited copy of *Lost in Space* but my plane is leaving in one hour without it. I call people in their hotel rooms from the plane so many times they answer their phones with 'No, it hasn't turned up'.

When I land and Frank meets me at the airport, I vomit.

'I lost Dave's video . . . I left it at someone's booth . . . it's gone . . . I'm dead . . . he's dead . . . we're all dead, dead, dead . . . killed and dead . . . (vomit).'

And then Frank reminds me. 'They'll have to find you first!'

The next day, just before we board the plane for Singapore, the video is reported to be in safe hands and on its way to my New York office. I kiss the phone. I never tell the client. I go joyfully to my seat in business class and snap for champagne . . . and keep them coming . . . For the next three years, they'll have to find me first. Goodbye, New York!

Welcome to Your Breezy New Lifestyle

Frank gets all his merit badges at once when he shows us into our new apartment. We have ample storage, large rooms and huge balconies, and every window in the entire joint has an unobstructed sea view. *And*, we have carpeting. This may not seem worth mentioning but it is rare here. No more crawling around with the kids on a cold, hard, marble floor. If that's the icing on the cake, then the cherry on top is Sadie's pink bedroom and the pink velvet headboard over her queen-sized bed.

Frank is all aglow as the three of us cheer and hug him. 'Hooray for Daddy!' We dance. He can't hide his pride and relief. He shows us around every nook and cranny and gives us a tour of all the wonderful features in our new home. He has taken it upon himself to purchase things we need, like a microwave, toaster oven and blender. He has had phone jacks installed on the balcony so I can work at night, watching the ships' lights, and, when it's clear, see Indonesia twinkling in the distance. We have remote-controlled lights, airconditioners, ceiling fans, boom boxes and VCRs. The place is filled with cables and thin little palm-held devices that are the only way to turn everything from the overhead light to the coffee maker on and off. Forget where you put one of these remote control suckers and you're screwed. What the heck is wrong with a toggle switch? I guess the marketing people are sure that the only way to edge past the competition is to appeal to the paraplegic and terribly lazy.

After the 'oohs' and 'ahhs' I'm faced with brochure overload. I flick through dossier after dossier about the stuff that is to make our lives easier. Ninety-eight pages of text come with the microwave; 160 pages come with the sound system. I decide to tackle it room by room, and start with the kitchen. I flip through the microwave book. The convivial little introduction starts with 'Welcome To Your Breezy New Lifestyle'. I get bored after the diagram of the appliance broken down into pieces labelled AA–ZZ. I just pull the microwave and all the accessories out, tossing styrofoam peanuts around and ripping through bubble wrap (saving enough so the kids will have a new toy tomorrow). Frank is watching me with that enormous – but now starting to get on my nerves – grin on his face. It must hurt to have it like that for so long. His eyes are moist when he points and says, '*This* one came with a mirror. Special promotion.'

I give him a sceptical look. This isn't Frank; it's Ernest. I move on to the blender and in that box there is a Filofax. Frank is still over the moon.

'Special promotion?' I ask. Frank's head goes up and down in the enthusiastic affirmative.

I'm not unhappy about these little extras but I am confounded by their relevance. I mean, I can understand the whole 'But wait . . . there's more! If you order now . . .' thing. But there was always a correlation between the freebie and the product, something that would, say, enhance your cooking experience. But a full-length mirror with my microwave? A Filofax with a blender? Hey, I just checked my schedule, no time to chew, better get out the blender – ha ha.

They have a totally different idea of marketing over here. They think it's sheer brilliance to have slogans like: 'Make it a Hock Toey night!' or 'Buy Chow Wang and you'll never go back!' The guys who thought up these bon mots are probably promoted to Grand Poo Bahs of their agencies. 'Yu Xin, you are like tiger,' says Goh. 'These ads are the lizard's gizzards. They do "the bump".'

I don't want to get sardonic so soon after landing, after seeing how happy my new husband Ernest is, after committing to three more years. I tell myself to shut up and enjoy. I assemble my mirror in the kitchen, position the microwave on the counter and watch myself nuke. I look pretty good. I get so far into it that I even think, 'Gee, if I get two, I'll look twice as good and nuke up twice as much.'

After a while, Frank finally leaves to check in at the office. We only landed yesterday and life feels out of focus for me, like I'm acting it out but missing my cues. I get tired of pulling boxes apart and trying to catch those wily little grains of styrofoam. I grow weary of figuring out where to put things and identifying their usefulness. Even dreaming of sweeping through my home in a white silk gown with rabbit-fur cuffs, flipping stuff on and off, fails to thrill after a while.

But I'm determined to make the place homey and get rid of the boxes. For something different, I turn my back on the new gizmos, begin hacking away at the containers sent from home, and start taking things out, beholding them as if for the first time. 'Oh, I remember this potato peeler . . . Yes! I am so glad I didn't leave the masking tape behind . . .' And then, as I line it all up, growing soft and nostalgic, I see the little bonus: every bowl, fork, knife, spoon, masher, peeler, grater, candlestick, cheeseboard, piece of linen, towel, toy, book and CD is covered not only in old grease and old crud but also carpets of brand new mildew. I open a box marked 'Sadie's Toy Chest' and scream. A dozen dolls stare up at me.

These are not the faces of innocent childhood playthings. Each lovingly named, cherished, treasured doll, from the American Girls to the Barbies, has turned sickeningly mottled – as if painted for jungle warfare, or worse – with mildew. I can only see the whites of their eyes. Evil is in that box. I kick it over. Their chanting dies down, but the magic eight ball rolls out, telling me: 'Whatever you think, is right.'

It will take forever to get all this stuff cleaned. I see my bunny fur balding and my silk greet-your-husband dress stained and smelly. I see my rhinestone heels getting caught up in a herd of rusty Brillo pads. I see my breezy new lifestyle turn skeezy. I must attack this mess . . . I must attack this mess . . . I walk steadily, slowly. My eyes are unblinking as I advance, chisel in hand, poised at ear level, ready to chip away at a five-month-old blob of guacamole or fossilised noodle – or maybe I'll just maim Baby All Gone.

'Why you brought so much?' comes a voice from the living room.

'Pearl!' I cry. 'How did you . . .'

'Ah, we begin again,' she says.

She opens several bags filled with household cleansers and pulls a chisel out of her hip pocket. We both watch it gleam in the light for a moment.

Taking hold of myself, I ask, 'What about that family from Texas?'

'So cheap, *lah*. They got maid now, Filipino. Here my new card.'

Her rates now include unpacking expats – $400 a day. I look around the room, thinking about it for a minute. If I say 'Forget it', she'll disappear again, but if I take it, she'll keep appearing again. I look around the room and shell out $500.

'Keep the change, just stay with me for the day.'

I take a bath with the kids and share their dismay and

disappointment that bubble bath doesn't work here. How can that be, you wonder? Because there is no water pressure. It took seven hours to get two inches of lukewarm water. Still, we feel better. After the bath, the kids sit in their car seats in the hall and we pretend they're still on the plane. 'Have a nice flight!' I call out.

'Mommy, don't go!'

'Have to, sweetie, but the stewardess will come around.'

'*Mommy!*'

'We're just playing. You aren't on a plane. I have tons to do around the house. Now have a nice flight.'

Finally, I set about making the home a home, for Sadie, Huxley, Frank and me. A place where we will play and grow and laugh and tickle and . . . and that's when 'The Night Chicago Died' comes to Fortune Gardens. I'm shocked out of total recall. I can't remember all the details – just like I can't remember the seconds before I hit a car full of Hassidim in Baltimore. I only remember their yarmulkes dangling at unnatural angles. It was horrible, there were bobby pins everywhere. There wasn't a dent on their car, but their headgear had gone astray. I was shamed. And I call myself a Jew! I stepped out of my car with some difficulty since I was nine months pregnant. The officer told me I had an expired licence. The men said, 'God forbid, she should keep driving that . . . that . . . weapon, going around killing innocent people.' I rubbed my stomach. The officer took my keys away. The men took my insurance premium.

Back to this crash . . . Okay, I remember I plugged in the wedding-gift cappuccino machine. I was eager to get Huxley's room ready for him for his nap so I plugged in his fish tank. I plugged in the 200-year-old-from-Rittman-to-Rittman china lamps after placing them on overturned boxes I had lovingly draped with colourful matching batiks. I started to charge up Frank's electric shaver and tested the printer and tried sending a fax to my mom and playing some old albums on the stereo, but I didn't get far. The hissing and burning and popping, the sizzling and frying and sparking. Glass flying, plastic melting, coffee everywhere . . . it all happened so fast.

So it would seem Singapore is on a different power system. Most profoundly retarded people know this.

Frank walks in the door. The studio audience gives him rousing applause. They elbow one another knowingly. 'Now the jokes are coming,' they say.

After a beat, Frank gives the camera a look. I remove his shoes. I hand him his drink. I'm over-solicitous, anticipating his every need, the perfect wife with a big old boo boo that has to be 'splained. I promise him his favourite thing in the whole world if he promises not to yell. There's grousing, nervous pacing, aye carumbas. The best I can hope for is an endearing tone when he shouts out 'Whah was chew thinnin' about?' because I just destroyed about $3,000 worth of appliances and whatnot we brought from America. And I seem to have caused some electrical damage in the apartment because *nothing* works now.

'All I wanted to do was have you come home to a nice place. *Wah, wah, wah.*'

Ah, what's going to happen next? Pearl! She looks up and smiles and flicks the switch on our $800 vacuum cleaner. Flash, boom, bang, the thing explodes. She stands there cloaked in a soft, downy fluff of Westchester debris, sooty but for the whites of her eyes.

Frank turns to me and says, '*Everything?*'

'No, no . . . no, God, no . . . the kids are fine. They were in their car seats. Wanna beer?'

'Definitely,' he says.

'Okay, I'll just go down to the little store. I'll be right back.'

I have nothing in the apartment to feed anyone, busy as I was destroying it all. Hey, there's a special promotion on eggs. Buy ten, get two free. I think, 'Well, that'd make a dozen, so, yeah, okay, thanks, but isn't that rather like "Buy the shirt and we'll throw in the buttons"?' Marketing genius, huh?

Back at home I hand Frank his VBs and step out onto the balcony. I don't want Frank asking me to explain again how I can be so stupid. I don't want to watch Frank pass through the stages of his grief. With the first beer, there will be a stoic acceptance but it will be understood that I am not to leave the room because I must bear witness to the strength he musters. With the second beer, he'll tour around the apartment silently, bereaving all that is lost, running a finger over this or that. With the third, he'll come back to me as if I've had enough time to accurately answer the question: How can you be so stupid? If there are more beers, he'll just hold on to the kids for dear life and shudder at the thought of what could've happened in this house of horrors.

When I go back in, Frank's placing a sheet over his big old Klipsch speakers. I put on my Sauconys. I'm going for my first run in Singapore. Pearl's all right and is cleaning again; the kids are fine. I'm pretty much no good to anyone; it's best I leave. 'Bye, everyone.'

The elevator ride is too short. I'm outside. I'm not going to do this; it's crazy. Even though it's after five in the evening and the wind is picking up and the sun is covered by cloud, it's so hot. I'll keel over. I don't deserve to die. I should stay home, enjoy the food and have boozy playdates for the next three years. It'll be the age of my complacency, my sleazy new lifestyle. An older woman approaches the lift, smiles and says, 'Oh, you so fit. Running, is it?' I nod.

'Good! Good!' she barks.

How could I disappoint this little old auntie?

Right. Okay. Let's do it. I trot through the parking lot and skip down the steps of the underpass. I take the ones leading up to the park path by twos. I'm already dripping but I recognise myself and don't feel half bad. Reunited with my animal soul, the atavistic particles of my psyche, carving my way across the land with speed and power. I really don't feel a thing but my engine burning. Perhaps that's because I've only been at it for three minutes.

I stick to the joggers' path and loudly cuss at the bikers who are disobeying the *roools*. The lanes are clearly marked, both on the ground and on signs conveying in words and symbols, impossible to miss, that joggers are *here* and cyclists are *here*.

But neither group listens, natch.

'*Jogging path!*' I scream as I pass a cycler. '*You belong over there,*' I bellow and point. Every time I get angry I run better. So, I keep myself angry. I curse at everyone and everything. I shout at the hawkers that their food really reeks. I loudly proclaim to the toddlers wandering about that I am barrelling through and they better watch their step. I feel great.

Then I hear, 'Hi Fran!'

It's Samantha, the lady I met after my first power swim at the pool. I had since discovered that she wasn't really part of the baby pool bunch but was their friend all the same. I'd taken to her. She was an inviting sort of person. I enjoyed hopping out of the pool and saying, 'Earned my beer today' because she always countered with something upbeat and convincing like, 'Ya did excellent. That's what it's all about.'

I join her and tell her that this is my first run in Singapore and apologise for my slow pace. She smiles and says, 'You kiddin' me? It's a great pace. You just take it easy now. It's a killer when you first start out.' Then she looks at me and gets a worried frown. 'Don't you have any water?'

'I never carry it,' I answer. 'Yeah, I can be *that* stupid.'

Then, with the same 'shame on you' expression, she asks rhetorically, 'And you don't have any powders either?'

'I used a roll-on.'

She tells me that I'm asking for trouble without water and energy-infusing, secret-ingredient-Z-containing, $600-a-scoopful powder. 'And it tastes just like tonic water.'

'I'm fine. Really. Water is something I use to rinse my mouth out after brushing and tonic is what I sprinkle on gin.'

She laughs and hands me a *shmattah*.

'What's this?' I ask.

'Oh, it's pieces of my son's underpants that my helper sewed together. I brought two.'

'Why, thank you. How kind.'

She dabs at her face with it and I can see that anyone would need two. I'm already watching large drops of water fall from my eyelids.

Samantha's stride is low and quick. She's deceptively fast and because we're running side by side, I match her beat instead of using my own slow-motion leprechaun style. I'm succumbing to the pace and the heat. I start talking mindlessly to rise above it.

'Your helper?'

'My maid, Bet.'

'Oh, do you work?'

'No, I have three kids. She frees me up so we can enjoy the good part of the day.'

'There isn't supposed to be a good part of the day until it's night,' I say.

I can't imagine having a Bet, someone doing everything I'm supposed to do, depriving me of the pleasures of being a martyr. Washing our things, doing our shopping, making our meals, babysitting, sewing *shmattahs*, cleaning the toilets, scrubbing the oven, ironing the shirts, sewing on buttons, mailing our letters, waxing the car, killing bugs. She'd answer the door when Frank came home for an afternoon rendezvous, overhear our discussions about money, witness my terrible temper and, no doubt, join the small but vociferous encounter group called 'I Worked For Fran', or 'IWFF', which has now become a verb meaning 'to have lived to talk about working for Fran', as in, 'Yeah, I was pretty IWFFed, but God, cigarettes, coffee and all you kind people have helped me lead a normal life.' I've had supervisors call me in. 'You will have to be let go if you tell anyone again they are "dumber than a bucket of hair".' If only I had a chance to tell my side of the story. Which is, she was!

'I do home schooling for my kids – or rather, unschooling – and Bet helps with that sometimes,' Samantha continues. (What is unschooling? Does she tell them one plus one doesn't really equal two, and don't let those power-hungry mind-control freaks in the education system tell you otherwise? I'm very curious but I don't ask because *really* I want to know more about maids.)

'Don't you feel, I don't know, inhibited with a maid around?' I ask.

'Oh my gosh, no. Bet's part of the family.'

'Does she eat with you?'

'No.'

'Do you take her on outings?'

'No.'

'Do you celebrate her birthday?'

'Oh, that would be a grand idea.'

'So . . . she's sort of like a useful pet.'

We laugh.

She tells me more about maids. Most come from the Philippines but some come from Sri Lanka or Indonesia. You don't have to give more than one Sunday a month and public

103

holidays off. They learn how to be excellent cooks and would throw themselves in front of a bullet to save your child. Most of them speak passable English and learn languages quickly. They're generally well educated, because even a nurse or teacher stands to make more as a domestic servant in Singapore than at the top of their career in their home country. Samantha tells me that they flock here hoping for work and I'd be doing them a favour by hiring one. Not just because I'd be offering a job to a needy person, but also because I'm an expat. Apparently, a number of locals have their maids sleeping on the floor of their kids' rooms or calling a hard chair in the kitchen a bed. Every week there are stories about employers beating up their maids. Just the other day, there was one about a nurse who bit her maid.

So, in Singapore, I'd be a good boss.

I'm wondering if Samantha will run with me again, maybe tomorrow after Caroline's playgroup. I had found out about it when I ran into Caroline at the store. She hurried up to me while I was at the register and whispered, 'Don't get those here', pointing to my two potatoes. 'They have them at Cold Storage for half the price this week.' I didn't want to seem unimpressed with the tip, so I nodded conspiratorially and put them back, saving myself about a nickel. She called out, 'Playgroup at mine tomorrow, three o'clock till five, block three, seventh floor.'

'What apartment?' I asked.

'Seventh floor,' she repeated as she put helmets on her children for the stroller ride home.

'Hey, are you going to Caroline's playgroup?' I ask Samantha.

'Oh, no, that's much too structured for me,' she responds.

'Really? I thought we'd just sit around, have coffee and cake and make sure the kids share,' I say.

'Exactly. It makes me so mad,' she says, getting visibly angry. 'Why should my child *share* just because it's play-group?'

Ah, *un*playgrouping.

'I see your point. Well, I, for one, won't have my child participate in such conformist activities like Simon Says or singing "If you're happy and you know it do whatever I tell you to".'

She laughs. She isn't offended. She can run, she has a joie de vivre that could wake the dead and she's sweet. Her kids are just the right ages to play with mine. I love her right then. We chat about this and that and the time flies. Turns out she's one of seven daughters of an Irish migrant couple who moved to Canada, is a vegetarian and breastfeeds her kids until they're five. She's got her ideas and some of 'em are plenty out there, but I hope we'll do this again.

'Do you want to run again tomorrow?' I ask when we get back to Fortune Gardens.

'Sure, this was great. See you at the Boonlap entrance at five. Bye for now.'

I'm a different person when I walk into the apartment. I have a friend and I have an answer about why I'm so stupid: 'Because I'm a jock, Frank.'

After I shower, we open a bottle of red and have a drink on the balcony. The disaster, though always to remain part of the fabric of our lives, is behind us. Frank talks about work. He tells me that the new staff is typically Singaporean and didn't say a word to him all day except, 'I'm going for my lunch now.' I tell him about playgroup tomorrow and my great run with my new pal. We pour another glass and then hear, 'All done already. I'll go now.'

'Oh, Pearl, I forgot you were still here, sorry,' I say.

She giggles and shifts from one well-planted foot to the other.

'What do we owe you?'

'$400 for expat moving, $100 for babysitting, $100 for cleaning and $10 for under 24-hour notice.'

'Hey, wait a minute, I already paid you $500, and I didn't call you, you just came,' I protest.

'Okay, okay, $207.'

I pay her. She's carting off $707 today. A maid costs $350 a month. And they do your shopping, make your meals, babysit, lick your stamps and smash your bugs. But Pearl's what I've got. 'Pearl, can you come tomorrow so I can do some heavy-duty grocery shopping?'

'No, tomorrow no good.' Her beeper goes, she whips off her apron, slips on her shoes and as she's doing the combination lock on her purse, she asks, 'Alabama, that US, right?'

I nod.

'When can you come again?' I ask somewhat shrilly, but the elevator door is closing between us and I can't hear her answer.

We put the kids to bed and settle out on the balcony again. Gosh, this is nice. It is our home. The chairs we're sitting on are cushy and we put our feet up on the two unused ones. We look at the stars and then at each other, and smile. This is going to be a good life. I bring out some snacks and another bottle of red. I light my first and best cigarette of the evening. I lean against the balcony and look out over the grounds, the water fountain, the shimmering pool, and, in the circle of light outside the grocery store, there is Pearl. She's standing in front of a stunned, red-necked foursome, her card between her fingers. I ask Frank, 'Do you think we should look into a maid?'

'Absolutely,' Frank answers without hesitation.

The next day, the kids and I play and shop, which is hellish because I need so much and they behave so badly. Huxley breaks five bottles of ketchup and Sadie tries to pick them up for me. The trolley wheels won't move and I have no idea where to find what I need. In the end, I get flustered and leave the cart in the middle of the aisle and buy a frozen apple pie to take to Caroline's. I have no idea how to convert Fahrenheit into Celsius so I just wing it and the result is a dry, fruity brick that would break your toes if you dropped it and your teeth if you didn't. Before stopping at Caroline's, I head to the little store for some ice-cream to apply like make-up to my ugly pie and go to block three, floor seven at 3 pm with the kids. I needn't have worried about finding her apartment. She is indeed on the entire seventh floor. After ringing the bell a dozen times, I just let myself in. The shoes scattered all around the enormous foyer remind me that I'm supposed to take all of ours off. I call out, 'Anybody home?'

A fortyish Filipino woman in a servant's uniform bustles out to greet me.

'Ma'am, Caroline is in here. Can I get you anything?'

'No, we're fine,' I say. 'Can I just put this in the fridge?'

We walk for 20 or so minutes from the foyer through the dining room, the rec room, the bar, another hallway, another den and finally to the kitchen. After adjusting the lifetime supply of Diet Cokes, I find a place for my pie.

'This way,' the maid instructs.

We go through another hallway and find ourselves in yet another den where Caroline has her feet up on a coffee table, toes sandwiched with cotton balls, and the kids are sitting comfortably on the sofa watching a Thomas the Tank Engine video. There's a rack hanging on the wall with several dozen remote control devices, labelled 'drape opener', 'aircon', 'DVD', 'VCD', 'VCR', 'TV', 'fan', 'light', etc.

'Hi Fran,' Caroline says. 'Bethy, you left off here.' She

points to a toe and the maid resumes buffing and polishing Caroline's right foot. The doorbell rings and Bethy continues her pedicure.

'Bethy, I can't get it, can I?' Caroline says.

'No, Ma'am, the polish is still wet. I'll get it.'

'Maids,' Caroline says, saying it all, as Bethy walks down the hall.

Amah-rama

A couple of weeks later, I wake up early to make a very important phone call.

'Jessica here.'

'Hi, um, is this Embassador Services?'

'Yes.'

'I'm Fran Rittman. My friend, Samantha Burns, recommended you to me.'

'Looking for a maid, is it?'

'Yes, we . . .'

'Do you currently have one employed?'

'No. I've been doing without for some time now.'

'I see.'

'You don't know what it's been like.'

'Tell me what you –'

'Oh, God, it's so good to talk to someone who understands. I've had to figure out how to use things and grocery shop and next week, I have playgroup. At my house!'

'Yes. Tell me –'

'The other day, I bought a chicken at the grocery store and when I unwrapped it, the head and feet were still on.

I screamed but of course there was no one there to help me. I panicked and threw it out the window.'

'What I mean, Mrs Rittman, is could you tell me what you are looking for?'

'An *amah*. A helper. A maid, dammit! Haven't you heard a word I've said? Listen, if you can't help me, tell me who can. Who has the maids? Who?'

'Don't shout, Mrs Rittman. We have several girls who are looking for work.'

'When can I meet them?'

'I think it would be a good idea to tell me what you want and then I can put together a group for you to see today.'

'Can't you do it sooner?'

'Mrs Rittman, calm down. A few more questions. Where are you from? Canada, is it?'

'No, no, *no*, of course not. What sort of question is that? I come from New York, as in the American New York. Doesn't that count for something?'

'Yes, that's helpful. Do you have kids?'

'Yeah, Sadie and Huxley.'

'And they are . . .'

'And they are Sadie and Huxley. My kids are called Sadie and Huxley. Can I talk to someone in charge, someone who speaks English?'

'I'm the owner. I understand you perfectly. I was just trying to get some information so we can arrange interviews. Now, Sadie and Huxley, they are how old?'

'Young! Very young. And, that's not all; they're a year apart. They're wild. Don't tell your maids that, okay? They're smart and good as far as they're concerned.'

'And do you need someone to cook western food?'

'What? Like beans and barbecue? I'm from the northeast. Frankly, I don't care if it's cornpone or clam chowder, really, I just . . .'

'Mrs Rittman, it's important to have some understanding of your background and needs. We have girls who have only worked for Chinese families, who know no English, who don't know how to cook the food you like. We have girls who don't have experience with small kids. It's best to identify your desires.'

'Anyone is fine. I'll just meet them all, okay? What's your soonest appointment?'

'You can come in half an hour if you'd like.'

'I can't make it there in half an hour! What're you, crazy? I have kids to feed and change and I have to pack a small bag full of everything they could possibly need for an outing. I have laundry to do and dishes to wash. I think I can be there in 45 minutes.'

'That's fine, Mrs Rittman. We'll see you then.'

'This isn't just a wild goose chase is it, Jessica? You really have maids.'

'No, this isn't a wild goose chase, Mrs Rittman. The girls are all here ready to meet you.'

'No kidding?'

'We'll see you soon.'

'Frank!' I jump onto the bed and shake him. 'Frank, wake up! I called a maid agency. We have to go *now*.' I start a little jig on the bed and sing, 'We're gonna get a maid . . . We're gonna get a maid . . .'

He just bounces around.

'Get up!'

'Whaaa?'

'Didn't you hear me?' I shout. 'We're gonna get a maid . . . We're gonna get a maid.'

Frank gets up to brush his teeth and I leap from the bed, dash out into the hall and jump onto Sadie's bed – 'We're gonna get a maid . . . We're gonna get a maid!' – and skip from room to room – 'We're gonna get a maid . . . We're gonna get a maid!' – and down the hall and back into our bedroom, where Sadie is now jumping on the bed, chanting, 'We're gonna have woast wabbit . . . We're gonna have woast wabbit.'

I can hear Frank spit out his toothpaste. I pause to interpret. We, and I'm sure millions of other couples, can tell a lot from our partner's spit, even from a distance. This *ptchew* held amusement and pride. He's done his part for Sadie. She can now recite sacrosanct lines from classic *Bugs Bunny* episodes.

Frank has memorised about 600 hours of old TV shows, from the earliest *Looney Tunes* to the *Flintstones* to *Dragnet*. Please let this be because his brain is so large it can hear something once and recite it perfectly. The alternative possibility depresses me deeply. I picture a waxy, skinny kid glued to the television with no drive, no energy. His mom occasionally storms in to say, 'You've seen this episode 15 times already. That's enough, go out and play.' But Frank can't hear her because he's talking along with the script, in perfect timing and with perfect mimicry. I might as well face it, there is no way he could have consumed all this television even once and still had a childhood that included the outdoors.

I get the kids dressed and fed and jam stuff into my backpack: diapers, milk, toys, snacks, extra clothes, peanut butter sandwiches, juice boxes, crayons and colouring books, Pringles. After a quick cup of coffee we go.

We walk into Tuskin Shopping Centre at 10 am on a Sunday. No stores are open. I think about being in my high-school building at weekends for special track meets. Everything still, waiting for real life, noisy life, to begin again. Embassador is on the third floor. We go up the escalator to find a hallway teeming with Filipino women, sitting, sauntering, socialising, preening, slouching, sleeping. They have many things in common: dark, thick, wavy hair, caramel skin, wide, wide smiles and, ooch, way wrong clothes. The outfits they're wearing are new and are not shabby or dirty or for the impoverished only – it's all normal attire but put together wrong, fitting badly and, most of all, never what you'd wear for an interview. Striped shirts with flowery skirts. Pantyhose, skinny heels and shorts. Clothes for the disco or last decade's weight – or maybe they just got dressed in the dark. I wonder if that one is really trying to find a job as a maid? Dress slit up to the *pupick*, heavy make-up, clingy, see-through blouse . . . Now you're just the kind of gal I need to take care of my husband, but what about the cleaning, dear?

They make way for us as we head down the hall. Conversations stop abruptly, hands fly self-consciously to stray hairs and puckered shirts. As we walk along, they try to outdo the last praise bestowed on the kids. We start with 'so cute' and move on to 'Jesus has blessed you with gifts greater than . . .' One young thing swoons. One shouts, 'Pick me!' There are a few 'I love Americas' and a general chorus of 'hellos' with noticeable effort applied to sounding American.

After wending our way through the crowd, making sure the kids are still with us and trying to look at each one with a 'Oh, you could be it!' expression of hope, we find Jessica. She is out in the hall as well, unmistakably the queen bee around here. Physically, she towers above all of us and weighs in at Frank times two. In contrast to the general garish-glam look of those milling about, Jessica wears her hair short and styled like all the boys in my third-grade picture. She actually has a straight part way over on one side. She carefully smoothes the hair over with a penny comb and a beefy hand.

'Mrs Rittman?' She mats down her hair once more before extending her hand for me to shake. 'I'm Jessica.'

I feel myself shrinking. This woman knows I am a bitch already. She is definitely not someone I should have spoken to

113

with any disrespect. This is a woman who owns a business, takes care of thousands of young, destitute women from one of the worst-run countries in the world. This is a woman who doesn't give a shit about being a macho, fat Asian broad in homophobic Singapore. This woman thinks I'm supercilious and as redundant as snack-size baggies. She's going to punish me here and now. She's not eyeing Frank up and down for new hairstyle inspiration. She is sizing him up. She can see he's a lascivious cad who wishes I still had my cheerleader outfit and would relocate, in a heartbeat, somewhere that allows you to pinch 16-year-olds. We'll have interview after interview with titillators only. I really wanted a big fat mammy to bustle about. Someone who maybe even, on a blue day, would think to make me chocolate chip cookies.

Jessica ushers us into a room VIP style, telling the girls to give us space, back off and settle down. She closes the door and motions for us to take our seats. There are placards on the wall bearing trite little quotes you'd find on last year's overstock of calendars, like, 'It is better to apologise and know that your beatings will heal than to not make the most of tomorrow.' There are lots of Catholic symbols – Marys and crosses – and Bible passages. The message as a whole: He served, you can too! There is a sign on the bathroom door advising 'Do not stand on the seat. You might slip in' with a line drawing of a person doing just that, the end result being that they are up to their ankles in the toilet bowl.

Once we're settled and have the kids engaged in snacking and colouring, Jessica hands us six binders. These are the dossiers of the women we are about to see. Each folder contains the answers to a questionnaire the candidates filled in previously: What would you do if a loved one back home died? Why did you leave your last employer? What can you cook? Can you give massage? Do you have any diseases? What would you do if there was an emergency? What does your father do? Are you married? What do you do on your day off? All the answers are the same. If a loved one dies, they would send money. They left their last employer because they didn't get Sundays off. 'I can cook spagedi.' 'I know massage.' No diseases. 'In emergency, I call 499 and Ma'am's cell phone.' 'My father, he was a farmer.' 'I am not married.' 'On my day off, I go to church and then study computer.'

Lunetta is our first interview. She has a tube top on and jeans with the label 'Pincme'. She smiles, showing all 900 teeth and lots of gum. We shake her hand. She looks at the kids and says, 'Oh, Ma'am, they are so good, so cute.' I thank her and begin: 'So, Lunetta, I really like being the mom. What I want is privacy. I want you to be like the shoemaker's little elves and just keep our place running smoothly and babysit when we want to go out. It isn't a big job, I don't think. You won't be overworked. Before you commit, though, you must check out the room we have for you. It's not the best. It's behind the kitchen and it's private and all, but it's small. Would that be okay for you?'

I've already hired her in my mind. Then she says, 'I make spagedi.'

'We like that but I will be doing all of my own cooking. Are you good with kids?'

'And hangbresers.'

'Great, great. Do you have kids of your own?'

'I'm not married.'

'Yes, but do you have kids?'

'I'm not married.'

'Okay, what would you do if one of my kids took a fall and started bleeding?'

'I would say, "Stop that now, eat chure spagedi."'

'Thanks.'

The next one comes in, Rose, aged 32. She is giggling nervously and immediately approaches the kids.

'So cute. Girl! What's your name?'

She's looking at Huxley, who is not reliably responsive yet. So, Sadie pitches in: 'I'm the girl. Name's Sadie. Huxley's a boy.' Sadie resumes her sticker book activity.

Rose laughs nervously over her gaffe. This is nothing new. Most people think Huxley's a girl over here. I keep his hair long, and he has pretty, chiselled features. It's not the end of the world to mistake him. I try to tell Rose this but she's already collecting her things and backing out the door.

Next is Diane. She is wearing a sweet cotton dress and pointy shoes that couldn't possibly accommodate a real foot.

'Diane, it's good to meet you,' I say and shake her hand. 'Tell me a little about yourself.'

'I graduated from university in the Philippines with a Masters in Fine Arts. I have two kids, four and seven. My husband died from lung cancer a year ago. My father was a farmer until he lost his legs to diabetes. I am one of eight children. I can cook spagedi.'

Of course I want to cry. Of course I want to hire all of them, but this is about saving the right person, someone for whom I can really make a difference.

'Masters in Fine Arts, what do you want to do with that?'

'I want to work in Singapore for an American family.'

'Will you be able to save up money and pursue the arts?'

'I send money home to my husband.'

'I thought he passed away.'

'Yes. Your children are cute. I love children.'

Then Posie comes in. Slim and sweet, dressed gaily but with decorum, with common sense. Posie smiles at the kids, sits straight and tall, smooths her skirt over her knees. Her black hair, which is neatly tucked behind her ears and falls to her waist, gives off a healthy shine and just-washed scent. She has some light lipstick on and from time to time she toys with a delicate, tiny gold cross necklace.

We ask her the usual questions and her answers are predictable but not unsettling. She would, for example, in the case of a mishap, call the emergency number instead of saying, 'Now, run over here with those scissors and eat chure spagedi.'

Huxley walks up to her and shows her his scribble. She warmly puts her hand on his shoulder and bends over to get closer to the work and to his little face. After a beat, she looks him in the eye and says, 'This is beautiful, Huxley.' He beams.

We meet a few more shy things who don't say a word, or speak to us in Tagalog, or who are nice but seemed tired.

When we leave the room, a thousand eyes widen in hope and wonder. I wish I could convince them that it would be an unpleasant experience working for me. American, shmerican – I am a Viking.

We find Jessica, who leads us to her office. Frank signs some papers, writes out a cheque for the bond and we're told we can come by tomorrow to collect Posie. We walk out with Jessica. The girls are beginning to gravitate toward her, silently, anxiously. Jessica raises her hand and points to Posie. She says, '*Ikaw ang napili nila.*' There is cheering. Frank whispers, 'It means: they chose you.'

I whisper back, '*Flintstones* episode?'

He shakes his head. '*Hazel.*'

Posie steps out to us. We embrace modestly. 'See you tomorrow,' I say.

As Frank, Sadie, Huxley and I walk down the hall, hand in hand, a fierce jab of trepidation sucker-punches me. What am I doing? I don't want someone in our house disturbing our unique, demented dynamics. I don't want the kids touched tenderly by anyone but friends and family, and I don't want Posie to become either. I'm all they need. I don't want to say, 'Shhh, the maid will hear' or 'Throw that away

117

before the maid sees it.' But the deed is done, the ink is dry, the bond is signed, the date is set, the maid is coming, ready or not. It'll be fine. Yes, everyone does it. It'll be fine. I swivel around to give Posie a smile, but her back is to me. She has her hands on her hips, clutching the bottom of her skirt, which is now hiked quite a ways up. Her butt is swinging from side to side as she shimmies down the hall, Soul Train style, singing, 'I'm gonna work for expats . . . I'm gonna work for expats . . .'

By the time Frank turns his head, she is swallowed up by the herd in the hall.

The Amah, the Bitch and the Homophobe

It's like Narnia. Behind every kitchen lies Amahville. Just go through a little door next to the refrigerator and you'll find their busy land. Each of the five buildings that make up Fortune Gardens is cylindrical and hollow in the middle. The maids inhabit the interior section, which opens onto the inside (think 'courtyard' and bring it down many, many notches). We, the employers, have balconies that look out at the sea, the sunsets, the playgrounds, the park. I can see who I'll run into at the store, who has a nice tennis serve, if Samantha and Greg's balcony light is on. The maids look inward at each other, downward to the lobby, or, if they lean over the waist-high wall, they might catch a bit of sky. Listen closely, you can hear the Tagalog, the giggling, the gossip, the radios. Take a peek and see the washing hanging out on bamboo poles, the neatly organised tools of trade and the clever use of discarded boxes, shelves, broken chairs. Can't you just smell the *beehoon* cooking?

To get to Posie's room, you open a door next to the refrigerator and go down an open-air walkway, at the end of which is a sliding door. Inside is a small box. At one end is a grilled window looking onto floor upon floor of other grilled windows. At the other end is another door that leads to the elevators.

'*Here's your room*,' I shout to be heard above the airconditioner. The part of the airconditioning unit that's in our living room quietly spreads comfort and refreshment. The part that is just above Posie's door and across from her bathroom spews out suffocating wind and rumbles like a dying freight train. Despite our electricity bills topping $1,000 a month, I keep the aircon on all the time because, frankly, it makes me nicer and Frank's company pays for it anyway.

'*And here's your bathroom.*' There is no door, just an alcove with a spigot on the wall and a squatter next to it. Nothing separates the toilet from the 'shower' or the user of either from the stares of the folks in Amahville. Posie is also to share her sleeping quarters with the dishwasher – a highly uncommon appliance in Singapore, though I doubt that makes her happy to find it as her roomie. The dishwasher was once in the kitchen, but wasn't built-in; it was just sort of plonked in the middle of the room. There was no other place for it unless you wanted to go through major renovations and I guess the owner didn't want to. It looked stupid where it was, as though I wanted to be sure everyone knew I had a dishwasher, the centrepiece of my culinary collection. We only used it a few times; the thing failed to wash more than it broke. In fact, I never saw any evidence of water having entered or left it. Granted, I had no idea what the control symbols indicated. They were awfully intricate but entirely too impressionistic, like a Japanese painting, full of haiku and wisdom – a half sun covering a flower with a hummingbird sucking out nectar, with a bee on its tail. But I'm sure I never pressed the one that meant: 'Dry clean, rattle violently, break dishes.' One day, we just put it out of sight.

'*Put your bag down.*' She has arrived with nothing more than a suitcase the size of a small birdcage. She follows me back out, through the door and into the kitchen where all is quiet and crisp, the sea surrounding us on three sides.

'What can I get you? Something to drink? Coffee? A piece of fruit?'

'Nothing, Ma'am, I ate breakfast at Jessica's.'

'Is that all of your things?'

'Yes, Ma'am.'

'Really?'

'Yes, Ma'am.'

She stands there looking at her shoes.

'Wow, great to be so unencumbered. Huh, I would love to be able to fit my life in a pillowcase. I mean it. Oh, the bits and pieces that have such talismanic pull for me. Can't leave any of it behind. I don't mean to say we have a lot of clutter here. Except you should see Frank empty out his pockets every night. He's like a kid. The things he wants to keep. Always dumping in a different place. I used to throw it away but he got pissed off when he couldn't find receipts or something. I don't mean you need to worry about him getting angry with you. No, Frank's easygoing. Huh, I'm the one with the temper. But don't get worried. It seems to be a little under control – until about three, which is when I tend to get angry at some damned thing or another. I know all about the count to ten thing but at 3 pm, doesn't matter. If you cross my lane while I swim or you cross my lane while I drive, if you cut in front of me at the supermarket or if you spill your milk, once I start yelling, I just can't stop. It's like an orgasm. Not that you should worry. Though I suppose it'll be best if you stay out of my way after three. Actually, I thought we might really never be in the same room at the same time. If you see me coming, just float on over to another room and make yourself busy. By eight at night, you go back into your part of the house. You can go out – use the door in your room, okay? – and meet the other maids. Have dinner, do something nice, but you can't come into our part of the house. Just be sure you have everything you need back there by eight. Okay? I don't want you to worry about going hungry in the middle of the night and not being able to set foot in our kitchen, so, here, take this.' I hand her $800. 'Get yourself a little fridge, a toaster oven, a microwave. Hey, if you want, buy yourself a nice little rice cooker too. Whatever else you need. Okay, so why don't you go now and do all of that getting settled in stuff and I'll see you at five. It's Halloween tonight. You have to dress up and give out candy. Look, I'm sorry about the room. You'll get it feeling cosy. Okay, out you go. See you at five.'

'Ma'am?'

'Call me Fran, for goodness sake. You're part of the – you live here now.'

'Ma'am Fran, what is the Halloween? What is an uncucumber?'

'Huh? Good, good, I'm glad you're asking questions. Never mind, just go and do.'

I pretty much shove her out the door. I hate her and I don't know why. I'll just send her cheques to Amahville and we'll never see each other. I'll leave notes about everything and before I come into a room, I'll announce, 'I'm coming in here now.' I don't want to look into her wide-set eyes that are full of confusion or see her sad little suitcase again.

I take the kids to the major grocery store at Parkway in the bike cart. We stop off at the Children's Library, which probably has a better inventory than any in the US. Classics and new titles from around the world cram hundreds of shelves. Unfortunately, randomness reigns, and it's too chaotic to ever find anything in particular. The shelving system is as arbitrary as the whims of the staff. For example, the three

Muslim volunteers do it according to colour, placing the dark covers in front and the colourful ones behind (those without any covers at all are cast aside). Another set of volunteers shelve by price. When we have the true, children's-book-loving, certified librarians, the alphabet rules but sometimes by title, sometimes by author, sometimes by publisher.

After we take out the eight books we're allowed I ask the kids what kind of Halloween candy they want. They want lollipops.

'Yuck,' I say.

'Jelly worms?' asks Sadie.

'Nah, it's gotta be wrapped.'

'Jaw breakers!'

'Do you know how many kids choke on them a year?'

'Gum?'

'Against the law.'

I can't believe my kids. *Chocolate* is the answer. What complete idiots. *Chocolate*, I think hard enough to send the message through. *Say 'chocolate'*. The correct response is: *chocolate*.

'Those, I want those.'

'What a sticky mess that would be. The moms would hate me.' She was pointing to the Tic Tacs.

While Sadie is looking up and down, weighing up the endless possibilities, I toss in 20 bags of mini Snickers.

'Okay, honey, I got your favourites.'

'They are?'

'Oh, sure. Let's just go home now.'

The candy costs $200.

I push the stroller home while Sadie and Huxley look at books. The journey takes about 30 minutes and there's lots of hefting and hauling to get the thing over enormous obstacles: the canals, construction, curbs up to my knees, foreign workers sleeping on the sidewalks. I'm shaking with fatigue when I get home. It's the hottest part of the day and I've been walking alongside cars and buses, negotiating this heavy thing and trying to make it fun for the kids. I just need a quick drink of water and to sit for a minute.

'Can I have some water? Can I have one of those candies?' asks Sadie.

'Can you just wait a minute? Take, take, take, peck, peck, peck. I get thirsty too . . . Do you ever stop to think that I am a person?' She looks at me. 'Ohh, now you see it. Yeah, I am. Sometimes I even have to go to the bathroom . . . for longer than a minute. Sometimes I just want want want too . . .' I go on and on like this for I have no idea how long. I stomp and slam and bang down cups to punctuate the tirade. All I know is that, yeah, it's about 3 pm and, unfortunately, it was the kids who crossed my lane this time. When it's out of my system, and the kids are staring at me in fear and misery, I pour them a cup of milk and grab a bag of candy. The chocolates have melted, soaked through the wrappers; they're entirely unsalvageable.

'Mommy's really sorry. I'm really stupid too, huh?' I show Sadie the bag of thick Snicker sauce. I put my head in my hands and cry. I don't want to be this mother, this person who can't hold on to a single thought or emotion long enough for it to be any more real than an idea.

'Vance sells candy, Mom,' Sadie says. The world has answers for her.

'I know, sweetie.' I kiss her head. 'Let's go there for some.'

Vance is the man who runs the little store. He's always kind to my kids and to me. I flirt with him because I'm sure no one really ever has. It makes him happy and nervous at the same time. Like it should. We bring home ten bags of Pokémon-shaped lollipops for $40.

We're all jazzed up about Halloween. It promises to be a big deal here. How it works is that families sign up on a sheet posted at the store and there is to be someone at home giving out candy and someone to take the kids around to participating addresses. Five or six sets of lists are drawn up and we're to break into groups and visit the units on the sheet in the order they're written so as to keep the flow consistent. We're all to assemble at the barbecue pits at 6 pm to get into our clusters and receive our destinations.

I dress Sadie as a fairy with butterfly wings I bought in the US. I figured I'd have some brainwave for Huxley. I miscalculated my brain and at the last minute just cut some holes in an old pillowcase. It was perhaps the oldest surviving pillowcase on the earth. Frank's mom gave it to us for some reason. She's a bit like that, giving us things that I never dreamed I'd need and laughed at only to later say, 'That's just what I needed' and mean it. Like the olive tongs which are hideous, scary even, but work like a charm, or the 'Doesit' which can hang hundreds of pounds from your walls without making a hole. She had used this particular pillowcase well, apparently, because the silhouette of her head was visible on the pattern, like a cameo. I couldn't bear to sleep on it without the irrational sense that I had to keep my head where she did. But, with a few snips, it works perfectly as a caveman toga-like thing. With some face paint and a tie, Huxley becomes Pillowcase Boy.

Posie gets home. I am determined to stay sunny. I drape a sheet over her and pour fake blood on her chin. While I tease her hair out, I tell her about Halloween. I give Sadie and Huxley their cue to say, 'Trick or treat, smell my feet, give me something good to eat.'

'That's when you open the door and put candy in the bags, Posie. It's fun.'

'Yes, Ma'am.'

'Fran.'

'Yes, Ma'am Fran.'

I'm wearing black shorts and an orange T-shirt. Frank, who has come home early to join in, is wearing a hideous rubber mask he found in New York. He stuffs a few beers into a backpack and takes pictures of the kids. He thinks to include a few with Posie and the kids.

There is a considerable crowd, and everyone has gone all out – elaborate homemade costumes on kids and adults; papier-mâché goody bags with hand-painted monsters. We have 'Pillowcase Boy', a Hooters wannabe, a fairy who ditched her wings after two minutes and Frank asphyxiating in a rubber mask. I find Tilda, her husband, Hugh, and their two kids, Tom and Lucy, and shepherd Frank and the kids over to them. They're standing next to Lisa, Roy and David (Huxley's age), a Canadian family. Unlike most of the couples at Fortune Gardens, both Lisa *and* Roy have jobs in Singapore. They're bankers. I introduce Frank all around.

'How's it going, Lisa?' I ask.

'Who knows. I only had ten minutes to get home, make dinner and put together the costumes. I got a call just as I was about to leave and had to finish a project.' She says it like I wouldn't have a clue what this is like. To the naked eye, I am living the typical expat-wife life, but the truth is I am waking up at four in the morning to work and staying up until 12 at night to finish, and doing a bit here and there throughout the day, and stressing about this wrinkle or that disaster in my job. I have no fewer than 50 emails to respond to on any given day, and 30 pages of contracts, not to mention manuscripts to download and read and send out. But because I am also at the pool, at the playground, committing to playgroups and socialising with leisurely ladies, no one really seems to get it.

'Yeah,' I say, 'I have two contracts to vet tonight. I'm hoping this doesn't last too long.'

'But you're so lucky. You can do your work whenever you want.'

'Are you kidding me? I start to panic if my kids aren't in bed by eight. I know it just makes my night longer.'

'At least you see your kids.'

'You get home and the work is done. For me, it's always there, faxes, emails, phone calls . . . always hovering.'

'I have to go to Jakarta tomorrow.'

'Yeah, and stay in a nice hotel.'

'I guess you haven't been to Jakarta. Not exactly like hanging out at the pool, eh?'

We have to stop there because Samantha, our ringleader, has just given a loud whistle between her teeth. 'Hey, everyone. Listen up. Get into a group with about ten kids. Some moms will be handing out right here, then you go to the units on your list. Have fun!'

I break into a little sweat. I don't know how I'll find a group. No one can really call me their friend yet. I wish someone would say, 'Fran, come on' but it seems understood that all the good, dear, old friends will be together. They are taking photos of each other and asking me to hold the camera. I get the picture.

Frank takes out a beer and cracks it open. I am mortified. Here we are doing a wholesome group family activity and he has to turn it into happy hour. No one else has a beer in their hand. Yeah, I want one too, but I'd never . . . not here at this event, our debut, if you will. Just as I am waiting for him to see my 'what a stupid ass you are' stare, he is reaching into his bag. 'Oh, God, not another!' I think. Actually, it's two more – one for Roy and one for Hugh. Then Valerie and

Sam come over to us. I introduce them to Frank: 'This is Valerie and you must be Sam? Frank, they're from Australia. They have a little boy Sadie's age, Andrew. He's in Sadie's playgroup.'

'How's it goin', mate, got another in your stash?' Sam says to Frank.

'Here you go. Like VB?' Frank says.

'Vitamin B, mate.'

Clive, Tess and Tag wander over.

I introduce them. 'They're from South Africa. Tag's Sadie's age.'

We all shake hands.

'Good idea, man. Can't go through another one of these without one. Feckin' bore.' Clive reaches in and grabs a beer. Hugh, Frank, Sam, Roy and Clive give a little tribute to VB.

'Best feckin' beer on earth.'

'Course, it's *Austrayan*.'

'Aye, that goes down good.'

'I don't know about you lot, but I reckon it's not halloween without a little treat.'

They toss their cans away. Sam reaches in for another.

'Bag's empty, mate. I'll shout the next round. Wait for me, doll.' He kisses Valerie and off he trots to the little store.

We have our group, thanks to Frank. Not to me, the one who perfectly timed my pool and playground appearances to coincide with the ebb and flow of the beautiful people. Todd and Caroline wander over. 'Oh, Frank, this is Caroline and you must be Todd. They're from Virginia. Jason is Sadie's age and Zooey is Huxley's.'

'Heard you brought some VBs,' says Todd as he reaches into the empty bag.

'Help is on the way,' Frank replies.

All the ladies congratulate me on hiring a maid.

The Japanese moms have to pass out treats at the

barbecue pits because they don't have maids at home. Their husbands won't allow it. And tonight, as on any given night, the husbands are totally unavailable, so there's no one home to answer the door. The Japanese men are seldom seen. The women can be found playing doubles together for the entire day, leaving the kids in the middle of the court, then treating themselves to Fattys, the restaurant above the swimming pool, for lunch, more tennis and Fattys for dinner. Their family core seems to be made up of seven women and 16 kids. But, my God, they're all gorgeous. How can their husbands stay away?

The Germans, the Indians, the Dutch, the Swedes, the Singaporeans don't show any interest in this Halloween thing, but the Japanese love it. We are a well-ordered throng as we move along the brick path accepting the Japanese offerings. Plink, plink, plink. It is finally Sadie and Huxley's turn. A green package about the size of a stick of gum is tossed into their goody bag. It's seaweed. Off the scales in nutrition.

'Hey,' I say to Tilda, holding up a seaweed. 'If it isn't 350 calories a serving, you can't call it a treat.'

'Bloody hell,' she says, 'if it isn't *chocolate*, it's a trick.'

Though it takes us over two hours to cover the schedule, everyone has a ball. By ten, the bags are full, the costumes dragging and all the doorbells have been rung. A scary story is told to the kids back at the barbecue pits and a lucky draw is held. The winner gets just what he needs – more candy.

11.30 pm: Hugh, Tilda, Tom and Lucy; Lisa, Roy and David; Valerie, Sam and Andrew; Clive, Tess and Tag; and Caroline, Todd, Zooey and Jason are all at our place and Frank is manning the blender.

12.30 am: The kids are sleeping in various nooks and crannies. We're dancing to loud music.

1.30 am: The security guard knocks at the door and demands we quieten down. This gives Clive a chance to tell some jokes. 'There's this Jew, a kefir and a feggit . . .'

'Clive,' I say, 'you might be insulting some people in this room.'

'I can see no one 'ere's a kefir or a feggit. Anyone a Jew?'

'Yeah, I am,' I say.

'Well, you'll like this then, the Jew makes off with all the money.'

2.15 am: Tilda and I eat all the chocolate from our kids' bags.

2.30 am: I'm sitting on Clive's lap trying to explain to him why these jokes are not nice. Valerie is sleeping. Tilda is mixing another drink and seems hardly affected by the evening. Caroline's saying, 'Put the music back on!'

3 am: Sam and I are dancing. We've danced the entire album of *Hair* but we're on the reprisal. When I'm not looking, Frank unbolts the door and allows our captive audience to leave.

3.05 am: Last time seen on clock . . . until . . .

4 am: I distinctly hear a door open and shut, behind our kitchen, in Amahville.

And the US is Where?

The days have taken on a pleasant rhythm. The kids are adjusting to Posie. In fact, they have quite a nice little time together, the three of them. That means I don't always have to take them with me when I do the shopping. Sometimes Posie even takes them while she does the shopping. But I wonder what's eating me now? I can't name it.

Perhaps all I need is just a little Thanksgiving in the air. Family time. Some leaves to crunch, a sweater to pull on, a football game to ignore, Kraft cheese promotions everywhere I turn. And then I can wake up the next day and be hot again. This is not the first Thanksgiving I've missed, but maybe it's the first I *miss*.

Halloween was plastered all over Singapore – the retailers love it. But forget about seeing so much as a feather to mark Thanksgiving. November 1, and it's beginning to look a lot like Christmas . . . and Deepavali.

It's not like I'm expecting giant pilgrim floats or even baton-twirling or marching bands. But maybe give me a ten-cents-off coupon for stuffing. The rebuff seems loaded with meaning. Everyone here just loves being able to ignore us, the US. And, gee, was that not me up there in line at the

Mooncake Festival last month waiting for my free moon-cake? And since I seem to be the only one who *likes* the double-yolk, bean-paste tarts, and since I am truly enthusiastic about honouring the fall of the Mongol Dynasty, I celebrated by having several. With wine. And that was *after* attending the very long ceremony at the pool in the evening, supporting the efforts of dozens of kids, some too shy to remember their routines, some too enthusiastic to keep with the program. There was lantern lighting, karate, ballet and choral performances, traditional dancers, flautists and a costume contest. We made it a group affair and thought we'd enjoy the evening with cocktails and nibblies, but the guards came around and told us to pack it up. 'No food or drink allowed at the pool.'

'But what about the stacks of mooncakes?' I asked, hoping for a reprieve just this once.

The others were already putting lids on and spoons away, telling me to give up.

'I have to point out that a mooncake is food,' I continued.

That does not compute. That does not compute. He stared.

Sam opened a fresh VB. The guard jerked to life, swivelled quickly toward the sound.

'There is no food or drink allowed at Mooncake Festival,' he said flatly.

'Right,' said Sam, 'I mistook "festival" to mean "a time to make merry".' He drained the can, crushed it and tossed it into a bin.

At the crackle of Clive reaching into a chip bag, the guard switched his focus.

'There is no –'

'Yah, dis is how we do it beck home,' Clive interrupted, waving a Tomimo Korn Chip ('Made the Mexico Way, Product of Malaysia') across the food still left out on the table.

The guard told Dana she couldn't smoke. 'I'm not,' she said, taking a drag.

Another guard, this one skinny and officious, Singapore's answer to Don Knotts, came hustling over, looking quite agitated. He stopped at me.

'Your kids are not registered,' he said, hiking up his pants and minding his posture.

'So?' I said.

'They cannot compete in the costume contest.'

'They're not competing; they're just standing up there,' I argued.

'They cannot compete in the costume contest,' he said.

'Well, I understand that they aren't eligible to win (the grand prize being two dozen mooncakes which – don't tell a soul – I would love) but, c'mon, they're just tiny kids. We weren't here in time to sign in,' I pleaded.

'Only registered children can compete.' He straightened his collar, squared his shoulders. A drip of perspiration rolled down the side of his face.

'*They are not competing*. Look, it's almost over,' I reasoned (and reasoning usually works here?). Indeed, prizes were being announced.

'Only registered children can compete.' He looped his thumbs in his trousers, shimmied them up his hips.

'Yeah, I didn't hear you the first 100 times. Okay, I'll get them off.' But I didn't. And he didn't come back. Sadie won second place.

Everyone in Singapore who wants a special day (birthdays excluded until further notice) gets one, complete with a hefty, bold acknowledgement. German Woodcrafters Day, Chinese Take Your Middle Child to Work Day, Indian Girl Power

Day, Guernsey Pasture Appreciation Day – whatever, it's acknowledged. Except the Americans.

In fact, one only needs to make a mental note of the two days when there *isn't* an observed holiday here. Jolly old Singapore. It's a place that tolerates, encourages and embraces cultural differences within three ethnic groups – Chinese, Malay and Indians. Each of them has a variety of religious and traditional celebrations, and when you add expats to the mix (but do ignore America) you will certainly find a way to never have to show up at the office.

You've got your Taoists, Buddhists, Christians, Free-thinkers, Hindus, Muslims, Sikhs, Parsees, Confucians and mixtures of all the above to consider. You've got your standard hometown pride to commemorate, too – National Day, May Day and such. Let's just scroll down and check out some of the events . . .

Festival of the Hungry Ghosts: Taoist; hell goes on holiday, ghosts escape.

Thimithi: Hindu; an excuse to go fire walking.

Deepavali: another score for the Hindus; turn on lights and remember good always triumphs over evil.

Hari Raya Puasa: Muslim; month-long daylight fast, perfect for midnight snackers and those who can't fit into their *tudongs* any more.

Vesak Day: Buddhist; pray, meditate, get buddy-buddy with the big B.

Thaipusam: Hindu; a must-see, honouring Lord Subramanian who represents virtue, valour, youth, beauty and power; people walk around with kavadis, semicircular large steel frames decorated with fruit, flowers and peacock feathers (do not stop reading, I am getting to the good part) supported by steel spikes and hooks (stay with me) inserted into their cheeks and tongues with skewers, while their feet are punctured with iron nails.

Birthday of the Monkey God: Chinese; put away the lap-top and write your charms in blood; mild skewering is okay.

Chinese New Year: granddaddy of them all; celebrated for two weeks. Holy hangover! Fourteen New Year's Eves!

You also have your Ch'ing Ming, Dragon Boat Festival, Hari Raya Haji, Navarathri Festival, Pilgrimage to Kusu Island, Maulidin Nabi and then Christmas and everyone else's New Year.

'Frank, do you think we should go away for Thanksgiving?'

'Yeah, maybe.'

I go to the phone.

'Who're you calling?'

'Hi, is Caroline there?'

'She's having her nap,' says Bethy. As I am leaving a message, I hear Caroline's voice in the background. 'I'm up, Bethy. You let it ring six times so now I'm up.'

'Sorry, Ma'am.'

'Hello,' Caroline sighs into the phone.

'It's Fran. Hey, sorry to bother . . . wake you. Just wondered if you'd have a good idea about where to go for Thanksgiving. We thought we'd get away.'

'Oh, well, there's lots of places but I was going to call you later today to tell you about Pam's.'

Pam is a mom in the playgroup, from Idaho. She has a thick head of delicious strawberry-blonde hair, a perfect smile, flawless skin, and a sweet, confiding disposition. She's married to a guy we all like; he is loose and talkative. Every-thing he says sounds like it's coming through a bong hit.

'Yeah?' I venture.

'She's having her annual BYOD/BYOM party.'

'What's that mean?' I ask.

'Oh, I keep forgetting you're new. It means bring your own dish and bring your own maid.'

'Dish?'

'Yeah, like pot luck.'

I am terrifically happy to be included in this expat Thanksgiving. A big American get-together will be the next best thing to family. Anyway, Thanksgiving back home is no longer what it used to be, for, sadly, little by little, my mom has gone entirely, completely, 100 per cent fat-free. The feast looks the same. I mean, if you passed by our dining-room window and took a gander at the turkey all trussed up like she was giving birth because Mom had tucked an orange into her gaping crevice, for flavour, I guess . . . I hope . . . or the swirls of mashed potatoes, or the Caesar salad loaded with croutons, or the yards of bread, you'd be sure we were assuming our holiday weight gain in one sitting. But, if you happened to look behind the salt shakers (containing non-sodium salt, which adds nothing to the food but does satisfy the urge to flick something on your dinner), you'd see a bright yellow bottle with a blue label that might give you pause: no-calorie, no-cholesterol butter spray. On Thanksgiving?

That's just the tip of the iceberg. The parmesan cheese on the salad: soy. The dressing: vinegar and guar gum. The turkey: sculpted out of 89 packages of Healthy Choice, fat-free deli meat. The potatoes: mashed with Butterbuds, non-fat, no-calorie butter substitute. The bread: braided pita. And the dessert: fruit. Okay, there is also my brother's favourite blueberry pie, which is a sore point with me. I mean, let's *never* disappoint Harris, never mind that I love chocolate chip cookies . . . but that's a matter for me and the sofa . . . it hardly bothers me at all now . . . I'm an adult, for God's sake . . . with kids of my own . . .

The food may have made its fat-freedom march, but we could still savour the tastelessness of the conversation around my mother's table. And that was what we came home for. Dad stopped saying, 'You've got to open a restaurant, Eunice.' Harris stopped asking, 'Can I have this last one, Mom?' My head stopped saying, *all this food is going to interfere with my alcohol absorption.* So, we moved right on to banter, escalating voices and terrific belly laughter. We rattled off embarrassing stories, exchanged barbs, challenged wits, offered unsolicited observations, revived old anxieties, created new ones and laughed like we never laugh with anyone else. We 'got' each other, and our spouses were chosen for better or worse because they fitted just fine. No one in my family married a mate who didn't withstand several tests of dinner-time verbal archery. When Dad was still alive we had the most fun. Talk about ripe for the picking. If we didn't touch on his hypochondria, it was only because we were on a jag about his temper. Sure enough, he'd get mad and storm out, until our cries of 'Come back, we're making fun of someone else now' combined with hunger softened his resolve.

Below-the-belt humour was always so well exercised, so precise, on those wonderful occasions. I'm sure most American families have a similar sentimentality and their lively feasts parallel my own. Why, even Frank's family, a group that never eats together, never goes out to dinner and considers the phrase 'happy birthday' too full of unseemly emotion, have what I'd call a normal Thanksgiving. One year we were on a roll, targeting his 90-year-old grandmother. We were on the floor – it was really just too much – when she forgot she couldn't leave in a huff without complete assistance. In a word, good, wholesome American fun. Like we all do in the US. So, this party at Pam's would take the sting out of a minor case of homesickness for sure. All these Americans . . .

The morning of the party, I decide to make a few dips in the 'no, never, no more' territory of my mom's offerings. There's one she found a hundred years ago in the *TV Guide* using nothing less than an entire jar of mayonnaise, and nothing more, except red dye number 9. You serve it with Ritz crackers. Where can I get Ritz crackers?

'Hi, is Caroline there?'

'She's napping.'

'Oh, I'll call back. When does she take her evening nap?' I joke.

'Usually at five, Ma'am, but today the party starts at three.'

At 2.40, the five of us get into the car with bags of beer, wine and my appetizers. I found the Ritz at Prestons. They're so old, the packet still has a recipe for Mock Apple Pie on it. Earlier this afternoon, I thought, what the heck, and made it. Looks good, kinda mooncakey actually. Posie is holding the dips on her lap in the back, the kids are snuggled under each arm. She manages to buckle them in before I can get out of my seat, having forgotten to do it myself. She also manages to keep the dips from tilting. She's wearing a bright red, silky dress that is perfect for her figure, her colouring and the occasion. I'm in a long-sleeved black spandexy dress, perfect for a New York cocktail party in November, and tall shoes, of course, perfect for standing, posing or sitting but awful for walking. And the dress is downright asthmatic in a hot car – in fact, it has stopped breathing altogether.

Pam's house is about 12,000 square feet of high ceilings and marble floors. Her furniture was collected. Everything is eye-catching, worthy of comment. Let someone else remark. I have dips to put out. But when she comes over to greet me, I do it: 'Pam! This is a gorgeous house! Omigod, it's huge. I love this table. Is it jade? *Wow*, I want that mirror!'

I don't covet the stuff, I'm just nice, that's all, and obviously these things matter to her so I want to make her feel good. But I *will not* say a word about her kajillion-carat diamond earrings or her sapphire-and-diamond pendant. Instead, I'll try to see if her ass is big. I sneak a glance. Nope.

'Those dips look great, Fran. Ritz crackers! As they say, "Everything's better on a Ritz."'

Dear little Fran and her dips and her adorable box of Ritz crackers. 'It's everything *sits* better on a Ritz,' I correct her.

'Right. Do you know everyone here?'

'No, just Caroline, I think.'

'Let me take you around.'

I am still holding my dips with the crackers parked on top as she leads me by the elbow, my spiky heels clicking and scraping on the smooth, spotless floor.

I meet Jane and Ted Walters, Sally and Tim Parker, Amber and John Pines, Paula and Scott Richards, and several other couples who all share some commonality that I can't quite place yet, like using the same barber or tailor but more personal than that. They probably all grew up together with moms named Beverly or Joan. The men had dads who called them 'Sport' and the women had dads who called them 'Princess'. Sure, my sister and I were called Princess, but usually by boys in pick-up trucks, behind our backs and typically shortened to JAP. Dad called Harris 'Butch'.

I am the only woman with a hemline closer to my chin than my heels. The others wear something that's just right for the church tea. I have a mass of gnarly hair. They have hairdos. On my right wrist, a sports watch that can tell me the differentials between a week's worth of track running, remind me to stretch, list the micrograms of salt I've lost and locate my perfect heart rate. On theirs, a tennis bracelet. I am wearing high heels and they are all – oh, yeah, the barefoot thing. Dumb Fran, stoopid Fran, you don't wear shoes in the house in this part of the world. If I take the shoes off, the dress won't look half as good. I'd rather be rude.

'Pam,' I whisper, 'you mind if I keep my shoes on?'

'Of course you can,' she punches me lightly. 'Anything goes in this house.' Her answer is so prompt, her smile so ready and real. What a gracious hostess. But I'm thinking she might have thick ankles. Let's have a look. Nope.

The men are all in banking or IT and the women are all Friends of the Museum or do part-time PR at the American Club. Wandering around, I hear the women's excited chatter about the upcoming shopping trip to the Philippines, the best ballet teacher and 'I'm sure the brunch is just as good at the Carlton'. From the men, legs astride, beers held at mid-breast, the talk is mostly about how impossible it is to work for Singaporeans, what it would take to sign on for another three years, and 'I'm sure the golfing is just as good at Tanamera'.

I struggle to feel connected. Are you not my American brothers and sisters? Do we not share memories of vacations at the beach, the mountains, stretches of highway, signs reading 'Last chance to stop at Pedroes for the best Pecan Rolls this side of the border', freezing cold oceans, summer camp, sitcoms, and, of course, loud, hysterical Thanksgivings? Maybe after a few drinks someone will lead the way to ribald, irreverent, uproarious, ironic. Any minute now, look out . . .

'And Frank, what do you do?' asks Paula. (Ah, perfect, watch this . . .)

'I'm a lawyer,' he answers. (Okay, Paula, now make a lawyer joke. A lame way to start but it'll pick up . . .) Amazingly, people start gravitating to Frank. Folks are moving toward a guy who's announced he's a lawyer. What this crowd needs is a CPA.

Frank looks uncertain about the attention. Is he being lured onto thin ice? But he takes a brave advance and announces, 'As I like to say,' and I mouth the words, 'I protect American copyrights from the world's pirates.'

'Shiver me timbers,' I add.

No one asks me what I do because they assume I don't. The ladies compliment my dips and my shoes. I gush over their tennis bracelets.

I go into the kitchen. State of the art. Half of the maids are in there, synchronised in their tasks, slicing vegetables, preparing platters, talking animatedly in Tagalog, stopping briefly to smile beatifically and ask, 'Can I help you, Ma'am?'

'Well, now, let's see. You've minded my kids, passed around hors d'oeuvres, made my dinner, cleaned the ashtrays. Perhaps I'll need you to breathe or chew for me, but for now, there really is little else I could possibly require so, no, thank you.' I am about to unravel but instead run outside to marvel at the lack of lawn Pam and Jacque are enduring.

Maids are pushing kids on the 35-foot swing set or catching them as they land off the trampoline. A few are putting on a puppet show in the life-size stage. One is rocking a newborn. Sadie and Huxley are hanging off Posie, one on the front and one on the back. They're having a ball. The maids are having a good time, too.

I head back inside and find Frank having a lively conversation with Jacque, who now seems to be pretending to smoke a joint as they talk. After a while, Frank accepts the invisible joint.

'Dinner is served,' announces Pam.

We troop into the dining hall, a space large enough to seat 50 people comfortably. The table is set with a china pattern so intricate it seems a great trespass to slop food on it. As soon as everyone is seated, the men ceremoniously slap down their cell phones just above their knives. Pam sits between Frank and me. She whispers, 'Can you believe them? I hope you're having a good time. Thanksgiving is hard for all of us.' Was that something between her teeth? Damn, she closed her mouth too fast.

Pam's maid brings out the salad. Tricolore with roasted

tomatoes and a few pine nuts. A cell phone goes off. Everyone's hand shoots forward, but Joe is the lucky winner.

'*Hell*-ooo,' he says, giving us a phoney put-upon face before excusing himself so he can talk loud enough in private for all to hear.

'Wrong number, was it?' I say. Laughter. I heard it. It wasn't just my own, was it? Before we can crescendo, another phone goes off.

'Phil here . . . yeah, ten hundred barrels, fine, and, hey, book me dinner for next Tuesday at The Grill in Tokyo.' Phil grabs a roll, butters it, and talks a doughy game for a few more seconds.

Before he finishes, it's Alan's turn. 'Did he try the bona-plop switch yet? No, of course he didn't, did he. Well, have him try that . . .'

'Frank, look! Your pigeon's back and she's got a message,' I say. Frank, who has nothing next to his bread plate but crumbs, nods with a hint of appreciation. This is Thanksgiving. You don't bring your cell phone and your palm pilot to Thanksgiving. You bring funny barbs and big appetites, you unbutton your jeans, you flop out on a sofa.

Soon, the women's voices weave between the phone calls, discussing the latest *amah* drama.

'When Toodi asked for New Year's Eve off, I had a cow,' comes floating down the table.

'All Jake's underwear turned pink. She hid it in her room.'

'Well, at least yours isn't pregnant!'

Sound of 25 forks dropping. A pregnant maid means immediate deportation. That is the law. Maids also can't consort with citizens or permanent residents, stay out past eight at night or have men in their rooms. Restrictive as it sounds, these are the laws for maid employment in Singapore. It's why we had to take out a bond.

'Please don't say anything to anyone,' she asks the 25 of

us plus the assorted maids milling about, one of whom is probably hers.

When we finish eating, the kids perform a song in Tagalog for us. Oh, jeez, and now are they going to prattle off a *few of their favourite things* . . .

'Pam, would you mind if I sent Posie home? I'll take over. I'd just really like to be able to get near my family.'

'Sure, I totally understand. Let's all send our maids home. Everyone,' she calls out, 'Fran had the great idea of sending the maids home.'

The expressions pass through befuddlement, horror and then intrigue.

'Golly, why the heck not?' says Sue.

'Yeah, that's right. Let's,' says Katherine.

'Do we dare?' asks Deborah.

'It's Thanksgiving,' I say. 'Family!'

'But what about the cleaning up?' whines Janet.

'We can do it!' I say. The crowd becomes a tiny bit frenzied. The very idea of self-reliance is invigorating. We call in our maids, give them taxi fare. They refuse to leave. We insist. They stand firm. We call the taxi service. They manage to get everything cleaned and orderly before the taxis arrive, coffee brewing and desserts laid out on the buffet.

'Are you sure, Ma'am?' they all ask as the cabs idle.

'Yes, go, go . . .' we say gamely.

'. . . before I change my mind,' I hear someone say.

Later, we sit politely in the living room. The kids are sweaty and swinging on candy highs and lows and asking to watch television. No one unbuttons his or her pants, no one busts a gut. No one pierces his or her body, no one writes in blood, no one walks on fire, burns fake money or dances while wearing a scary dragon costume. No wonder Americans are ignored.

I might join the crowd.

Take Two

Wednesday nights are for Fran and Frank staff meetings. First, we loosen up with an hour of tennis followed by two jugs of Tiger Beer and two bowls of palm-oiled Camel Brand crunchy nuts at the New Barrel Pub. We read the minutes of the last meeting, discuss old business, bring up new business, digress and meander, continue in a peripatetic fashion as we force the last half mug down, adjourn, go home, check on the kids and watch *The Practice*. I eat a tuna melt and Frank picks at a piece of buttered toast. We go to bed at 11.

This particular night, we dispense with reading the minutes of the last meeting because I remember it clearly and Frank remembers it wrongly. Let's just say I was right and leave it at that, shall we? My agenda had two items on it but I crossed out 'try a new sandwich'. Frank hates my tuna habit. At the first sound of the can opener, he makes up the sofa bed; he screams at the sight of me peeling a hardboiled egg. I had trained myself to eat these things only on nights he was travelling but then I started to slip, to let go, and now, after being married for seven years, I am often spotted carelessly sitting cross-legged on the floor in a long, faded T-shirt and saggy briefs, flipping the TV dial, hunched over a bulging, smelly sandwich. I am going to try a new sandwich, soon – maybe not tonight, but soon. I need to make that commitment to the marriage. I need to try harder to like maybe just cheese. Did Cantor Donald not prophesise before our wedding that there would be many sacrifices along the path? He was so right. Just cheese, yup. And a shorter T-shirt. And tighter undies. Next thing you know, I might even brush my teeth before bed.

The remaining issue on my agenda is planning a vacation.

'Frank,' I say, shifting my chair closer, 'let's go away.' He is noisily eating his peanuts. He has this habit of popping them in one at a time and sort of coming down on them with a hard surprise attack – K-E-R-R-R-U-N-C-H – followed by a rapid-fire chomp, chomp, chomp. He couldn't do this in the US. Unlike American cocktail peanuts, these palm-oil-coated ones aren't greasy; they look shellacked. I watch his mouth hammer at a few more nuts before he feels he can leave it for a minute and turn his attention to me.

'Sure, sure, sounds good.' He gulps down some beer and opens his leather-bound daily planner. 'When were you thinking?'

'Next week?'

'I can't next week, I'm in Jakarta,' he says, pointing to the word 'Jakarta' and the line drawn through the week as incontrovertible proof.

'Okay, the week after?'

'Alrighty. I'm in Taipei from Tuesday until Friday,' he says, tapping at the Xs on his daily planner and circling the word 'Taipei' for me. Yes, exhibit B, indeed. 'But after that I'm clear until Sunday.'

'Great, so we'll go somewhere for a long Saturday. Let's book the living-room sofa.'

'Just until I have to go,' he points, 'to Bangkok.'

There was a woman I used to see at the pool who was

somewhat unfortunate-looking. Suddenly, she wasn't there any more. Her husband sent her and the kids packing. I didn't have a chance to get to know her but now and then I had heard snippets of conversation about her between Valerie and Tess, who were her good friends. Apparently, she discovered her husband cheating. She caught him with his pants down at home. She was supposed to have been in a clinic getting some radical new treatment (for you-know-what – cellulite – the poor thing), but she chickened out.

Word is the husband just rolled his eyes and, somewhat bored of the game already, said to the closet, 'Come out, Dorrie, gig's up.' Dorrie popped out.

'Dorrie, I believe you know my wife?' He nodded from one to the other.

'Hi Ma'am. Don't worry, I always change the sheets, Ma'am,' Dorrie said.

At first, he was extra careful, backed up his false alibis with sincere little scribbles in his Filofax, irrefutable testimony to his arduous travel, his dedication to home and hearth.

'It's okay, Dorrie,' he'd whisper at some hotel in the city, 'my datebook says I'm in Jakarta. I left it lying open.'

'You left it out? Ma'am will think I don't clean the things away.'

I shake the image from my head. Not Frank, not us. We talk. We're friends.

'What about over Christmas? That'd be a great way to celebrate, don't you think?' he says. K-E-R-R-R-U-N-C-H, chomp, chomp, chomp.

'Can't. There's the children's party at Lisa and Roy's and Caroline's Christmas Eve cocktails and I'm on the planning committee for the expat Christmas Day party. It's in the function room. It's all sorted out.'

'Sounds cosy.'

'Wait, before all of that, you know, we have your birthday.'

'God, you know what I want to do for my birthday?' Frank looks off, squinting dreamily. 'I seem to remember some sort of promise . . .'

I squirm in my seat a bit. 'Anyway, we're having a big dinner party at our house.'

'Really?' he snaps back. 'In fact, that is *exactly* what I want to do. I was just going to ask you if you'd mind inviting everyone we barely know over, doling out a fortune feeding them and getting them drunk, and spending the rest of the night cleaning up a big mess. Please, please promise me – because this is my 35th – that you'll also get really stressed out all day long and leave me with the kids.'

I nod and cross my heart.

'You know me too well,' Frank smirks.

'Um, then,' I continue, 'we're all going to Anywheres for dancing.'

'You are a mind reader! I love dancing. I *especially* love it in a group situation.'

'Yeah, the Burnses, the Markses, the Hendricks, the Landrocks, the Tildons, the Stones and Irish Kell . . . everyone!'

'Who is anyone!' A beat. 'And then, Fran?'

'What do you mean, Frank?'

'I'm turning 35, Fran.'

'Yeah, but we didn't really think you would, did we, Frank?'

'But I am, Fran. You made a promise.' The good Cantor Donald also prophesised that if we did not keep our sacred oaths to each other, our marriage would falter.

'Oh, look at the time. We gotta get home if we want to

watch *The Practice*.' I call to our regular waitress, 'Tanya, we'll settle up now.'

At home, I eat a cheese sandwich.

While Frank was in Jakarta, I caught up with work. While Frank was in Taipei, I shopped for his birthday, Hanukah and Christmas. He never called and he didn't leave me his itinerary. I wanted to talk to him but even his secretary didn't know where he was staying.

While Frank was in Bangkok, I marinated a brisket, made three different polenta pizzas, baked five dozen chocolate chip cookies and whipped up batches of dips. In all, I swam six miles, ran 100 miles, invented recipes for fried oyster falafel, crab-stuffed hushpuppies, anchovy puffs and beer-battered popcorn (don't bother, it's better with mayonnaise and white bread), caught the kids off the slide 500 times, pushed them on the swings 900 times, erected a kingdom of sand castles, wiped ice-cream off small fists until my hands became forever grafted with cheap paper napkins, and took the kids to the zoo, the bird park, the science centre and to see the 'snow' at Tanglin mall.

I wished Frank were with us then. We stood there with a meringue of bubbles on our heads, surrounded by thrill-starved Singaporeans – children, adults and even disenfranchised youths – whooping it up together in the communal lather, pushing and shoving to get closer to the 90-foot-high plaster Santa whose pipe was the source of the white stuff. If you got real near, you'd get a blast like a pie in the face. A father and two boys about ten and 13 mowed Sadie down in their rush to experience 'snow'.

'Hey, asshole,' I shouted. I must have gotten the name right because he turned around. He looked at me innocently, curiously, his cheeks and nose inexplicably rosy. His expression turned impatient – the Santa was waiting, could I please finish my sentence? I couldn't. I forgot what to say next. Then I thought of something. I shouted it loud and clear. 'It's soap, you moron! See?' I threw a snowball at him, which just glopped on my feet. I started to show him how futile it would be to build a lather-man. Sadie tugged my arm. Tears started to flow down her cheeks. Everyone looked at me. The mall music – 'White Christmas', 'Silent Night', 'Jingle Bells' – came to a screeching halt. Santa stopped belching snow and fixed his plaster gaze on me.

> *'Twas two nights before Christmas,*
> *And all through the mall,*
> *Not a creature was stirring,*
> *Not a sound in the hall.*
> *There came a pop, pop, pop,*
> *From the bubbles of snow*
> *That made everyone happy,*
> *Till Fran let them know.*

It's soap, you moron . . . It's soap, you moron . . . The words echoed through the streets, into every village and every home. It's soap, you moron. I grabbed Sadie and Huxley and slid away to the parking lot.

After a while, once hot chocolate had been sipped and marshmallows dunked in the festive lounge of the Regency, the kids stopped crying. I tried to explain to them that in America, you call someone an asshole and they don't pause to wonder what possibly elicited such a rude reaction in a fellow man. They just say, 'Yeah, well, screw you.' Right? So, Sadie, Huxley, I was out of my element, you know? Like when you find yourself in the wrong playground or something. Get it? Here, I don't know what's going on. They cock their head, look all perplexed, say 'Sorry, sorry' and continue pushing the guy in front, who's pushing another guy in front. I mean, Sadie, Huxley, you tell me, are they really innocent or is it their strategy: to get you to feel too humiliated to continue firing away? Sadie tried so hard to keep up with me. She nodded her head and said, 'Mommy? Is Santa from the US?'

'There *is* no S . . . I mean, I don't think so.'

'Mommy?'

'Yes, puddin'?'

'He might not like it if you call him an asshole.'

'Let's not use the word again, okay?'

But the very next day, we were driving down a road that suddenly became one lane due to construction. There was no warning sign. I came head to head with another car. I happened to be in the correct lane. If I backed out, I'd be moving into the cross street and major traffic. He could have just pulled into a driveway. But he refused to budge. So did I. We sat there gunning our engines. Mortal enemies, only death could choose the winner. He sat, he gunned. I put the car in park and leapt out, pointing my finger at him. 'Hey, idiot! Get the hell out of your damned car, you stupid asshole.' He rolled his windows up. I jumped onto his hood and did a little monkey dance. 'Get the fuck out!' I screamed. Lots of passersby were rubbernecking now, plus two outdoor restaurants full of people. A second later, someone ran out of a nearby house and entered the man's car. My opponent rolled down his window and asked me to please get off his hood. I said, 'Yeah, just as soon as you back up.'

'Okay,' he said pleasantly, beginning to back up, with me on the car. I hopped down.

'Yeah, it *better* be okay!' Walking back to my car, I threw in another 'asshole' just because I had one on deck. Then I got limp. I mean, what was all that? Was he just waiting for his friend and innocently, albeit stupidly, thought I wouldn't mind waiting too? Maybe he finally realised I was too dangerous to push around. Or, maybe it was a solution – save face for him, show me for the lunatic I am and then we can all get back on the road. Whatever it was, it felt a lot like swinging hard and missing the ball. I was hungry for my next victim. I had no idea what to say to Sadie, who was searching my face for an explanation. I looked at her and then back at Huxley. 'Come on . . . I'm sorry, but he was! Okay, okay. My holiday promise: Stop getting so mad. No more bad words.'

The day before Frank's birthday party, I put my brisket in the oven. I had told Prestons I'd need a big one. Since I didn't know the conversion from pounds to kilos, I thought 'Australian' a good standard of meat measure.

'There will be ten Australians,' I informed the butcher. He gave a low whistle. When I got there to pick it up, he solemnly unfurled the thing with respect and dignity, a veritable beefy flag ceremony. Then a couple of minions picked it up, hoisted it on their shoulders and paraded it down the aisle like they were carrying the Pharaoh's palanquin.

'Hey, there's no way this is gonna fit in my oven,' I said nervously.

'No problem.' A band of merry hatchet men arrived and chopped it into four smaller pieces. I took it home to the tune of $400.

The trick of making a good brisket is to wrap it securely in foil, cook it on a low heat, and leave it alone.

I steal out of Michelle's playgroup after three hours and slip back into the apartment to check on my brisket.

'Posie?' I call.

She appears in the kitchen. A second later, I hear a door close.

'Was that our door?' I ask her.

'I was napping,' she says.

'That's fine. I just wondered about the noise.'

'I didn't hear noise. I was asleep.'

'No, just now.'

'Yes, I only just got up.'

'Yes, but I heard it while you were in here.'

'I had to nap. I have female pains.'

'Oy *gvalt*, okay. I'm just checking on the meat. Take some aspirin.'

The perfect scent isn't hovering so I reckon it isn't done. I hike up the oven to six and take the kids to the playground. When I get home, four aluminium pans are sitting on the counter.

'Posie!' I holler. She appears from her side of things, still looking tousled and groggy. 'Did you take this out?'

'I smell a burn, Ma'am.'

'It's not your fault that you don't understand brisket.' I say it more as a 'calm down, Fran' mantra than for her sake, but nevertheless I can hear my voice take on a dangerous trill.

'I think it was in too long, Ma'am.'

'*It's really not your fault that you don't understand brisket, Posie.*'

She peels back a corner of the foil.

'*What are you doing?*' I jump up and down, the first steps to the monkey dance. 'You think you can uncover my brisket? Who do you think you are? You, who knows nothing about brisket!'

'Yes, Ma'am. I want to show the burn.'

'It's not burned! It's got a still-a-long-way-to-go smell. I know. *You* don't know. I know!' I cover it tightly, not even looking at it because eye contact with an unfinished brisket immediately gives it the kybosh.

'Posie,' I say, with tortured, measured calmness, 'I'm throwing a birthday party for Frank tomorrow. This is –'

'Sir was born two days before Jesus?' Her eyes light up; she claps her hands in glee.

'Yeah –'

'Very blessed is he.'

'Yeah, *this* close to being King of the Jews . . . anyway, I have a big dinner party tomorrow. You'll have to work with me, okay? Right now I have to meet up with Samantha for a run. *Don't touch the brisket!* Understood?'

'Yes, Ma'am. Have a nice run. I'll give Sir and the kids dinner and their bath.'

'Frank won't be home until late tonight.' Her face falls.

After letting Samantha talk for a few minutes, I contemplate confiding in her about something I cannot get off my mind. Her life, as usual, is full of treasured moments, little gifts and endless satisfaction. It's terrific stuff to keep you leaping through a long, hot run. But today, my thoughts are wedged in too tightly to allow my spirits to lift. She's talking about how her daughter, Heidi, helped a sick cat give birth to nine healthy kittens. Meanwhile, I'm remembering something that happened very recently in Manhattan, just before we came back to Singapore. I was walking down the street and heard someone behind me. 'Yo, yo, yo, hey baby. You the one, baby . . .' He went on for a while like that and I was loving it. Then I realised that any self-respecting woman shouldn't. So I turned around to glare at him but before I could work up a scathing look, he said, 'Oh, you *old* . . .' Crestfallen, I faced front and continued on. He was a nice molester, though. He tried to make me feel better: 'Dat's not to say you don't have a few good years left, baby. You okay. Aw, I was just teasin'.'

153

Before Samantha can tell me the name of the ninth kitten, I cut her short and blurt, 'I promised Frank I'd bring another woman to bed when he turned 35.'

She gives me quite a shocked look. 'Oh, no, no, no, don't worry. I wasn't asking you. How funny. I mean, not that you aren't his type. Jeez, anyway . . .' And I begin to explain. Who knows how the pact came about, but, over the years, it's loomed and hovered like my own personal cloud. I feel like if I don't come through, the wild child he married will be forever gone, replaced by this 32-year-old frumpinstein who reminds herself that Wednesday isn't tuna day any more and carries moist towelettes. Samantha laughs and dabs her forehead with a *shmattah*. I continue, 'After ten years of promising, it's like judgement day . . . am I still a ride on a Harley or a tilt on the recliner rocker?' She offers me her second *shmattah*. 'Thanks,' I dab. We used to stay up late and spend Saturday mornings drinking Baileys and having sex. We once did it in an alley in the city. And another time in the file room at his office . . . On a train once! Jeez, before I met him, I had two men. At one time. Okay, I'm going to do this. I'm going to just call some service and make a memory. Yeah, and this 23-year-old, flawless, never-had-a-baby – never mind that my babies were too big to even call babies – Asian, lithe girl will knock on my door wearing better clothes and better legs. And me, the nice old lady of the house, can pay her and see her safely to a cab.

We arrive back at home. I thank Samantha for listening and she wishes me luck, adding, 'You know, Fran, Frank loves *you*.' She says she can see it in his eyes.

Like what I saw in Darren Wynoski's? Darren was my sister's boyfriend from college. He campaigned for a ménage à trois with Bonnie every time he called and I picked up and every time he visited. He was a Mack truck of a guy who led the football team to victory, an African–American adopted by a Polish family late in his youth. I don't remember what

154

happened to his own parents, but he took on the name Wynoski and did his best to be an African–American Pole, which is hard without many role models around. Now, if I had brought home a 600-pound, made of kryptonite, black guy, my dad would have thrown me across the room and locked me in for a fortnight. Which was why I always snuck around. But this was sweet-sweet Bonnie and no one really ever got mad at her. My parents thought Darren was great.

One day he came over for dinner and we were all on the front lawn tossing a football. I fumbled and the ball hopped over a little shrub and smashed my dad's study window. Darren scooted down and reached in to get the ball. We were called to dinner and went inside. No sooner had the corn landed on the table, but there was a knock at the door. Dad went to get it.

'Sorry to disturb your dinner,' said the sergeant, detecting Dad's paper napkin tucked into his shirt. 'Neighbour reported a thief at your house. A large Negro fellow in black shorts, seen breaking your window.'

Dad explained that he was our guest and a ball had smashed the window. The officer hesitated, looked squarely into my father's eyes to be sure he was telling the truth and hadn't been coerced into protecting the criminal. Unconvinced, he pulled out his card. 'Here's my name and number if you remember anything else.'

A few years later, without intervention, Bonnie married a Jewish boy from New Jersey.

I still have some of tomorrow left to find my solution. I also have a bazillion things to do. I walk in, sniff. Yes, it's done to perfection! I place the pans on the counter. I walk away. PS, you don't view the brisket until the next day. It's all a matter of trust.

155

I wake up at 5 am, have coffee, check emails and faxes, and feel sorry for myself for being up so early, until I hear someone get into the elevator and realise I'm not so alone. I go for a run, come back to a still-sleeping household and write 'HAPPY 35th BIRTHDAY' in red lipstick on every mirror in the apartment. I wake Frank up with a birthday kiss under the covers and, while he showers, I make him his favourite breakfast – an onion omelette with cheese, sausage and bacon, beans on toast, and coffee with Baileys. (But forever damned be the simple hardboiled egg!) He says he has to go into the office for just a few hours, which is surprising since he claims to have never gone to school, classes or work on his birthday. I could use his help watching the kids while I work on the party.

Still, it's early and there's no need to start stressing out. The brisket is done and just needs carving, the appetizers just need thawing, and other odds and ends can't be done too far ahead anyway. We'll need to get the beer and wine and ice and set up, but I tell myself to calm down, there's still ten hours till showtime. Besides, I have Posie. She's no dummy, she's a pro, she's dying to be busy. I don't use her enough, in fact. So, yeah, let's send Posie out with a shopping list. I need to unwind.

'Posie,' I call.

She appears at my side. 'Yes, Ma'am.'

'I need you to do some shopping for Frank's party.'

'For Sir?' she says, brightening.

'Well, for the party. Yeah.' I tell her what to get, and write it down as well. 'I'll need corn chips, they cost about $4; cheddar cheese, $7; smoked salmon, $7; caviar, the black kind, $10; Greek-style yogurt, $3 . . .' I draw a sketch of the type of baguette I want and extend my arms to show her 'this big'. I write down the names of all the wines we need and their prices. I tally up for her the money she will likely need.

I grab the coffee can where we keep some household money and hand her $300. 'Now, that should cover it. See you soon.'

The kids and I go out. It is a cloudless, glorious day – hot as ever and perfect for a morning at the pool. Everyone is already there. My friends are poaching in the shallow end of the baby pool and the kids are teetering on the edge of the turtle pond. I sunscreen Sadie and Huxley, put Hux in his inflatable armbands and waterproof diapers, and set them free. I take my place next to Valerie.

'How goes it, matey?' she asks.

'Ugh, I've got some problems,' I answer. I didn't know I'd be going down this path but she caught me off guard with the 'How are you?' I could have said 'Fine', like most normal human beings. But I have always been so touched by the term 'How are you?' that I've never been able to remember the word 'Fine', or that I'm not supposed to pause, contemplate and launch into a monologue. When I say 'Well', it's not my final answer; I'm not saying 'Fine'. I'm beginning: 'Well . . . I had an awful day already . . .' Sometimes people walk away, but, hey, they asked an intelligent question and I'll talk as long as I bloody well like. Valerie is too relaxed and too firmly planted between my hips and Tilda's to do much else but listen.

I tell her about the promise I made ten years ago and how it has not been forgotten but, rather, has snowballed in meaning. I tell her about the man who followed me in New York, and we laugh.

Tilda asks, 'What's so funny?'

'Well, you know it's Frank's birthday . . . you are coming over, aren't you?' She nods. Tess, Caroline and Dana make their way over. 'You're all coming tonight, right?' They nod.

'Sorry, Valerie, but I'll have to back up.' I repeat it all.

'Frannie, only you would feel old on someone else's birthday,' Dana says.

Sadie paddles over. 'What's so funny, Mom?'

We burst out laughing.

'I know,' Tilda says, 'why don't you have Sadie and Lucy asleep in your bed when we get back tonight?' Lucy is her daughter. Her kids, in fact most of our guests' kids, are coming over tonight. By the time we all go to Anywheres, they'll be sleeping on floors and sofas and beds, to be taken home later in parents' arms. The sense of extended family at Fortune Gardens is probably the single most precious aspect of my new life. In the light of day, around my friends, I feel the complications easing up. They are upbeat and pull the humour out of me easily and appreciatively. The environment is safe, perhaps because it is relatively temporary but also anchored by how important each day is to small children. We are well suited to each other and are quickly becoming essential to one another, sharing events and histories, dreams, learning the depths and oddities of each other's character, without ever having to revisit places in the past where we don't want to venture. To them, I am not the person on the freezing cold deck worrying that life was not working and working was not life. The beauty and relief wash over me. And then I start picturing each one naked with Frank.

'Put two Barbies on the pillow,' Valerie guffaws. She's got nice shoulders, good stomach – too good, actually.

'Dress up in a wig,' Tess offers. She has a beautiful face, luxuriant hair. Nu-uh.

'Have Collin dress in a wig,' Dana adds. If Dana covered her eyes and strapped down her boobs . . . she'd still have those lips.

I am surrounded by sensuous, lovely, adored women, mothers, my age. I feel better thanks to their efforts to package my issues up as a gag. But somehow, in the course of my life with Frank, this 35th birthday quest was merely a salient example of my vow that I would never grow up. Cantor Donald prophesied: 'Changes will challenge the ties you forge today.' Amen, Cantor Donald!

Frank calls to say he won't be able to come home early. His friends are taking him to lunch. 'Oh, okay, but don't eat anything. I'm making a special dinner.'

What friends?

'Schnitzels?' he asks.

'Well, no, but you'll like it.'

Panicked that I hadn't thought of how much Frank likes German food on his birthday, I decide that when Posie returns I'll send her out again for something German – maybe pretzels.

I remember Frank's 30th birthday in Manhattan, before kids. I had invited dozens of friends to a dinner I organised at Frank's favourite restaurant, The Heidelberg Inn on Second Avenue at 86th Street. I had just discovered that I was persona non grata at my job with The Very Famous Agency because I pissed off a very important person in the department. I told him I couldn't get him coffee, that I was busy. When you're a hopeful assistant at The Very Famous Agency, you're supposed to say, 'Thank you, Sir, can I have another?' *Thwack*. But I lacked the correct upbringing to knowingly humiliate myself. Anyway, by the time we all convened at the Heidelberg, I was pretty much out of work. I whispered in a few ears, 'Listen, I don't think I can pay for all of this . . .'

'Don't worry!' was the constant rejoinder.

I had decorated the tables with cloths and streamers made up of cheques written out to Frank Rittman for $1 million. He had always wanted to be a millionaire by the time he was 30. I had questionnaires for everyone to fill out about their experiences with Frank. We drank, we ate good German food and danced with the oompah band. Word must have spread about my predicament because everyone shoved wads of bills into my pockets at the end of the night. After the last guest had left, Frank and I had a nightcap and I took out my roll to pay the bill. 'It's a wonderful life,' I said. 'I made $400 on this party!'

Where is Posie? I wonder. I look at my watch. It's four o'clock. I have to get moving on slicing the brisket. I thought she'd like to watch me do it but I can't wait all day. I select the best knife for the job, even though brisket really just falls apart; it's the nature of the meat. It's what makes it so good. I take the tinfoil off the first pan and spear the hunk. The fork doesn't slide in as easily as I would have expected. In fact, it takes a great deal of effort to penetrate at all. One . . . final . . . puuush . . . from above on a chair. At last! Next, I move it to the cutting board. I slice. I slice. I slice. I get another knife. With a little more downward pressure, I should manage okay. I get another knife. What is it with these things? I go to Frank's toolbox. I start sawing, axing, hammering, screwing, wrenching. Each pan is the same. I am exhausted and there is nary an Aussie-gram worth saving.

Posie comes in.

'Oh, thank God you're here, Posie. I am in a terrible state. I have to get back to Prestons right away . . .' I stop because I notice she is unpacking *four* bags of corn chips. Maybe there was a promotion. 'I'll be much faster if you stay with the kids. *If* I can even make it there and back in . . .' I stop again because she is taking out the *third* container of yogurt. 'Posie,' I say sharply, 'what is going on?'

160

'I ran out of money, Ma'am. I couldn't get the wine.' She puts the seventh block of cheddar cheese on the counter.

'Posie! We went over this. The little dollar sign means how much *money* not how *many*. Oh my God! I even counted it out in front of you. We have ten jars of caviar and seven packages of smoked salmon but no wine. People will be very thirsty, Posie! You better take this back.' And then I think to add, so there can be no confusion, 'Take the *extras* back. Get the wine. Take the kids with you. Good luck to us all.'

I drive like a maniac to Prestons, squeal into two parking spots and hoist a trash bag full of mutilated dinner over my shoulder like a carnivorous Santa. I walk in and swing it onto the counter, madly ringing the bell for service. The butcher comes out. 'Ah, so good to see you. Come back for more –'

'You have the nerve to call this brisket?! This cow must have been roaming the streets of Calcutta for the past 90 years before you fellows swooped down!'

He laughs.

'It's not funny! I have a dinner party. Ten Australians, *remember*?'

'Don't worry. Don't worry. Brisket sometimes do that.'

I start to cry. 'Don't worry? How can I not worry? Shit!'

'Take this.' He hands me a perfectly gorgeous roasted tenderloin worth twice as much as my brisket. 'And this.' He gives me a large platter of grilled vegetables. 'Oh, you might as well take this since it so late now, no one else come in for it.' He gives me a tray of roasted potatoes and 50 jumbo shrimp.

Now I am really crying. 'Oh, thank you, thank you.' He hands me a tissue and I wipe my eyes. I hear his service bell ring. An angel just got his wings . . . It's a wonderful life.

161

With all this prepared food, I have time to get dressed. Posie even sets things up, sort of, kind of, not quite the way I would have done it but not altogether half bad, that is to say there is much room for improvement but it's not a disaster.

Frank is the first to show up. He apologises for not being around and asks if it all went okay. I say, 'Of course it did. We had fun, didn't we?' The terrified faces of Sadie, Huxley and Posie go up and down automatically. 'How are you?' I ask.

'I'm feeling double happiness,' he says.

My stomach clenches. Frank kisses Sadie on her forehead and Huxley on his big fat cheek.

As the night wears on, no one shows any interest in eating. A few nuts here, a few dips there would have been fine for this crowd. We become increasingly loud, my girlfriends hoarsely whispering, 'What are you going to do?' and me answering, 'I don't know yet!' The dancing is starting but I whistle us over for dinner anyway. The food is perfect, really, and I take full credit. Frank says he particularly likes the sauerkraut canapé. I think he's being sweet, but I'm glad I thought of it at the last minute. By 12, no one really feels like going dancing any more.

'I'll vomit if I dance now,' Sam says, opening a VB.

'That place is full of poofters,' Clive adds.

'Look, you have thousands of CDs. We'll dance here,' says Tilda.

'I brought dessert,' Dana says. 'Wine and fags!'

Tilda puts on 'Voulez Vous Coucher Avec Moi' . . . Ha ha, very funny.

We take turns playing our picks and soon, cautiously at first, I'd say we're rocking. Until Tilda puts on Crosby, Stills, Nash & Young, and I hear someone laughing at 'Love the One You're With'. There isn't a good way to move to most of this CD, so we take a breather.

I go into the kitchen and get the cake out. I don't expect to, but I start to weep. Frank hasn't glanced my way, he hasn't told me I look good, he really hasn't said much to me at all. He doesn't seem like a man who wants to be with me whether or not I bring a friend along. But as I light the candles, his arms encircle me from behind and he turns me to dance with him in the privacy of our kitchen. 'Hey, what's wrong?' I don't answer. I breathe into his shoulder. To 'Suite: Judy Blue Eyes' we sway fifth-grade style.

I won't let the past remind me of what I am not now.

His hand caresses my back, seventh-grade style.

I am yours . . . I am my beloved's . . . and my beloved is mine.

He kisses me, like my husband. Like a man 35 years old, in love with his wife. And I remember the most important thing Cantor Donald said, the most important vow: I am my beloved's and my beloved is mine.

I kiss him back like a 32-year-old; a 32-year-old who doesn't like to share.

By 2 am, everyone has left. Frank and I ignore the mess and venture into the kitchen for a Baileys. As I pour, he presents me with three gifts. 'Early Christmas,' he says.

Inside the first package is a can of tuna from Taiwan. In the second, a can of tuna from Thailand and in the third, a can of tuna from Indonesia. Proof positive of his travels. I am laughing when he hands me the can opener and says, 'Go on, try them.' He brings out some mayonnaise and crackers, puts them on the counter. We start to fool around. He undresses me and we make spectacular love on the kitchen floor. As we lounge, in a daze, bare-bottomed on the cold floor, leaning against the counters, I know I am off the hook. So, I try a little from every can.

Bed of Posies

'Merry Christmas, Pat!'

'Bill, pick up the phone,' Frank's mother calls out. 'Fran and Frank are on.'

'Well, tell them I only want to talk to Huxley.' I hear Bill's slippers scuffling down the hall of their Westchester home.

'Now tell me, how *are* you? Bill, *Bill*, for goodness sake, Bill.'

He is either taking another nip of good cheer, turning on the TV instead of getting on the phone or dipping his finger in a dish meant for later.

'That's for later,' Pat admonishes. I hear Bill pick up the phone in the den; there's the faint sound of a game show in the background.

'Where's Mama?' Frank asks, referring to his 93-year-old grandmother.

'Where she always is,' Bill grouses. 'Here. *Here* for our 49th Christmas. *Here* for our 49th summer vacation. *Here* for our 49th wedding anniversary. And if she isn't *here*, Pat's *there*.'

'Merry Christmas, Bill,' I say. 'So, how is everyone? What are you doing?'

Pat gives a tremulous sigh, a beleaguered sound. 'Oh, nothing much. It's a quiet Christmas.'

There is no doubt she's exhausted and feeling put upon. Why? Because she does all the work, because getting anyone to contribute to the Christmas spirit in that house is about as easy as kicking yourself in the behind, because she is telling herself for the hundredth time that it is better to give than to receive, and because she is growing weary from saying things like 'What an adorable cat-shaped garlic tree; it is just what I wanted' or 'What an adorable cat-shaped piece of driftwood; it is just what I wanted' or 'What an adorable cat-shaped ink blotter; it is just what I wanted'. Now add to that the fact that we took her two adorable grandchildren 10,000 miles away after living in the same postal code for two years and, frankly, I'm amazed at her composure.

'Is Walter there?' Frank asks, referring to his brother.

'He was but he told me the food looked inedible so he went to Pete's Tavern. He did give me the most adorable cat-shaped potholder. It's just what I wanted.'

'I don't know why you bother with this every year, Pat,' Bill says. 'Where's Huxley?' he asks.

'Bill, Huxley can't talk yet,' Pat corrects.

'Well, put Sadie on the phone. I want to talk to him,' Bill says.

'Sadie is a girl!' we all say.

'I know that. I like to tease.'

'You guys, Huxley *can* talk,' I defend. 'He doesn't just jabber; he speaks in complete sentences and never forgets to put in adjectives. He even knows his days of the week.' I put the phone to Huxley's mouth. 'Tell Grandma and Grandpa the days of the week.'

He swats the phone down. I pick it up. 'Huxley, come on, tell them the days of the week.'

A big drop of drool lands on the receiver. 'Come on, Hux.

165

Sunday,' I coax, 'Monday . . .' He puts the phone in his mouth. 'I guess he's tired. Anyway, he says it like this: "Sunday, Monday, Dinnertime, Saturday." It's so cute.'

'Oh, the dear.' Pat's voice catches.

'Yeah, he's my mush. Everyone loves him here.'

'Yeah, 'cause he looks like Buddha,' says a small voice.

'Is that you, Sadie Dean?'

'Hi Grandma. Merry Christmas.'

'What did you get from Father Christmas, Sadie Dean?'

'Mom said we don't have a chimney so he had to come through the garbage chute. I got Barbie and a kitchen set and that's all, I think.'

'Sadie, what about the clothes and books and backpack?' I remind her.

'Well, that was all I liked.'

'Pat, we had the best time here. I wish you two could have come.'

'I know. I couldn't leave my mother,' Pat says.

'Forty-nine Christmases, 49 Easters, 49 Thanksgivings. Every summer. She even sits in my chair,' Bill laments.

I cut him off. 'We had a Christmas Eve formal cocktail party at our friend's apartment. Oh my gosh, you should have seen the decorations . . .'

Caroline is famous for her holiday zeal. Weeks before Christmas, she had a different set of themed earrings on every day: Rudolphs that lit up, wreaths made of pine, Santas that said 'ho ho ho' when she tugged her earlobe. Her apartment was chockablock with paraphernalia on Christmas Eve, from the tree that swayed to the music, to the one that had ornaments in the shape of her family, from the electric train that went through all 10,000 square feet of her apartment, to the authentic Santa sleigh that vibrated when you fed it coins. She had replaced her curtains with ones bearing a winter wonderland pattern. There were matching slipcovers and pillows. She somehow had icicles hanging from the ceiling. My favourite decoration was the life-sized manger with robotic holy men and a stereo playing 'We Three Kings', 'Little Drummer Boy' and 'Silent Night'. Caroline was decked out in a fur-lined red dress. She and Todd had the space, they were very generous and genuinely enjoyed having a crowd. Todd was jolly though rather busy. When he wasn't handing out red and green Jello shots, he was untying Barbie from the train tracks. Just when he thought he could mingle, he spotted something amiss in the manger. 'Hey, Clive, put Mary back. She doesn't like that.'

Thousands of kids were there because the maids had Christmas Eve and Christmas Day off. We all brought a dish and some drinks. I brought homemade potato *latkes*, applesauce, *ruggelah* and three bottles of my brother's Snow Farm Wine that I hid away in boxes when we moved. The party started at five. I wore a yellow cocktail dress that was short but smart, and a black pearl necklace and sapphire diamond earrings Frank brought back from Bangkok. Several of my friends' parents were there visiting so we adopted them for general grandparent duty.

'. . . Yeah, it was nice . . .'

'Well, it was so good of you to call,' Pat says, wrapping it up a bit abruptly.

'Where's Huxley?' Bill asks.

'Merry Christmas, Bill. See you in a few months.'

'I'm getting old. I don't have a few months.'

'Bill, you've been saying that since I first met you ten years ago.'

'Just hang up, Bill. I'll bring dinner,' Pat says. 'Goodbye . . .'

'Hi Ma!' I say into the phone.

'Frannie! I was just doing my exercises. I usually turn the

phone off when I do them but I thought that I hadn't heard from you in so long. I was just telling Sonya how Hanukah came and went and I didn't hear a word from you. I don't even know if you got my card. Did you get the kids anything with the money I sent? I would have sent a gift but I wouldn't have known if it got to you. At least with a cheque I can see if it was cashed. You didn't cash the one I sent for your birthday. Ah, speaking of birthdays. Did Frank get my card? Did he have a good birthday? I hope you didn't drag him around to all your things and you just let the poor guy relax. From what Pat tells me . . . can you believe I have to hear about you from your mother-in-law . . . Frank must keep up with her. I know she does that email you want me to do but you know me, I'm just learning how to use the VCR. Pat says you and Frank are always out on the town. Poor Bonnie and Harris, they're too busy to go out. They don't have maids. We've had six feet of snow already. I'm out shovelling every day. It's good exercise, besides, I don't trust the boys who come around. This neighbourhood isn't safe any more. But I don't know where to move. Oh, I have to hang up in a sec, I just noticed the time. I'm late already. You didn't tell me how you are? Or the kids. Typical! I love you. Talk to you next week.'

I had hoped to get a quick chance to assure Mom that I was swell. I had always been such a source of commotion, disturbance, worry, grief, stress, fear (why else have kids?) all my life that I wanted to make amends and prove that I had my act together. I was a long way from convincing Mom. Even if I said nothing more than 'I was just about to go to the store' she'd be sure it was another hair-brained, crazy scheme I was cooking up.

'Well, guys, let's get dressed for Jenny's,' I call out.

Frank puts down his paper. 'What?'

'The Boxing Day party. At Jenny's. Remember?'

'No.'

'Well, it starts at noon.'

'No.'

'Yeah, it does.'

'I mean, I'm not going.'

'Why not?'

'I don't want to.'

'Why not?'

'It's going to be the same people from the Christmas Eve party and the same people from the Christmas Day party.'

'I guess there will be some cross-over attendance, yes. What's your point?'

'What more could I possibly have to say to these people after one night apart?'

'Oh, come on, get dressed. I'll write out some conversation cards for you or you can just sulk against the wall. Anyway, you don't want to be all alone on Boxing Day.'

'I don't know what Boxing Day is. I *do* want to be alone. I would *love* to be alone. Alone with you and Sadie and Huxley.'

'That's so sweet to hear. Listen, I'm going to –'

'Go out for your run,' Frank finishes.

'Yeah, and I was going to meet you there because I want to run for a few hours today. So I've packed a bag for you to bring to Jenny's so I can shower there.'

'No.'

'She said it would be okay.'

'No.'

'What now?'

'Don't run. Stay.'

'Jeez, Frank. I can't make a day out of a sofa and a newspaper. I need other ingredients. Don't be mad.'

'Don't keep Samantha waiting, Fran. I'll see you at noon.'

'Thanks.' I give him a long kiss because I still have a minute before Samantha will be at the gate and because I can't bear to just leave him standing there with his arms out-stretched in the void.

'I didn't think I'd make it out,' I say when I see her.

'Oh, my gang isn't even up yet.'

'What time do your kids go to bed?' Mine had been up for hours already.

'Sometimes they just don't. And sometimes they sleep all day.'

'That doesn't worry you?'

'I read a book, *Your Body, Our Cash*, all about how big companies want us to be awake during the day so we can buy things.'

'I never thought of it that way.'

'Sure, look how the commercials for toys and junk food are on during the day. And the stores . . .'

'Open in the day,' I add, wide-eyed. 'Yeah, you know, you're right! Still, I could write a book: *Kids Who Don't Sleep Don't Get Toys . . . and Other Things Children Should Know to Make Their Lives More Pleasant.*'

'Fran!'

'What do they do at 1 am?'

'Oh, we make bread or play chess or watch television.'

'We? So how do *you* function during the day?'

'Bet!' We laugh.

Our plan is to go down East Coast Park and over Mt Faber and take a cab to Jenny's from there. Now that we're doing one long run a week, it's critical for our sanity to find inventive routes on this small island. Last week, to make up a two-hour run, we went through a mall from end to end, on each floor. I thought it was brilliant. We got aircon, we had some steps, we got to leap over things like wheelchairs and small children, and we could window-shop. Plus the bathrooms were much better there than in the park – better soap and some even had toilet paper.

Not too many people are in the park this morning but it's still a scene. There are four kinds of groups that can be found here no matter what the time, no matter what the weather, no matter what the holiday. First, there are the public workers, lean, swarthy men from places like Sri Lanka, who live in encampments in the park. Their ghettos are hidden from public view by trees and shrubs but if you peer between the branches, you can see them laying out their straw mats, cooking over butane stoves, smoking *bidis* and washing out the cloths they wrap around their waists and then tuck between their legs. I don't know what they call that look; it's like Aladdin before he got rich. In the earliest hours of the morning, like 5 am, a crew of them sweep the paths free of detritus; another set, reams of black garbage bags artfully coiled around their heads, like walking dispensers, change the bin liners; and still another just stand there harmlessly, but unnervingly, curling their lips as they watch me run past.

Okay, so that's the worker bees. Then you have the people, usually poor families and teenagers, who pitch tents and camp out. They bring everything that's not nailed down and set it up just like it is at home, outside the tent. They put sofas and crockery, televisions and radios, tons of meat and rice and snacks and drinks and breakfast items onto a trolley and sail over to their plot of land, be it the tarmac, the sand or the grass. They stay up all night (so as to avoid the consumerist mind control of the big retail establishments?) eating and singing and eating some more until they pass out wherever they please, be it the grass, the tent, the tarmac or the sand. I'm sure they wake up with thousands of welts, a gift from the carpet of red ants that patrol the landmass, and the thick clouds of mosquitoes that rule the ankle zone of Singapore.

Then you have your bathroom attendants. They live with their families in the rest stations. It is not what most westerners would consider a home. Yes, they have running water, yes, they have lots of indoor plumbing, but they sleep in a hot little cell between the Gents and the Ladies and probably live on the snack food they sell: very instant noodles (just add saliva); Twisties and cuttlefish floss (you got me, but it's written on the package and you don't find it at the dentist's).

Finally, there are the ever-present teams of Tai Chi practitioners. I've been in the park in extraordinary weather and at the frightful hours of dawn and dusk, and there they are. I love them best. Happy herds of people past 50 in T-shirts that designate their class name, making small, tight movements to tape-recorded instructions. The cassette they listen to was produced before anyone used the word 'digital' for anything but a clock. The hisses and pops, static and blur are so grating, I can't imagine these disciples get the zen for their yen, but they are such a jolly lot that I feel grateful to witness their simplicity as I sweat and drip on another endless workout.

We leave the park, run along the highway on Shears Bridge and get honked at. 'Oh, look, it's Lisa and Roy. Hi!' I wave and blow a kiss. We run past Suntec City Mall.

'Fran! Samantha!' come a duo of voices.

'Hey,' I say, still running, to people sitting outside drinking coffee.

'Who were they?' Samantha asks.

'I think it was Simon and Melanie.'

'Oh, I helped her breastfeed.'

'That must have been a while ago, 'cause just the other day, I helped her up after she and Simon passed out in front of the koi fish. I found them at five in the morning when I went out for a run.'

'Where were their kids?'

'Pearl. Wonder what that night totalled.'

When we get to Mt Faber, Singapore's idea of a mountain, we trudge up the hill. Cable cars leave from here and stop at the World Trade Centre and then Sentosa Island, a little freckle of land used until 1970 as a military base. As logic would dictate, it is now a pleasure resort–theme park. Most people say it sucks: too expensive, too run-down, what a waste of space. While I see Sentosa Island that way too, I love it for those very reasons. I remember our first visit. Sadie enthralled a snake charmer who directed a python to slither up her tiny body like a stripe on a barbershop pole. I bit my nails but she begged for more. We took a hike down the 'Dragon Path', following an ancient archaeological site where the first dragons were discovered. Really. There were plaster-of-Paris skeleton remains of 200-yard-long mythical reptiles and partial human skulls. Really. And then we went through Sea World. It took about one minute and cost $50. It features a moving platform that takes you through a glass tunnel of ocean life. I read every placard aloud to the family and we took another spin in an effort to amortise that $50. Then we went to the surfside burger place that would have been better without the insanely loud technobeat. We had a deep-fried lunch, hung out on the beach, rented paddle boats, collected things. And then found ourselves covered in tar.

We went to the hotel there and used their facilities. They had a shower outside of the pool area and we scrubbed until the black ooze on our feet and butts was the colour of nicotine stains and not quite sticky enough to pick up more than a few thousand grains of sand. The kids wanted to go to the pool, so we carried ourselves like guests, haughtily looking at the towel man, wagging our fingers at the cocktail boy, and no one thought otherwise as the kids went through the waterslides and frolicked in the pool. After that, we changed back into our clothes and kept looking at each other, saying, 'This is our new life. This is great!' All right, so we got a little gooey, a little sunburned, but all that was of no concern as we sat in the Thai-styled lounge area, open on three sides to the South China Sea, a few ceiling fans spinning, the band, Kep Tan and To Nil, singing 'Muskrat Love'. We lapped up the sunset with a bottle of happy-hour half-priced Moët and two Shirley Temples, toasting our friends back home who were bundled up with drippy noses. We spotted our first family of wild monkeys, picked up the car and went home, wondering what exactly everyone thought was so funny about Sentosa. Okay, the next day I had tar on my butt and deep-fryer fat in my veins, but it was worth it.

'Hey Samantha, next run we should go into Sentosa.'

'Oh, no, you couldn't pay me to go there.'

'Why not?' I feel defensive.

'They make you keep pets on a leash.'

'Listen, Sentosa has hills. Not just stairs, but hills. Think of it! We could go through the mall, around the docks, over Mt Faber and –'

'Golly, I didn't see it that way. Sure!'

By the three-hour mark, we are back at the base of Mt Faber having circled Labrador Park a few times. We get some water and call Comfort Cablinks for our taxi. After you call Comfort Cablinks once, they think they know you. Here's how the second and ever-after conversations go:

ME: Hi, I need a pick-up.

DISPATCHER: Is this 9-082-4116?

ME: Yes.

DISPATCHER: Coming from Fortune Gardens, is it?

ME: No. I'm coming from Mt Faber.

DISPATCHER: You stay at Fortune Gardens?

ME: Yes, but I need a taxi from Mt Faber.

DISPATCHER: (tapping on a keyboard) You are staying at Mt Faber now?

ME: I'm just standing here waiting for a taxi.

DISPATCHER: Okay okay. Pick-up location is Mt Faber. Going to Prestons?

ME: No, that was yesterday. Today I –
DISPATCHER: You don't go to Prestons today?
ME: No, no, I need to go to Bayshore.
DISPATCHER: (tapping) Your husband is Frank.
ME: Yes.
DISPATCHER: You are Mrs Frank.
ME: Not technically, but that's okay.
DISPATCHER: You live in Fortune Gardens.
ME: Yes, I do, but I'm not there now.
DISPATCHER: But your maid is at home.
ME: Yeah. Can you get me?
DISPATCHER: Please hold for your taxi number.

Five seconds later, a voice comes on and says, 'A blue comfort cab with a small dimple on the left rear side and an advertisement for Tiger Beer, licence plate SHA 489098, will be arriving in five minutes' time.' One minute later, it is there. The driver greets you, 'Miss Flank. You not go to Plestons today?'

His computer screen, inexplicably, has a picture of you in your home, in your PJs on a Sunday morning. Comfort Cablinks is Big Brother. They get you where you're going and they know where you've been.

Jenny lives in Bayshore. It's a lot like Fortune Gardens except the apartments are bigger and they have two restaurants. Instead of being numbered, their blocks are named after gems. The precious ones – Ruby, Emerald and Diamond – are taller and face the sea. Opal, Jade and poor little Quartz-ite have a view of their superior crystals. I met Jenny through Tilda. She has three kids. The older two, Trent and Neil, are Sadie's and Huxley's ages.

I get there before Frank and the kids, but others are there.

I stand dripping in the vestibule. I don't have my clean clothes to change into but Jenny brings me a towel and a glass of water.

'Fran, Fortune Gardens is just two blocks away. Why didn't you go home first?' Jenny asks quite reasonably.

I know I'm being set up here. I will say, 'Believe it or not, finishing at a different door makes running here just a tad less monotonous.' And the British will say, 'Bloody stupid to run in this heat; you wouldn't catch me doing that.' And the Americans will say, 'You are so disciplined. I wish I could find the time.' The Australians will say, 'You call that a run, mate? Back in Sydney I ran 40 kilometres in under two hours.' The Germans will say, 'Vatz de difrence. You get olt; you die.' The Canadians will say, ' '.

As I towel off, I see lots of kids, hands in chip bowls, drink boxes dented and overturned on tables and chairs, moms reaching for toys, pouring out juice and picking up muffin parts and unclenching fists for more muffin parts.

'Jenny, where's Steven?' I ask.

'Working.'

'Sudden emergency?'

'No, just the usual.'

I'm puzzled. I turn to Tilda. 'Hugh here?'

'He's watching the soccer at Muddy Murphy's. It doesn't start until three but last time Everton beat Manchester, Hugh was at Muddy Murphy's three hours early.'

'I'm not following you,' I say.

'When he watched Everton lose to Manchester, he was at Father Flanagan's.'

'Okay . . . still not there yet.'

'What's not to get? Everton won because Hugh was at Muddy Murphy's and they lost because he was at Father Flanagan's instead. So now he has to go to Muddy Murphy's wearing his green tie and have three rum and Cokes and three beers three hours before the game if he wants them to beat Manchester. I'm not going over this again with you, Fran, either you understand or you're daft.'

'Where's Collin?' I ask Dana, afraid to show Tilda my confusion.

'With Hugh.'

'But I thought Collin roots for a different team?'

'Not the point,' Tilda pipes in. 'Collin was with him at Muddy Murphy's when Everton beat Manchester so he has to come.'

'So, are any men coming?'

'Oh, I highly doubt it. Jenny, it's just tea for mums and kids, right?'

On cue, Frank walks in and hands me my bag of clean clothes, takes the kids' shoes off and asks where he should stash his 12 cans of VB.

He opens one, Jenny's maid appears and takes the rest of the beer into the kitchen. I motion for him to follow me down the hall, into the bathroom. I close the door. I turn on the shower and undress. He smiles. He moves toward me. I can't decide if I should tell him he's taken the day off to go to playgroup or if we should have sex on the bathroom rug first.

'I'm dirty,' I warn.

'So am I.' He smiles.

'We left the kids out there.'

'We'll make new ones in here.'

'I'll get nailed for exceeding my limit.'

'You'll get nailed either way.'

'Frank, can we stop? We're not really one-liner people.'

'Yeah, but it was fun.'

'Kinda. Anyway, listen, I have to tell you something.'

He starts to unzip.

'You're the only man here.'

177

'That's right, baby.' He yanks his pants down.

'I mean at the whole party. Actually, it's not so much a party as a tea. For women. I mean, you can stay. That'd be great . . . Frank, *Frank*, don't be mad!'

He's hiked up his pants, buckled his belt, and left the room.

'Your fly's undone,' I say softly to myself.

I get out of the shower and change into my 'of course all the handsome men will be here to look at me in this' halter dress, take my cup of tea and sit on the floor with the kids and moms. I turn a tinkling ball over in my hand and absently roll it into a block castle. Strike. Frank's gone. A kid is crying. Doesn't sound like one of mine.

Valerie's cell phone rings. 'Hi doll.' It's Sam. I've noticed he calls her several times a day. At first I thought he did it to check up on her. Now I think it's ardour. Maybe both. Frank never calls me from work. He rarely calls me from his trips either. I hardly even know where he goes. If I call him, even if I'm at my desk doing more work than he ever does, he'll say, 'Yes, Fran?' and I better come up with a darned good reason for the call. I hear Valerie, 'Me and Andrew are at Jenny's . . . Oh, before that? I guess I had the phone off. Sorry. What? Oh, that's too bad . . . never mind . . . love you too. Bye doll.' Her smile falls as soon as she flicks the phone closed. 'Oh, poor Sam,' she says. 'We can't go to Phuket now. He's got a big client coming. I have to make them dinner at our house.'

'When were you supposed to go?' Tess asks.

'Tomorrow morning. You have no idea how hard it was to get tickets anywhere this time of year. Never mind, we'll have a New Year's Eve party at our house instead. Can you guys make it? New Year's Eve at mine!' Valerie calls out.

I'm still the newest kid on the block; I'm still unsure of myself; I'm just about the only American and I don't know many recipes or have much to add to mommy-and-me activities so I have to forgive myself, though Frank never will, when I hear my own voice say, 'And New Year's Day at ours!' I say it loud enough for the neighbours to think they were invited as well. I am already thinking bagels, lox, scrambled eggs, quiche, cheese and deli meats, pasta salads – oh, I wonder if I could find *challah* and make some killer French toast – and Bloody Marys and mimosas. Excellent idea. Except for the Frank factor.

When I get home, I take the kids upstairs and put them down for a nap. There is a note from Frank. 'Went to work' it says. I sit on the sofa and look at the phone. I pick up a manuscript. I put it down. I wonder if I should call Frank and see if he's really mad or really really mad. But if he's just really mad, calling him might hike it up to really really and so forth and so on. I look at the phone. I start the manuscript. It's short. It's called *Heartland*. It's a picture book about sad hearts and happy hearts all living together in harmony. I know I'll pass on it. And the lucky author will be a bestseller. Everything I reject turns into a bestseller. It's my gift to publishing. If I take it on, you're destined to be mediocre. But if I hate it, it's good. 'What am I doing?' I think, 'I have to start getting the shopping done for New Year's Day.' I put the manuscript on my towering 'to do' pile.

I go back to Posie's part of the house to tell her I'm going out and that the kids are napping. I hear her radio. I hear a drawer open and shut. As I'm about to knock on her bedroom door, I hear the toilet flush.

'Posie?' I call. She peeps her head out.

'Yes, Ma'am?'

'Oh, you're in here. I just heard the toilet flush.'

'I didn't hear you. I have the radio on. I just cleaned the shower.'

'Why would that make the toilet flush, Posie?'

She is staring over my shoulder.

'Why would that make the toilet flush? I don't get it,' I say.

'Then I did the shopping. No more baking soda. Gone already.' She looks at my knees. I hear the tap running in her bathroom. I open the curtain-cum-door.

'Posie! Who is this?' A man wearing nothing but a towel stands before me.

'Who, Ma'am?'

At last I have a good reason to call Frank. 'I knew I was hearing doors and elevators at all sorts of times,' I say.

'So what should we do?' he asks.

'Look, she's a young girl. Why shouldn't she have a boy-friend?'

'What'd he look like?' Frank asks.

'Dark, curly hair, I don't know. Anyway, she showed really bad judgement but I think . . .'

'Big guy?'

'Yeah, I think. Do you agree we should give her a second chance?'

'Did he look like a foreign worker or a local?'

'He was too put together to be a foreign worker, nice-looking clothes, but I don't know. Why?'

'Nothing. I might have seen him too. A pretty boy. Yeah, sounds like the way to handle it. See you later.'

That's it.

I lecture Posie, frighten her a little about what would happen if I reported this, and fold my arms, waiting for something nonsensical to come out of her.

'I yam ashamed. He is my boyfriend. I love Sadie and Huxley.'

To be fair, she says all the right things – sorry, in love, would never harm your kids. I give her a hug. 'Hey, I was young once, too. Go to his house next time, okay? And no more lies.'

When I tell Frank about it all on our balcony that night with our Boxing Day cocktails (I have been forgiven for dragging him to the party and, in exchange, I promise not to work, yet again, that evening) he looks out in the distance and then to me. 'Let's go away over New Year's. We can just get in the car and drive up the coast of Malaysia to . . .'

I have a freezer full of bagels and smoked salmon, a cupboard full of caviar and a pantry full of champagne. I have spent close to a thousand dollars already. I look at him, about to spill the beans. But, flash! Bam! Damn, what do they say about the mother of invention? I don't know, but she's adopted me this minute.

'Why wait? Let's go to Phuket. Tomorrow!'

'We could never get a flight,' says Frank.

'It's all done, Frank.'

I am going to enjoy being the one to finally bring home a happy surprise, some prime Rittman-family-bubble time at one of the best resorts in the world.

Trans Spotting

'Fran, I don't know how you pulled this off,' Frank says as he hands me my customary pre-take-off Bloody Mary at the Raffles Class lounge. Sadie is piling up a plate of potato chips and Huxley is eating water crackers. It's mid-morning and though I shouldn't be fazed in the least, I'm still fascinated by the abundance of food. As if auditioning for an all-Asian *Oliver*, people line up silently waiting for bowls of steaming fish porridge. Trays of sushi vanish in the blink of an eye. Bread and cheese are lobbed off the cutting board. Prawn *mee* and fried rice fly haphazardly onto the floor. Clusters of cellophane balls, once snuggling crust-free dainty egg salad, tuna and pâté sandwiches, loiter round the trash bins. Handfuls of exotic nuts are scooped out of gigantic jars into palms and cocktail napkins. Cookies are balanced beside cups of tea and coffee on china saucers.

This is my fifth experience of Singapore Airlines' business-class lounge. I know the layout. I take my Bloody Mary and head for a spot in the smoking chamber. It's well venti-lated and kitted out just enough so that you don't feel like a bad doggy with your nose thrust into your mess, though not so much that it conveys 'Smoking's cool with us'. The non-smokers or the not-partaking-at-the-moment-smokers can see us through four sides of glass, like the nearly extinct species exhibit we are. I have stood in here before, holding my palm out to Sadie's with the glass wall between us, convict style.

I finish a quick cigarette and join Frank at a small table. The kids are sprinkling minced crackers on the floor.

'It says here, "Forget about going between Christmas and Chinese New Year. You'll never get in unless you book six months in advance." How in the world did you swing this?' Frank points at the travel book. I shrug and smile. He drains his glass and fishes around for a regular old peanut, flicking away the cashews and macadamias. KERRRUNCH, chomp, chomp, chomp. I don't eat. I love plane food too much to compromise my appetite. I have never really outgrown TV dinners. They were like getting a present. They were like a mathematical equation. It took a beautiful mind to come up with 'small tray = full meal'. TV dinners meant Mom and Dad were going out and we'd get to stay up late and watch shows that were way over our heads, like *Manix* and *Carol Burnett*. Mom moved on to Burger King when they claimed the corner of Liberty Avenue and Milford Mill Road, tempted by the lines on the meat that reflected their grilly-ness. That era was sadly replaced by the frozen pizza bagel and we might as well just have shot Saturday night to hell when we sat down to Lean Cuisines (the nascent stages of Mom defatting her kitchen).

Frank dismisses the meals served on planes. He doesn't like being held against his will by the little shelf, doesn't like being dictated to about what and when to eat. He's a card-carrying frequent flier, too jaded to put his chair in the upright position, can't be bothered to look over the movie selections, never even glances to the side as they roll out the linen tablecloths, lay out the fine china and crystal and place the bushel of stainless steel cutlery on the plate with a stimulating clatter. I'm quite sure Frank never gets all Pavlovian at the faintest squeak of the trolley wheels, salivating on cue like the rest of us mortals. 'Nyet. Nyet. Nyet.' To the hors d'oeuvres, the salad with marinated mushrooms and walnuts, the foil-wrapped Australian butterfish with apricot-brandy sauce, the coconut custard pie and the dessert-redux of cheese, fruit and chocolates. Of course, I've convinced him to order it and just put it on my side. I'll eat two.

'Fran, this place you have us in sounds fantastic, Relax Bay. It's a little far from the action but we'll rent a car.' He mixes us up a fresh batch of Bloody Marys then engages his pointer finger in the task of uncovering more peanuts.

'I'm so glad you're happy, Frank.'

Just 15 hours ago, I stole away to our upstairs phone and dialled Valerie. 'Oh, good, you're home,' I whispered.

'Hey, mate, what's up?' she asked.

'Do you think I can buy your Phuket tickets and take on your hotel room?'

'That'd be lovely. We paid the deposit already. I think it's still there. Let me check.' She held her palm over the receiver but I could hear the muffled conversation. Sam said, 'That's fine but she needs to transfer the tickets to her name.' Valerie got back on the phone and told me her travel agent's contact numbers. I called Mala from Sime Travel on her cell phone and reached her at a restaurant.

'Look, I am sooo sorry to intrude on your dinner.'

'Oh, that is not a problem,' came the distinct Indian accent.

'I want to surprise my husband with a trip and . . .' I gave my spiel and asked her if I could assume Sam and Valerie's tickets.

'I'll get the three tickets transferred into your name.'

Suddenly, I remembered. 'Oh, shit, Mala, we're four. The Markses are only three.'

'Ah, not to worry, it doesn't make a difference at the hotel and I'm sure there's still room in business class. I'll get back to you in about 15 minutes.' She did. It was done. Not a problem.

And then I had to call her again.

'Oh, I'm soooo sorry, Mala, please forgive me. I know you're probably sleeping and all . . . yeah, it's Fran. Wham, in the middle of the night, I remembered I forgot to tell you we need to come home on the 31st . . . Would you? Oh, that is sooo sweet. Take a cab and I'll pay for it. Is that your husband? Sheesh, not in the service industry, I'll bet. Thanks. I'll never use anyone but you!' I went back to bed, snug and secure.

Pretty rare in Singapore to find a 'hold the pickles, hold the lettuce, special orders don't upset us' kind of person. Even if they wanted to help, they just wouldn't know how to move beyond the standard, 'cannot cannot *lah*' . . . 'tickets paid for already' . . . 'in wrong name already'. Like the other day, as I passed the Fortune Gardens booking office, I decided, on a whim, to reserve a tennis court for later that night. Silly me, I had forgotten my card. I said, 'Well, I'll bring it down later. You know me, I play every Wednesday night.' Can you guess what they said? Say it with me: 'Cannot cannot (and don't forget the) *lah*.' I was rarin' for a fight, it was that time of day.

'Hey, you let us phone in for a court the day of,' I argued.

'Yes, you can book a court over the phone for that same day,' he returned.

'Well, you don't see the card when I call, right?'

'You don't need to present your card over the phone.'

'Right.' I took out my cell phone and dialled. I watched him answer the phone.

'Hello,' he said.

'Hi! It's me.' I waved to him, fluttering my fingers just inches in front of his nose.

He looked uneasy. Was he supposed to wave back? He wasn't accustomed to feeling silly like this. I continued.

'I'd like to book a tennis court for six tonight. Can you guess who I am?'

'Mrs Flank.' He stayed on the phone. He couldn't be accused of not following the rules. 'Do you want court number one or four?'

'Four.'

'Okay, court four at 6 pm.'

'See ya.' I hung up.

We gather up our stuff, drain our glasses and hike to the gate; it is time to board the plane. Every seat is taken in the departure lounge. Bored children are sprawled on the floor; gnarly-headed, shoestring, *Lonely Planet* types are sitting on their backpacks talking about how Phi Phi beats Phuket (Phi Phi is pronounced *Pee Pee* not *Fee Fee*, just like Phuket is *Pooket* not *Fuckit*) but Krabi's the best. And poised to take over the entire room and eat us if they must is a tour group of lovingly large, comfortably cushioned, wide-in-the-waistband ladies. But we get to board first.

We settle the kids in their plane seats and tuck toys around them. I say, 'Now, think lovely thoughts . . . Think lovely thoughts . . .' Sadie joins me, 'Think lovely thoughts . . .'

'Vacation!' I call out.

'Nana!' Sadie says.

'Nana!' Huxley says.

Frank doesn't play. There are certain things he'll never do in public, like juggling or crossing his eyes or shouting out a lovely thought.

'Sandy beaches!' I continue.

'Aunt Bonnie!' Sadie says.

'Aunt Bonnie!' Huxley says.

Frank straightens out *The Wall Street Journal*.

'Family games!'

'Grandma's cats!'

'Grandma's cats!'

Frank makes sure his cell phone is turned off.

The plane ascends. I give Sadie and Huxley a squeeze. As soon as the seatbelt light goes off, I begin my nervous traveller routine. If they think I'm about to go mental, they'll give me a drink faster. I become acutely fidgety, aerobically squirmy. I rock a bit but figure I don't need to be convincingly autistic. I look at the ceiling and then at Frank. 'It's going to be all right isn't it, Frank? I mean, it's going to be all right, right? Tell me the odds again . . . Just tell me one more time . . .'

'Beverage for you?' the hostess asks.

'Oh, that might do the trick. Yeah, can you keep my glass full?' I wring my hands.

Frank manages to frighten everyone away on a plane. He looks busy and important. He says no more than one syllable at a time, usually finding it unnecessary to go beyond 'yes', 'no' and the meagerly dispensed 'thank you'.

After four hours, the plane begins its descent. The captain announces that we're over the islands of Phang Nga Bay. These are among the wonders of Asia. The sheer-sided limestone monoliths rise almost a thousand feet out of the water. It was on one of these islands that a James Bond movie, *The Man with the Golden Gun*, was filmed. Phuket comes into view and I can see deep green islands, farms and forests, and long stretches of white beach sporadically interrupted by boulders, outcroppings and dramatic cliffs. The Andaman Sea is a pallet of greens and blues. Its surge rolls in gently, benignly. Its waves are sleepy, quite unlike the turgid, challenging breakers of the Atlantic. Phuket's history, like much

187

of South East Asia's, is full of spice seekers and fortune hunters. The first inhabitants are believed to have been Semang pygmies and Moken sea gypsies who lived in caves. They were later joined by Tamils and Malays. By the late 18th century, European sailors had discovered valuable commodities: ivory, gems and pearls. They were often relieved of these treasures by thorny pirates lurking near the shores.

Phuket has ignored the industrial world, retaining villages where the people live off the sea, living a simple life of fishing and farming, weaving and pearl diving, oblivious to the tides of change crashing through the rest of Asia.

Ears are clogging and I tell the kids to yawn, hold their noses and blow.

'Think lovely thoughts . . . Think lovely thoughts . . .' I chant. 'Elephant rides!' I begin the game for us.

'Bmmrlt,' Sadie says.

'Oh, you can stop holding it now.'

'Baltimore, America!' Sadie sings.

'Baltimore, America!' Huxley sings.

'Okay, bang me over the head, Sadie, I get it. But just think of all the things you've seen that your cousins haven't. You'll have so much to tell them.'

'So *now* can we go home?' she implores.

Huxley's no better – worse even, with that additional character flaw of being unable to think for himself. 'B*lah* b*lah* b*lah*' to a real plane but 'whoo whee' to the chipped fibreglass one outside the grocery store that vibrates for 50 cents. *That* they could sit in all day long. Anything but yet another hot island full of sand and monkeys and elephants. A swing set and a squirrel would do nicely for them. Hey, kids, wanna see the Great Wall of China or stay home and order in? Frank's kids.

'Sweetie,' I whisper in Sadie's ear, 'this is a time we'll always remember. It's about togetherness. Being a family. If you complain one more time, I will leave you with that man over there . . . Oh, Sadie, I'm kidding . . . a joke . . . stop crying . . .'

Like most resort airports, Phuket's is just a place that holds a lot of pamphlets and hangs advertisements on the wall. I collect 16 fliers within the first few minutes. Huxley's winning with about 900.

'Boy,' I say, flipping through some of them, 'we're going to be biii-zzeee.'

Frank is several yards ahead and I gather the kids and my bag and shuffle to catch up. 'Oh, listen Frank, we have to see some of these wats on Wan Phra Day so we can hear the monks pray and then we can go to the aquarium.

'Hey Frank,' I say as I move out of his way while he digs around for some documentation or another. 'We could do this one today: the national park. They have gibbons. The kids will like gibbons, don't you think? And then we can take a little walk up to the waterfalls. It's just a short trail, not much more than a mile or so.

'Oh, *here's* a good one,' I continue as Frank closes his briefcase and walks to the money exchange, 'Thai Village elephant show and cultural performance. We could do that before dinner or maybe we should . . .' Frank is talking to a man at a counter. I check to make sure the kids are still here.

'Hey, Huxley, what's that one? I don't have it.' I take a brochure from his clenched little hand. 'Oh, a museum, I don't want to do that.' He looks crestfallen. 'All right, all right, that'd be a great thing to do on Thursday.'

Enough with the child's play, we have serious things to go over. 'Frank,' I continue, 'maybe tomorrow we should do the town and Sea Gypsy Village.' Frank is scribbling on forms. He's trying to balance all the passports on a narrow shelf and his backpack is sliding down over his shoulder, as he grapples with the pen. I don't think he's heard a word I've said, so I add, 'And I'll be working out every morning from eight to ten so you take care of the kids. Thanks.'

We go through Customs and Immigration, get our luggage and look for the driver. I see 'MARKS' held aloft on a corrugated banner also bearing the name 'Meridian'.

'Oh, here we are!' I yodel to the man.

'Fran, that says Marks.'

'Yeah, they never understand me with this American accent.'

When we finally arrive at the Meridian on Relax Bay, we are greeted with a gong. A handful of tiny, delicate men and women serve us a welcome drink and drape us in flower necklaces as our luggage is carted off to the check-in counter.

'Have a nice stay, Mr Marks, Mrs Marks,' they beseech.

We get to our room, a suite at the far end of the building, facing the ocean. We have a large master bedroom, almost as large as the bathroom. There is another section – that would be the living room, I presume. It has a bar, fridge and two pull-out sofas. On the bar is a basket of what must be fruit since it has a heavy, sweet, biodegradable smell and lots of tiny flies hovering protectively nearby. The shapes and colours are monstrously alien, though. There is a note tucked between two gigantic hairy strawberries saying 'Welcome Marks Family'. I know who *I'll* be calling later today. Great job, Mala. Anyway, let's see that basket again.

Sticking out of a post that has been thrust into a green, human-heart-shaped, lumpy, tough-skinned fruit is a descriptive tour of the basket, a map if you will. Shall we explore? To begin with, the post is anchored in a *sugar apple* – you break it in two and eat it with a spoon, discarding the few seeds. Its neighbour on the left is the *sapodilla*, which is shaped like a kiwifruit – you peel the soft skin off and cut the fruit in quadrants. There are red *litchis* about the size of large cherry tomatoes. Shouldering them are two dark green, smooth *pomelos* – each is about the size of a small melon but the inside reminds you of a dry, ropy grapefruit. The hairy strawberries are *rambutans* and I can't understand if we're supposed to eat them hairs and all so I'll just keep away. Spilling over the rim is what looks like a dried yellow brain but is really a cluster of *long-gongs* – you press them open with your fingers and scoop out the inside, avoiding the seeds. There is a branch bearing *longans*, which are different from *long-gongs* in every way but sound. My favourite is the *mangosteen*, not just because the name suggests that the more mainstream mango was really a Jew who needed a cover, but because it is delicious. The size of an apple, with a deep purple, leathery skin like an avocado and a plastic-like green cap, it is to be cut around the middle and the segments scooped out. The taste is sort of like a grape meets a peach that's been hanging around a banana.

I've made quite a mess already but I take my fruit salad outside to the balcony to share. The balcony is large enough to accommodate a couple of games of badminton at once. I go to the edge to see the view. Relax Bay is sheltered by two opposing cliffs. Our beach is small, very small indeed. The sea is hugged and captured in the arms of the curving shore-line and granite walls. And, well, it appears to be rather contained, stagnant in fact. Okay, so that means it's safe, a better word than 'boring' or 'predictable'. I reach into my pocket to make sure the pamphlets listing things to do are still there. The pool runs the length of the entire hotel and has several different areas devoted to specific activities – if you can call sitting in a whirlpool bath an activity. There is a considerable number of guests. The robust ladies from the airport, for example, are here, of course, in my vacation, on my beach. It seems the sun has already taken its toll.

'Hey, Frank.'

'Yeah?' Frank calls from the bedroom where he is meticulously refolding and storing his clothes, having already used up all the good hangers for his trousers and shirts.

'What's black and white and red all over?'

'I dunno, what?'

'The other guests here. And guess what, they're the group from the airport. Let's check them out. To the beach everyone!' I direct.

We race down to the shore, buckets flying, kids laughing.

'I bet it's a package tour from Philly,' I challenge.

'No way. Americans don't come here. Definitely not,' Frank asserts, pride on the line.

'Hey, you wanna go to Sea Gypsy . . .'

Sadie stops and begins to loudly bawl. Huxley's bawling now, too. I stop to see what's the matter and start to howl. Frank falls onto his hands and knees. The sand is deadly, it is burning, it will cook a steak in ten seconds flat. We can't take another step. That would mean forward or backward. Standing still ain't no grand treat either. We all do what Frank's doing. He's the worldly one, after all.

Oh my God, definitely time for a new leader. Getting on all fours is stupid. Feet can take it much better.

'Run to the water!' I decree. Frank and I scoop up a kid each and sprint out to the water. It's warm and mellow and soon we have splashing and happy laughter, chicken fights and toss-the-kid; we dance, we wind down and then grow quiet as we swim with a kid on our backs out in the clear sea. No doubt why they call it Relax Bay. I swim in deeper. *Omigod, what was that?* I get a wake-up call. I've been stung by a swarm of something.

'Out of the water, everyone!' I holler in a panic.

'Is it happy hour, Mommy?'

'Frank, grab Huxley. There's jellyfish all over the place.' But as I look around, I don't see a thing. Frank is already close to shore and Sadie and I follow. We're all huffing and puffing. I sit on the wet sand. I look for welts that don't materialise, even though I'm feeling prickly and rashy.

'I didn't actually see them but all of a sudden, I was, like, attacked,' I try to explain. 'I'll just rinse off over there,' I say, pointing to a shower in front of the pool. 'Be back in a flash.'

A woman three times my size, with a sunburned face, is pressing the nozzle every now and then as she absentmindedly, unhurriedly washes off a patch of sand here, a blob of sunscreen there.

Her friend, who could be her stand-in, is stirring a straw in a young coconut, saying, 'Mel, vashtin pushtin.'

'Tchai schmmpt?' says shower gal whilst trying to catch a tricep that keeps flapping away. I'm going to be here a long time. A single leg will take another 15 minutes to cover.

'Um, excuse me. Mel?' I take a stab.

'Vah?'

Okay, I'm gonna call you Mel. She turns and flops a breast out over her bathing suit. The breast is visibly relieved to be free. It says, 'Achh.'

'Mel,' I speak slowly, 'well, I know I'm behind you, but could I just do a really quick shower? I think I got stung by jellyfish.'

'Shpentin *foon*?' Her eyes bug out in astonishment. She cups her breast in one hand, pulls the top of her suit out with the other and lets it fall, finishing the job with some smushing and aligning to achieve a parallelness. I hear the breast's muffled curses.

'Yes, I believe so,' I say.

'Sphpentin foon mar glch. Foy!' Mel adds, looking at her friend with some wonder, scepticism and genuine concern for me.

'Well, yeah, I didn't see them, though. Suddenly, I was just stung all over,' I say.

'Lpshun,' offers non-Mel, nodding her head. She wobbles down the steps. She gets close, examines up and down the length of my body. I don't have welts but now there is a rash of rather high-definition red dots covering my legs.

'Brooshtin, brooshtin. Vroom.' She pretends to shave her legs.

'No, come on, it couldn't just be from shaving.' I look up. 'Could it?'

She comes even closer and with all her might, twists her great oak of a thigh clockwise and indicates with her chin that I am to look down. I don't want to. Please don't make me. Please don't make me. I am being given the treat of glimpsing her inner, should-stay-covered-and-secret, inner *inner* thigh.

She is showing me that my rash is just like hers. Yes, we are all alike on the inside . . . we're a mere language away from being sisters, separated at birth.

'Flertwick shnard opu December. Crombt.'

'Damn right,' I say, 'even if it is December. It just doesn't look right. You gotta shave.'

'Tmirit, dunplop.' She fishes around in her plastic bag from duty free and hands me a tube of cream.

'I made my husband and kids get out of the ocean.' I laugh and they join in.

I meet Frank and the kids at the pool. Huxley's in his durable rubber ring with fitted leg holes and a steering wheel and horn so he can play captain. Sadie is practising her strokes and floating on her back. She's already fairly competent in the water. Frank is pulling the last dregs from a pina colada at the swim-up bar facing our ever-so-buoyant young ones. I take the seat next to him.

'Are you okay now?' he asks, concerned.

I explain about the ladies and their likely correct diagnosis and how Mel's cream eased the pain and itch.

'We have to get some of that sombremsh.'

'Huh?'

'The cream, sombrembsh. You know, yak fat.'

A young waitress approaches and I tell her I'll have a pina colada too. She says, 'Yes madame', as she hefts a keg up on the bar.

Sadie slithers onto my lap. We order her a virgin drink. She says, 'Why is that man dressed as a lady?'

I look around. 'Who?'

'Her!' she says, going for a sip.

I look around again. Frank knocks his knee into me, a 'shut up' sort of a nudge. Without moving his head, simply with dead-accurate eye directionals, I am being told to observe our waitress a little more closely.

'Hmmm.' I nod, letting them know I've spotted the transvestite. We're all staring a bit since 'her' back is turned. Next thing I know . . .

'*Huxleeey!*' His vessel has capsized. I jump off my stool, fly through the pool. Mel is there already. She flips Huxley back around so that his head is now above the water and his legs below. Hux is unfazed.

'Omigosh. Thanks, Mel. How long was he like that?' I ask as I take my seat next to Frank.

'Thrumpten, futhm, jasheva.' Mel tosses her arm around my shoulders and gives me a hard squeeze.

'Frank, this is Mel.' She extends her hand assertively to Frank.

'Oh, and here comes Bernie.'

Mel points to a table across the way where five ladies are playing something with tiles and dice and, if I'm not mistaken, pine cones. 'Grek?'

'Thanks. No, I'm just going to hang out with the kids,' Frank says politely.

'Well, maybe I will,' I respond.

They take their drinks and return to the other shore to their friends.

'Fran! You aren't really going over there, are you?'

'I might, just for a half hour. I mean, they're nice. They're fun. Happy. I like happy people. Is that so wrong? Come with me, the kids can go to the Penguin Club.'

'No thanks.'

'Anyway, I owe them. First they save me from death by exfoliation and then they get Huxley.'

'All right, whatever.'

We all get to talking. My half hour turns into an hour. When I return, there's a note. Frank's taken the kids to pick up a rental car.

Sadie storms in while I shower. 'Mommy!' She is breathless. 'The lady at the car was really a man. I showed Daddy.'

While I'm wondering what to do about shaving, Frank calls through the door, 'Fran, Mala just called. Said she was sorry her maid didn't bring the phone to the bath but you can call her back.'

Frank suggests we go to Patong for the evening. It's the most happening beach and funkiest section of Phuket. We'll park and walk up the main road, check out some craft stalls, look into a few of the gift shops, see what grabs us for dinner. This is Frank's idea. A stroll, you might call it, a play-it-by-ear night, a wander. Nothing wrong – except there is a certain pattern to these episodes, a certain plot, a formula when it's Frank and I in the leading roles. Maybe if there could be a better ending, a happy ending. Maybe this season will be different . . . we're older . . . it's a new setting . . . could turn out better. Okay, let's do it. Places everyone, and *action*:

TITLE: *The Wanderers – Negotiating Phuket*

After getting lost, they finally find themselves at the general destination. They cannot find a spot to park the car. Up and down side streets, trying to fit in spaces that are clearly too small, covering grid after grid. At last, a car space appears in front of a run-down garage. The spot is too far from town to walk. They stop two tuk-tuks.

FRANK: To Patong, main street.

DRIVER ONE: 600 baht.

FRANK: 400 baht.

DRIVER ONE: Okay.

Frank puts Fran and Huxley in the first.

FRANK (*jogs over to driver two*): To Patong, main street.

DRIVER TWO: 400 baht.

FRANK: 300.

DRIVER TWO: Okay.

On main street. Busy. Lots of tourists. Rows of stores.

FRAN: Wow, it is lively here. [Shit, is everyone here or what?]

FRANK: Yeah, this is where everyone goes. [Do I know my shit or what?]

FRAN: Oh, let's look in that store. [I need to show some enthusiasm.]

FRANK: Sure, honey. [Well, I guess it is too early for a beer.]

They enter Batik Boutique.

FRAN: Isn't this gorgeous? [As a wall hanging, yes, but to wear?]

FRANK: Yeah. [As a wall hanging, yes, but to wear?]

FRAN: You would look so hot in this, Frank. [Why do I bother?]

FRANK: Ah . . . I don't know. Kinda . . . not me . . . [She thinks I'm boring.]

SALES LADY: That will be 900 baht.

FRAN: 800 baht.

SALES LADY (*deadpan*): Oh, you're killing me. I have to eat. 850 baht.

FRAN: 845 baht.

SALES LADY (*deadpan*): Okay.

Many shopping bags later, finally, they wander into his store.

FRAN: Frank, are you even *thinking* of getting that? We

don't need any more trinkets, not here, not back home, not anywhere we'll ever live again for the rest of our lives. That is *ugly*. It is *junkie*. I would be embarrassed to have anyone see it and I'll hide it with the thousands of other wooden frogs and grotesque masks and bamboo boxes and opium pipes. I don't care if this is the fucking pewter capital of the universe, we don't need another beer stein.

Moments later they are on the street again. They stop outside a jewellery store.

FRAN: Do you think you get a good buy? [Gimme gimme gimme.]

FRANK: Yeah, goodbye money. Only kidding. [Not.]

They enter the store.

FRAN: I love that. [Gimme gimme gimme.]

FRANK: Want to try it on?

FRAN: Nah. [Gimme gimme gimme.]

FRANK: Go on.

FRAN: Okay. [Gimme gimme gimme.]

FRANK: [Did she just say 'Gimme gimme gimme'?]

They move on to another shop. Fran shows Sadie how her new ring captures the light. Frank leads them into a store. Cut to Frank pulling out the Am Ex again. The clerk folds up the oatmeal-coloured tennis shirt that looks exactly like the 400 Frank already has at home and wraps two fertility god masks that look worse than the 400 they already have stuffed in the closet at home. Obvious haggling. After two quick rounds of negotiations, close-up on clerk's face as he says 'Okay' with dull eyes. The kids are holding wooden frogs. Fran and Frank stop, face each other. The camera picks up the body language from across the street. We can see the dust recirculating as bicycles and cars whiz past. Frank leaves Fran and the kids on the sidewalk. She shifts her weight from hip to hip, agitated. Her dress is sticking to her. The kids are wandering around and picking up things they shouldn't. She's holding two frogs.

Half a minute later, Frank returns. He is wearing a baseball hat with SPAM embroidered on the front.

FRAN: Happy? [Just look at my ring, just keep looking at my new ring.]

FRANK: Yeah. [I love my hat!]

SADIE: Look!

Frank mans the double stroller across the street for a closer view of the cross-dressers hanging out at the Gonzo Bar.

HUXLEY: Whaa! Whaa! Whaa! [I'm hungry.]

FRAN: We better get him something to eat. [If there is a God, we'll have happy hour followed by a five-course dinner in a five-star restaurant overlooking the sea, beneath the moon, eating an abundance of fresh seafood.]

FRANK: Yeah. [There's a doughnut store.]

Frank directs the stroller to the pastry shop. Fran begins to boil. She questions the marriage. 'How could he not know that this will not do. What? After doughnuts we just go home? Doughnuts? In Thailand?'

FRAN (*hot, hungry*): Frank, for fuck's sake. Why do we want to give the kids this for dinner? We haven't even had happy hour yet. Let's look for something nice.

FRANK: Yeah, you're right, of course. [What the hell does a doughnut have to do with dinner?]

The camera catches the Rittmans looking at menus outside of restaurants. The Malee Seafood Village, The Royal Kitchen, The Tung Ka Café. They wander down side streets; sometimes Fran walks into a place and comes out shaking her head 'no'. Sometimes they all go in, look around and shrug 'not exactly what I had in mind'. The streetlamps are now turned on and we can see that a good chunk of time has elapsed. They are drenched, dirty, beyond hungry and thirsty, unable to think entirely coherently. Menu after menu – too foreign, too western, too fancy, too bright, too loud, too shlocky. This – more than the bore of shopping, more than trying to get excited about local crafts – this *is their curse*. Indecision. *This is how the story always ends.*

FRAN (*panicking now*): We *have* to just settle on something. Let's go to the end of the block and if nothing is right, we'll do that Ban Rim Pa. [If there is a God.]

The next cluster of restaurants is a pizzeria, an outdoor coffee shop and The Dino-Park, a mini-golf-cum-burger-and-rib-restaurant with a prehistoric theme. There is nothing remotely Thai about it.

SADIE: Yeah! [You will be the best parents on earth if you take me there.]

HUXLEY: Yeah! [Well, Sadie said it.]

Fran and Frank look at each other. They are tired, they admit defeat, they wave a wilted white flag. They go in and get a caveman banner with a number, golf clubs and four balls. The Rittmans hear the number painted on their caveman sashes called. It is time to return the equipment. They get briefly lost in 'The Land Time Forgot'. Sadie finally leads the way out. They take a seat.

FRANK: I'm going to get the 'no-wonder-we're-extinct' burger. [Life is good.]

FRAN: There's nothing for me here. [I hate everyone.]

SADIE: Hey, our waitress has hairy arms.

THE END.

As the credits roll, Fran, Sadie and Huxley are on the dark, dark street and hear Frank from far away: 'I was sure this was where I parked it.'

The next day, I feel awful.

Frank says, 'I'm not suggesting that your friends aren't entirely knowledgeable about the ocean activity in Asia, but maybe, just maybe, you should see the nurse.'

I go to the gym instead, despite being unable to bend. Frank takes the kids to breakfast. An hour later we meet up in the room, where I've collapsed on the bed with cold towels wrapped around my legs. I go to the nurse and discover there is something called sea lice. I've displayed a particularly bad reaction to them and should stay out of the sun for the day. I get a new cream. I sit in the shade. Frank and the kids go from the pool to the beach and say 'Hi' on occasion, if they remember.

I join Mel and the gang for a game of chrelpla in the shade. Mel can't believe she missed the signs. She pulls my leg up onto her ample lap.

She stares, disbelieving, 'Foon, dreguggle.'

'Yeah, it's okay. No one knows for sure.' I take my leg back.

'Mommmeeee!' Sadie hollers.

'Over here!' I wave.

Frank hands me a drink and asks how I'm doing.

'Why you spending all your time with the fat ladies?' Sadie whispers.

'Sadie! Sorry,' I offer the girls.

The gang looks down at the game. They murmur, 'Schent, schent.'

'She's just upset with me.'

'Schent, schent.'

'Please, it was nothing . . .'

'Sch . . .'

'Mom, it's your turn. We'll see you later! Dad's making a sand car for Huxley and a sand city for me.'

I'm much better the next day and wake up early for a run. By the time Frank and the kids wake up, they find me with my feet in a tub of ice. I've just been writing a fax to Mala:

Dear Mala: Perhaps you could spare just a moment of your time to clarify a few things for me. First of all, WE ARE NOT THE MARKSES. It was impossible to find a way to tell Frank I've had this planned for ages when everyone's running around calling us the Markses. AND, we are four, not three. Only THREE pillows had chocolate on them. The kids had to share! That isn't right. And, I only tell you this so you might avoid a future full of law suits, there are sea lice here. They almost killed me. PS, and the beach is small.

'What now?' Frank startles me. He is looking at the ice bucket.

'Um, this is really really stupid,' I say as I slip the fax – unnoticed – into a magazine.

'What?'

'Well, did you know it takes about 200 times around the beach to make a 12K? Killer on the feet.'

Frank takes the kids to breakfast and after a while, I hobble down for coffee. He's left already so I sit with Mel and Bernie and the girls.

At 11 we catch each other in the elevator. Frank suggests we get in the car and go to Nai Harn, go up the steep hill to the lighthouse, look at the view, have lunch and hang out on the beach.

I can't say that walking up to the lighthouse is easy but being able to look around and see only Rittmans at my side is worth it, and the view of the island is spectacular as well. We can see farms, rubber plantations, beaches, boats, white-washed cliffs and eerie protrusions from the sea.

We have lunch at a small, family-owned shack next to the imposing yacht club: *mii sapam*, seafood in gravy over flat rice noodles, *kao mok gai*, a Muslim dish of roasted chicken on a bed of saffron rice, mixed with crispy ginger, *pad thai*, pineapple fried rice and two Singha Beers. We wait a long time for the order and it doesn't come out all at once but we get to watch them wash and peel and chop as if it were Mom's kitchen. We love the food and vow to come back the next time we find a spare $5 – that's what it costs, including the tip.

After lunch, I find the courage to swim in the ocean. We stay for hours. Playing Puff the Magic Dragon, hiking along the shore, discovering treasure. We find a red starfish about the size of a dinner plate. I'm sure it's fake, it feels like rubber. We shower off at the yacht club, toss the toy starfish in the trunk and pile into the sweltering car, promising the kids we'll get them a milkshake at Dino-Park on the way back.

We are pretty zonked, everyone just staring out his or her window, when we come upon a building we haven't noticed before, not far from the hotel. It's about the size of a colonial mansion; perhaps it was the home of some rubber plantation king. But where it was once probably painted a bright white, it is now entirely black. How could we have missed the illuminated orange spaceship of a jack-o-lantern on the lawn with a mechanical green stem that lifts up and billows smoke and says 'Ha ha ha'? I can make out a small, humble, unobtrusive glow-in-the-dark sign that matter-of-factly states 'World's largest haunted house'.

'Cool!' Frank says, awestricken.

The next day, I run on the highway. Frank buys rafts and we all meet up for a bob in the sea. Sadie and Huxley feed Jumper, the elephant that travels around the hotel during the hours of ten through noon and five through eight. Jumper does a little dance and kisses Sadie; he bows before Huxley. He's only a little pachyderm, like the one in *Jungle Book*, and the kids want to be with him every minute.

We have lunch inside the pub. I'm playing pool with Mel. Sadie's eating her hamburger the way her father does, which is fine for him but not so good for our Sadie, who has less chewing experience and a smaller gullet. Therefore, she chokes. Mel hustles over and directs Frank on the proper manoeuvre. Out the chunk of food shoots, landing on Huxley's plate. Thinking, 'Oh, a flying meatball', Huxley eats it.

'Thanks again, Mel.'

She points up, crosses herself. 'Pater Heimlich.'

I give up my game and join my family.

Grabbing a fistful of fries from Sadie's plate, I fan out my brochures on the table.

'So, later on, I thought we'd go to the casuarina forest and see the water buffalo and the rice paddies and then go –'

Frank interrupts, puts his burger down and says in a stentorian tone, 'We're going to the haunted house.' No hemming and hawing, no compromise like 'Okay, and then on the way back . . .' He continues his lunch.

'Frank, there's so much to see here. I don't want to go to a haunted house. I mean, it's Thailand for goodness sake – snorkelling, ancient temples, cliffs, gibbons. Frank, think of the kids!'

'I want to go to the haunted house!' Sadie screams, throwing her head back, burger juice dribbling down her chin. Jeez, she'll choke again.

Huxley is drawing with ketchup.

'Well, I don't. It's stupid to be here and do that,' I say.

I tuck my pamphlets away and stir my salad. Not one mention – in the books, the brochures, the billboards or the hotel directory – of this attraction. Even Dino-Park had its share of blurbs.

'Fine, fine. Stop looking at me like that, Huxley.'

After lunch we go back to the room. A postcard is under

the door. It seems THE MARKS FAMILY is invited on a sunset cruise with the GM. Will it never end? I head to the phone. Mala's secretary answers. She concocts some ridiculous tale about Mala being at the dentist. Yeah, right. I leave an urgent message and take a shower. As I'm getting dressed in the orange-and-black overall shorts that Frank insists I wear, the phone rings. It's Mala.

'I'm sorry. I've had an awful day. I'm having a bit of unexpected dental . . .'

'Mala, Mala, Mala,' I sing, patiently, menacingly, with an 'I've got nowhere to go' sort of tone. 'Among other things . . . like, I'm sure I mentioned I'm a runner? . . . And this beach? . . . Uh, a little too small for, like, even a sprint . . . but, mostly, you FORGOT to change the hotel reservations. They have us as The Markses everywhere I turn. I told you that this was –'

'Oh, Mrs Rittman. I can explain. Hold on a second, Mrs Rittman . . .' She now speaks to someone else in the room, if you can believe her gall. 'General anaesthesia's fine, Doctor. Mrs Rittman.' She resumes our conversation, talking funny like there's cotton in her mouth. 'I'm sorry, Mrs Rittman, as I was saying, the reason . . . Oh, Doctor, that was a bit of a sting, not to worry, not to worry, it barely went noticed . . . Mrs Rittman, the reason for that . . . Count backwards from 99? Okay, that's easy . . . 99, 98, 97 . . .'

'MALA! The reason is what?'

'Oh, it's because . . .'

'She's ready, Doctor,' comes a female voice. The phone goes dead just after I hear a drill.

Oh, God, like what couldn't wait until she finished her fucking last sentence? Never again, Mala. You blew it, Sleeping Beauty.

———

It's about six when we make it to the haunted house. We're the only car in the lot. We bang on the knocker. After at least a minute the door opens. We see a European man. He towers over Frank and is paper-thin. His skin is pale and waxy. He wears a faded, shabby tuxedo. He welcomes us in.

'I have been expecting you. I am Dorian. This is my house. Come in.' His accent is elegant, heavy, like long, crimson velvet drapes. I can't place it.

'Please, please, follow me.'

He ushers us to a macabre café. The tables are glass-topped coffins. You can see remains inside the coffins, and tokens buried with the dead. Our table houses Marilyn Monroe. She's much skinnier now and in the company of her favourite dress, a rose and a novel. A waitress approaches. Dorian introduces her. 'This is Desdemona. She'll be your personal assistant. We require 20 minutes to wake the dead. Please enjoy our menu.' His accent loses a bit of its pomp: 'One house pour is free. Kids go half price. We're out of the chicken.' He turns on his heel and leaves.

Desdemona hands out the menus, rubs Huxley's head and produces the smile that so many Asians do when they see him – enthralled, enraptured, could it really be Confucius? She says, 'This is not for children.'

'Oh, I don't know. They like nuggets and chips,' I respond.

'Good. They can have that with me in the operating room. We are equipped with monitors so they will be able to watch you as you take your journey. But they cannot join you. So, what'll you have?' She pulls out a pen from behind her ear and a pad from her hip pocket.

'Frank, that doesn't seem right, maybe we should go.'

'Go now? After coming all this way? The kids will be *fine* with Dorian and Desdemona. Won't you?'

'Yeah, Dad, I want to watch. Don't you, Huxley?' Sadie says.

'Daddy knows you do, Pumpkin.'

Frank orders a Bloody Mary and I order a wine. We get the kids a whole bunch of things that hopefully will keep them occupied while we 'journey'. Desdemona sashays away.

'Another boy, Mom,' Sadie whispers.

'Huh?'

'Desdemona is a boy. I know it.'

'No way,' I say.

'Yes way.' She closes the argument.

Desdemona returns with our drinks. I look at her more closely and see the carefully layered pancake make-up, the scarf not quite obliterating the Adam's apple. She motions for us to follow her. She leads us to brain central, a small room with a few sofas and pillows and a dozen TV screens on the wall, like you'd see in the security room of a major institution.

The kids' food is laid out on a low table in a dignified, if not overly formal fashion, with pewter curlicued cutlery and cloth napkins and ice-cold water. Desdemona says, 'You begin outside. Dorian will show you the way.'

I hug Sadie and she stiffens. 'Go, Mother!'

I kiss the top of Huxley's head.

'We don't have to go if you guys are worried,' I say to the kids.

They're busy eating.

Frank pulls my arm. 'Dorian is waiting!'

'Mr and Mrs Rittman, you are to begin here.' He shows us a staircase. 'Otto will take you to your first room. Tarra. Have fun.'

We walk up the stairs and our world gets dimmer and dimmer. Otto is waiting on the landing. He is dressed in an old-time jailhouse uniform. He doesn't speak, but mimes for us to follow him. He opens a door, motions 'After you', and then slams it shut. He is not in the room with us. A small bulb is swinging overhead. There is a big bed and a young girl lying in it. The bed begins to rock violently and spin. The girl sits up, turns to us, revealing a hideous grin, black-rimmed eyes and long, tangled hair. She screams; I scream. She lurches forward and vomits. I quickly make for the door – jolted, disturbed – and find it's locked. Another door on the far end is opening, revealing a shaft of dusty light. I stride toward it. Otto is on the other side; he takes my elbow. Frank is behind me. Otto leads us a few paces and opens another door. Uncertainly, I follow Frank into another room. Otto disappears in a cloud of smoke. We're in total darkness. I hear footsteps. A desk lamp comes on, framing the silhouette of a man in a sweater. He moves toward us. 'Mother? Mother?' He stops at a swivel chair, spins it around and shows us the skeleton. Otto, at the other side of the room, motions 'This way, this way'. I hurry.

Down the pitch-black hall we go. I hear heavy footfalls behind us, faster and faster; chains are rattling, closer and closer, hitting metal, hitting the floor, the wall. I start to run and scream. What sort of mind would come up with all of this? This is not mechanical; this is not some cheap-thrill sideshow. This is a Broadway-production horror, and while I totally appreciate the accuracy and all the great special effects and, God, just the workmanship that went into all of this, I am freaking out because, like, what sort of person devotes all his time and resources to such a thing? A person who really might want to butcher another person? I can feel the chains coming near . . . A person who especially likes to prey upon the children of foreign tourists? When is a game not a game? The footsteps are upon me and I see something glimmering right in front of my face. It's a huge butcher's knife. I scream and grab for Frank – who isn't there. '*Frank!!!*' Otto pulls me into a small closet, where a man is typing 'REDRUM' over and over.

'*I want to go. I want to go,*' I cry.

Otto nods. He smiles. It's going to be all right. He's just a bloke. It's just a summer job. He takes my hand. We're moving along a hallway. He drops my hand. A screen slides open, revealing a window, through which we see the broad shoulders and head of a man. When he turns, we see he is wearing a hockey mask. 'It's Jason, Frank. Ha ha, it's just Jason, Frank. And it's not even Friday 13th. Get it? Get it? Frank?' I make a weird laugh. At this point, Jason is warm and fuzzy, especially behind the glass. But then he takes his hockey stick and smashes it through the window. He reaches out for me. I run in terror. I have to find a way out. I look around for light from a window, anything. Instead, I crash into Otto, just as I hear the first pull on a chainsaw cord. Frank crashes into me and we find ourselves in an old-fashioned elevator. It takes us to a basement full of scientific experiments, bubbling test tubes and Frankenstein, I presume. It is indeed a detailed laboratory complete with the good doctor mixing potions and the big guy himself getting electrocuted. I remember the monitors. Why exactly do they have monitors? Maybe in case a tourist escapes?

'Otto – Frank –' I pant, 'really – I think it's – like – time to go. The kids and all . . .'

Otto points to a door with an EXIT sign. A trap?

'Come on, Frank.'

Frank just stands there.

'Come on, Frank, please! What are you doing? Please!'

'I think we came in this way, don't you?' he asks Otto, pointing in a different direction.

'Yeah, but this is the way back to your kids,' Otto answers in a real normal voice.

I crash through the doors and hug and kiss my children. Sadie is giggling madly.

'We saw you screaming, Mommy. Daddy was laughing the whole time behind you.'

There are still no cars in the lot when we get out. I open my side. There is a horrible stench in the car – rotting, sewagy, definitely not old milk or stale crackers. The kids won't get in. We roll the windows down but it barely helps.

We get back to our hotel and Frank and I sit outside on the balcony. I tell him about how truly petrified I was. 'I mean, all the great things we could have done today – together – the pearl diving, the rubber tapping, the waterfall, the gibbons, the kids would have loved the gibbons. All the things Thailand is known for . . .'

He flicks his lighter. 'Oh well, that's not *all* it's known for.' He pulls on a big fat joint and we look out over Relax Bay.

We're all knackered the next day so we hang at the beach and the pool and wait for Jumper. I say goodbye to Mel and Bernie and the girls.

They're on their way east, to Thmptst. Frank and I decide to get a babysitter for our last night. We'll go to a restaurant the concierge recommends in Patong after doing a bit of bar-hopping. Bar-hopping is not wandering. It is structured. It's not about finding the perfect place, it's about hitting them all. The car smells worse and I didn't believe that possible. We check between the seats and under the car mats and find nothing.

After we've hit the Rock Hard, Alice, Moonshine Joint and Tequila, we arrive at a cabaret.

'Hey, that seems like fun. Let's go in.'

'But what about your five-star, five-course . . .'

'Oh, come on, let's just check it out.' We walk in and sit down at a small, round cocktail table near the stage. I feel good, buzzed, happy to be with Frank and, to be honest, happy that we're going home. After four days on the other side of the looking glass, I will relish straight old Singapore. Phuket is a beautiful place, but it casts a very strange spell – surrounded by sea but living on burgers, men dressed as women, Rittmans addressed as Markses. I can't even think about what might have happened without Mel . . . Hux drowning, Sadie choking. Sea lice? Deadly razor burn? The psycho house . . . but nothing – nothing – can prepare me for what happens next.

'Ladies and gentlemen, please take your seats. Our show is about to begin.'

The waitress gets our last order before the show. In a few moments, all is quiet in the room – except for a quick, loud sniff. And then a guttural hawking, followed by productive hacking, a couple of snorts and a loud hoot. The footlights come on. We see six *lad*ies dressed in red sequins. They are swaying, Motown style, humming softly.

'Ladies and gentlemen, the wonderful . . .'

Two spotlights converge on a man who has taken his place between the 'girls'. He is wearing a green, crushed-velvet dinner jacket. His hair is slicked to the side, he has topaz-coloured glasses and a moustache. He sings the first words to a Chinese heartbreak song. The audience begins excited applause . . .

'Ladies and gentlemen, I present . . . The Sensational Sebastian Gok and the Go-Gos . . .'

'Think lovely thoughts . . . Think lovely thoughts . . .' I start the chant. Sadie joins in: 'Think lovely thoughts . . . think lovely thoughts . . .'

'Singapore!' I say.

'Transextypes,' Sadie says.

'Dino-Park!' Huxley says.

'The corporate, non-transferable discount we received for being the Markses!' Frank suddenly joins in.

'My new ring!' I say.

'The starfish!' Sadie says.

'The starfish?' Frank and I look at each other.

'Yeah, the one we put in the trunk of the car.'

The smell – a dead, *real* starfish.

'Jumper!' says Huxley.

'The Go-Gos!' I say.

'A happy ending.' Frank and I clink our fifth or sixth glass of champagne.

Mark My Words

Simon and Melanie are bringing their kids over to avoid Pearl's holiday mark-up. Their daughter, Natalie, is a tawny-skinned girl with dark, soft curls and wide-set almond eyes. She is Sadie's age. Charlie, pink-skinned and bald, is barely any age at all. They are supposed to come at eight, then we'll get the little ones set up with Posie before shooting out. My bed is wearing the contents of my closet. Nothing seems right for New Year's. New Year's won't even *be* New Year's without my leather pants. They make me dance, make me want to stay up late. They even tell a good joke. They speak to me with their last vestiges of animal spirit. But it's so hot here I'll never make it out alive if I wear them. And while I want to be buried in my leather pants, I do not feel ready to go yet. Ah well, the Daisy Duke shorts will have to do – they make me yodel, swig beer and kick butt. Getting dressed for New Year's, to me, is like picking out the best stuffed animal to sleep with, the right song to have sex to, the right topping on your pizza. You have to be in touch with your mood-goals.

I blow out my hair real big and am generous with my make-up. The tiny faces of Sadie and Huxley, watching everything I do, get a make-over too. Frank hates that I let Huxley wear lipstick, but he also hates that I paint Huxley's fingernails. (I never told Frank that I taught Sadie how to put cream on Huxley's penis after his bris. He would think it had something to do with Huxley's unflagging fidelity to Sadie.) Anyway, I would rather see Huxley dolled up than left out. Huxley doesn't think it's perverse to acknowledge his feminine side. I unpack from Phuket, and finally relinquish the bedroom.

'Frank, it's all yours. They'll be here in five minutes.'

I pop in a video for the kids and wait and pouf my hair a little more. I make myself a gin and tonic. By 8.30, I am still waiting for them, and Frank. I'm looking forward to seeing Frank in what I strongly suggested he wear (suggestion being to lay it out on the bed): a black Jacquard silk shirt, black slacks and his signature cowboy boots.

Back in the days when Frank first started flirting with me, he didn't make too much of an impression until I noticed his boots. And how he'd walk in those boots. I met him at my first job in New York. He was on the cc list of every memo I had to type. My guess, from typing his name several times a day, was that he was an esteemed person of advanced years. So when my girlfriend, another secretary in the subsidiary rights department at M Publishing, introduced me to him, I was surprised by his youth and standing. We were all headed into a meeting. I was to write down everything that was said, and there was that tacit understanding that there would, of course, be no quotes attributable to myself in my notepad. That was just one reason no one laughed when I asked if the book title *Sniglets* was pig Latin for 'little Negro'. Another reason no one laughed was because *Sniglets* was a sacred cash cow. Mostly, though, they didn't get it and they never laughed anyway. But Frank did. He even riffed on *Sniglet* and Margaret Mitchell, using two cash cows in one irreverent joke. Everyone else was dead silent, looking at the dipshit Shelley Sherstein, the head (giver) of the department. She was the one who clicked by on stiletto heels and Heather-Locklear-circa-*Melrose* outfits. She was the one who snapped my bra while I was typing a memo, probably just at the FSR, Esq. part, and said, 'None of my girls will have their bra straps showing.'

Thereafter, from time to time, Frank would stop by and sit catty-corner to me. Like the day he came down wearing a walkman and just sat there. I finally acknowledged him when I finished typing the 29 names on the bcc part of the memo that I had to get out to fifty bazillion people along with ten pages of photocopying each that I hadn't done yet. I was a bit frazzled since it was nearly 5.30. He slouched into a chair, all full of nonchalance, which I knew was really 'damn I like watching you', and said nothing. I said nothing. I kept on madly typing. 'I am pleased to enclose the excerpt from *Fruiti de Lane* by Natalie Plattau.' (Whose last book, *Over There*, sold 75 copies – the exact number of her close friends and relatives – and was about her three years as an expatriate.) 'This is Ms Plattau's diary from her two years spent studying roadkill from around the world. Be sure to catch it in next month's *Uncommon Pets* magazine.' I had a few more lines to type and all the copying and stapling to do, but FSR Esq. started talking.

'Do you like music?' he asked.

'No. And I don't like colours either,' I said.

He laughed.

'See you later. You look busy,' he said. I looked up to make amends just as he was leaving. I would have put my head back down to the typewriter, but I couldn't help noticing his gait. It was eons slower than a New Yorker's. It was by degrees more casual. It was easy and fluid, unhurried, cool, unflappable. The cowboy boots were doing their thang, scraping across the floor, transporting FSR Esq. into his saddle again. I couldn't take my eyes off him. Though there was nothing nearly acceptable, sartorially speaking, above the boots, there was promise. We could do something with that rancher's bod – long, thin, elegant and broad-shouldered. Indeed we could. He loped away to the elevator. I put everything down and ran after him. We went to a bar. I got fired and five years later we were married but I'll not digress on all of that because at least 75 of you – the exact number of my close friends and relatives – already know all about the courtship of Fran and Frank.

Okay, Frank will be a little warm in these clothes tonight but he doesn't dance like I do – crazy, frenetically. I always thought I was a good dancer until the damn video camera made a point of proving that I am actually spastically jangling to a meter even the Chipmunks can't achieve. It's like everyone around me is hearing something different to what I am. It's like I'm furiously applauding instead of clapping to the beat . . . so fast my hands could turn into butter. Maybe Frank moves at the speed of light so it just looks like he's standing still, leaning against the wall.

Before I can finish my thesis about attire and why a caged hamster married Brer Tortoise, Simon and Melanie arrive. Melanie has the same dark skin, black lustrous curls and wide-set, violet eyes as her daughter. Her father was Scottish and her mother Maori, traits visible in her colouring and high warrior brow. Her mouth is expressive, her lips shapely but thin. She has a heart tattoo on her wrist and has an artsy demeanour, wearing flowing caftans and gauzy shirts that look very sexy on her. If I didn't appreciate her, understand her like I do, I might think she was dishevelled and her clothes frowzy. She has a good, impulsive, explosive laugh. But, if I didn't know her, appreciate her like I do, I might sometimes wonder what the hell she's laughing about. It could be something from yesterday, it could be the part about 'Your table is ready' or 'Is this your son's cup?' It doesn't take much. She's that easily tickled. And, well, it does come with the territory, you know, being creative and all, but some *might* say she's completely unstable.

Simon is British, but was raised all over the world, left in boarding schools and often sent to live with relatives while his parents researched . . . things. He has peach hair and light skin – in fact, he's pretty darned monochromatic all over. Indeed, at first glance, he's featureless, but if you squint and catch him in a shadowy overhead light, you can see that there *is* a nose, a mouth and eyes – they're just reticent, very British, very reserved. He shows signs of genius – intensity, wit, impulsiveness. I just wish I could understand the half of what he is saying. His voice is low, his accent is thick, he uses a few big words I don't know, and he's usually pissed as a potter by the time I see him. Simon and Melanie are in Singapore for only a short while and we hope that means what it usually does – three more years – but Melanie hates living here for some reason. Some people just do. I thought she liked it when I saw her sleeping under the stars a few weeks ago. You can't do that everywhere, enjoy a slumber in the great outdoors. Turned out she was too tired to make it all the way home and thought she'd just lie near the fish pond and her unfinished vodka and rest her eyes for a minute. It wasn't her fault that the sun was up before she was. Simon had a bit more stamina. He made it as far as the grocery store steps. Pearl was babysitting so it was okay.

Simon and Melanie are famous for their fights. They make me and Frank look like mourning doves, but that's just because we usually get on each other's nerves when there aren't others distracting us, like at home, in the car, on vacation, in elevators, etc. To Simon and Melanie, the world is their home, their car, their elevator, and that's all there is to it. Whether it's camping down with the fishes or shouting 'I'll fucking kill you! You fucking piece of shit . . .' over the seesaw at the colourful playground, they are honest, wear their hearts on their sleeves, and are down-to-earth and full of life. There's no one better I can think of to ring in the New Year with.

We'll be going to Sam and Valerie's party later. The big scandal is that Brenda decided to have a dinner party even though she knew about the Markses' party. *Yes, can you believe?* She even managed to bag a few seminal couples, enticing them with her idea of having an elegant New Year's Eve with a candlelit midnight dinner and fancy dress. It was predetermined who would go to Brenda's and who to Valerie's by the established bonds of friendship. The groups overlap, but if forced to choose allegiances, they will find themselves in different camps. Brenda's minions are more expatty, more *Town & Country*, know all the right restaurants, clubs, trips and schools. Valerie's group knows a lot about where you can sneak in wine and duck the corkage.

Frank is not ready so the three of us have a drink on the balcony. In fact, his delay is bringing us dangerously close to still being here when Sadie and Natalie come down, as they inevitably will, in costume to put on an entirely ad-libbed show that has no end. It's the performance version of 'The Song That Gets On Everybody's Nerves'. Here comes the whispering, the giggling. I hear Sadie back-kick Huxley into the wall, 'No, Huxley, you're not in this part!' They goof their way through a few minutes, only to be interrupted by a thunderous booming upstairs. 'I can't fucking find it!' It's just Frank banging around looking for something. Frank's always losing things.

'Out of the way, Huxley,' Frank says harshly. 'This doesn't have anything to do with you. Fran, do you have any idea where my leather satchel is? I have all my cards in it. I can't go out.'

'Come on, we'll just take cash. We're only going for a drink and then to the party. Frank, watch the show, I'll get money from the coffee can.' I go to the kitchen and take it down but it's empty. Shoot.

'All right, let's just take out cash from the machine,' I suggest. 'Carry on without us, won't you girls. Oh, Sadie, don't cry. It's a great show; practise for tomorrow.'

We leave and go to the ATM, but it spits my card back.

'This is just my luck. The machine isn't giving any more tonight.'

We head to a wine bar I've spotted to try for some tapas and champagne before going to Sam and Valerie's. When we're at the street, Melanie stops and flails her hand.

'What are you doing?' I ask her.

'Hailing a cab,' she answers.

'Why?' I ask.

'How else can we get there?'

'Melanie, it's three blocks away.'

'Yeah. Here's one.'

It passes us, lighting up its 'for hire' sign.

Not many more come by and after 15 minutes we use a cell phone and go through the whole Comfort Cablinks thing.

'Is this 9-082-4 . . .'

'Yes.'

'Going to Bayshore, is it?'

'No.'

'But you are 9-082-4 . . .'

'Yes. I'm going to –'

'Leaving from lobby J?'

'No, actually –'

'You have moved from lobby J, is it?'

'No, I'm standing on the street!'

'Is this Mrs Flank?'

Finally, it is understood where I am and where I'm going and before I hang up, the taxi is there.

The driver has to travel two miles in the wrong direction just to get to a spot where he can make a u-turn. He turns and doubles back, and when we get across the street from the very spot where he just picked us up, he makes a right, passes a school, a shop and stops. We're there. It wasn't even three blocks from where we stood, a five-minute walk.

The place is empty. I'm not sure why because it's really quite nice. There's a long, smooth bar and a couple of pool tables, votive candles and dark walls, oriental rugs and tables all along the periphery, with sofas and cushions. Maybe the crowds come later. We go to sit at one of the plush tables.

'Ah, sorry *lah*, that one is reserved, you see.' The waitress indicates the paper tent on the table that says 'reserved'.

I notice that all the good seats are 'reserved'. Only the plain tables scattered in the middle – the type that wobble when you put your elbows on them, as you sit hunched up in your cold, hard chair – are not. I don't want to be seated in the centre of a big, empty room in an uninspired metal chair, apologising for tipping the table, whilst staring at the good seats.

'Look, there's no one in here. We're just going to be about an hour, or less even,' I say.

'We reserve these tables for our members,' the waitress answers.

'Members? What's that?'

'It's $500 a year.'

'And?'

'And $500 the next year.'

'Okay, but what *is* a membership?'

'You get to have the reserved seats.'

'Yeah?' we all ask.

'And, you get a bottle of your choice of whiskey, vodka or gin when you join,' she explains.

'Doesn't that take business away, you know, if everyone gets a bottle of liquor to take home?' Simon asks.

'Oh, we keep it here behind the bar.'

'So you can charge for the mixers,' Melanie whispers to us.

'Bloody hell, $500. Do you have many members?' Simon inquires.

'We don't have members yet. We just opened a week ago.'

We crack up. Simon takes the sign off the table, sits on the overstuffed library chair and says, 'Here's the deal, love, if you get 50 members in the next 50 minutes, I pledge that we will give up our seats peacefully. How 'bout you get us some Moët? Thanks, me duck.'

The champagne comes to us warm. It seems the refrigerator hasn't arrived yet, but they bought a few bags of ice. We wait while it chills in the ice bucket. We gaze upon our uncorked bottle, silently. Our conversation is in there. As soon as the first sign of sweat drips down the neck of the bottle, Simon thumbs it open, pours four glasses and begins his stories, ranging from white-water rafting in New Zealand to going to sleep in Spain and waking up in New Delhi. I am too outclassed to win them over with my limp little tale about hitchhiking for two years. Compared with them, I was just faking it all that time, waiting for Daddy to spank me and bring me back to finish up college. But I tell it anyway; it's all I got. They love the part about when I fell asleep in a car and woke up in the middle of a cow pasture.

Frank tells his story from Switzerland. (He usually saves this for Christmas Eve.) He'd been travelling for a while and had developed a stomach upset on the leg to Switzerland. He dropped off his bags at the hotel and planned to kill time until his room was ready, an estimated three hours. On his way back to the hotel, he stopped at a pissoir. 'My, what a clean Johnnie On The Spot this is,' he thought as he unzipped his fly. And basking in the relative comfort of his environment, zipping back up his fly, he unleashed the fart that had been grieving him for so many hours. Unfortunately, and ever-so-unFrankly, the fart was, by definition, not a fart at all; it had substance. He made it back to the hotel and adopted a haughty tone so as to put the staff to the task before they could determine his soiled state. They poked around on the computer for a moment and told him his room was ready but they would need a moment to deliver his luggage. 'Fine, fine,' he flicked his hand, disguising his relief. He went into his room and immediately dropped his drawers and started running a bath. The doorbell rang. 'Bellhop, Sir. We have your bags.' He looked at his underpants. He heard another knock. 'Sir? Sir?' He wrapped a towel around himself, opened a window, grabbed a hanger and scooped the loaded under-pants onto the hook. He extended the armed hanger out the window and swung it around until the centrifugal force was powerful enough to send those babies flying. He returned the hanger to the closet and opened the door. He hadn't bathed yet and the man gave him a very Swiss–French 'pee-yew' face. Who cares, thought Frank. He felt better now and took his bath. He was even well enough for a little room service and a glass of wine and a tawdry pay-per-view movie. He fell asleep around nine. The next morning he woke up early, full of brand-new-day energy, and pulled the curtains aside to breathe in the fresh, dewy air. He looked out at the moun-tains, proudly showing themselves against a cloudless sky. He heard the clattering of silverware and muffled conversation. It was coming from below his window. Just one floor down was an outdoor terrace café where the waiters were setting up for breakfast. They'd just begun. In only a few moments, they would start putting plates, napkins, silverware, coffee cups, saucers, milk, cream, sugar and maybe a vase of flowers on the table just below Frank's room. The table just below Frank's room, where his briefs had landed. They lay there still, as yet unnoticed, smack in the middle where the vase of flowers would go.

Frank and I often say there are two kinds of people in the world: those who love this story and those who haven't a clue why it's being told in the company of fair ladies. It's no wonder we want to ring in the New Year with Simon and Melanie.

We order another bottle of Moët.

'Gone already,' says the waitress.

'Yeah, we're quick, so we'll have another.'

'No champagne left.'

'Not a drop. It was so delicious. Anyway, we'll take another.'

'We don't have any more champagne. That was all. Anything else for you?'

We convince Melanie that it makes more sense to walk back to Fortune Gardens. I try two more bank machines along the way and still can't get any money out. We get to Sam and Valerie's at about 10.30. It's pretty packed. A buffet of nibblies is spread on the table. I did think to contribute. I had ducked back to our apartment to pick up a tray of hard, brown bread squares, which I'd earlier brushed repeatedly with my homemade shabu-shabu sauce. I'd invented a new appetizer. Wrap a little smoked salmon around it and whoo doggy. In fact, my little cruncherretta put the stake in previously undiscovered fusion possibilities. I had German bread, Japanese sauce and Norwegian salmon. I put my tray out in a prime position, moving inferior appetizers out of the way, and retrieve my drink from Sam. I go to hang out on the balcony. It's the best place for people who want to talk and smoke – outside and distanced from the stereo speakers. Of course, you *listen* only by default if you can't manage to talk while you're drinking or dragging.

Sam keeps coming up and filling and filling. He dances through the room asking us to taste his concoctions – a soursop daiquiri, a mango margarita, a papaya colada. And we do, because we can tell he'll be sad and sobered if we don't. He makes a toast to his lovely wife, swoops up his still-awake four-year-old son, Andrew, and dances with him to some hometown favourite. When the song's over, Andrew returns, dazed, to the sofa to sit with his mother, who seems to be content as a spectator.

Melanie and I start dancing. She's doing that Deadhead sort of dance where you pretend you're a weed in the wind or something. I try it. I know I look more like a dust mite in a hurricane; my heart rate is already at 170 and we're only listening to Olivia Newton-John.

Frank has just come back with a shoebox full of our CDs. Clive hunkers down next to him, looks from side to side to see if he'll be spotted, and surreptitiously pulls out another stack from his inside pocket. Joe furtively pulls out a few of his own. Veterans of Sam and Valerie's New Year's parties come out of the woodwork and hand over their smuggled-in disks. Not that his music isn't good. I'm sure he likes it. Now the stack is as high as the corn in July. Soon, we're dancing to everything from Prince to Queen, from Cake to Cream, from Phish to Meat Loaf. Oh, if Brenda's party could see us now, they'd all agree they made the more suitable choice if they were to act their age. We're bouncing on the sofa, jumping off chairs, picking up candlesticks and salt shakers, holding them like mikes. I'm livin' the song and singing loud, it's a cold and lonely night. I'm not even aware of the major dings I'm making in the Burmese teak coffee table as I stomp in queble time about doing what I can and worrying about it in the morning, I mean, ain't no doubt about. Then, everyone's down for the count, moppin' brows, falling back onto the sofa. Sam and I stand alone before them on our Burmese-teak coffee-table stage, gathering up all the anguish of that teenage night when the devil sat on our shoulders, feeling blessed, feeling 17, feeling barely dressed. I crouch down as low as I can, and know it just as well as he that we're gonna go all the way tonight . . . I pick up a champagne flute, and finish the song, doing both parts. When the song ends, we get applause. I dance with Frank to NRBQ and take a break outside for a smoke. I'm about two puffs into it when harpies come – the first strains of *Hair*. I stub out my cigarette and meet Sam in the middle of the living room. Melanie's good for 'Age of Aquarius', but then it's a two-man show for me and Sam – until Clive croons in with 'Colored Spade'. I don't even know there's an audience when I make my way with all my heart and soul through 'Once Upon a Lookin' for Donna'. When I do look up, Sam is gazing at me, puzzled. *What are you?* Valerie is still awfully relaxed on the lounge, barely even making a dent in her durian daiquiri. When the title song comes on, Sam and I traverse the room, leap athletically from surface to surface, land on the floor together as if it's been rehearsed a dozen times and embrace at the end to shattering calls for an encore in our heads. The party continues with more dancing and singing and drinking and chips sloppily scooped into dips. Midnight comes and goes unnoticed.

Brenda is just serving her starter, a fried slice of foie gras with a raspberry drizzle over toasted, crust-free farmers' bread. They're listening to Vivaldi, drinking champagne. Everyone still has good hair. Brenda's husband, Tim, looks through binoculars and tells Brenda, 'Oh, it looks pretty beat. Everyone's on the sofa watching the coffee table.'
'What are they eating?' asks Caroline.

Frank towels me off and offers me water, like a good coach. Knock, knock, knock. There's an insistent rap at the door. A guardly hammering.

'Let's guess which one. Winner gets $100.'

'I say it's Mr Quiff!'

Knock! Knock! Knock!

'Let's hide in the bathroom and make him think he's crazy.'

'No, no, let's get naked and slither on our bellies down the hall.'

'Wait, wait, I got it,' Sam says and goes to the door. Some of us were hoping for a shot at $100 or at least a little naked slithering, but he takes matters into his own hands. He opens the door, slowly approaches the guard, seems about to kiss him on the lips and says, 'I told you not to come here. What if my husband catches us!'

Valerie, who is the most sober of us and has her child and lease to consider, intervenes. 'Oh, we're sorry. He's just kidding. We'll keep it down. Here, take this.' She hands him a box of chocolates. 'Happy New Year!' The guard backs out, nodding and smiling. One of the good guys. He wants us to know that beneath his uniform . . . once the pistol holster is removed . . . and the club put aside . . . his cap taken off . . . shiny shoes left outside the door . . . walkie-talkie disengaged . . . chain of keys returned to their hook . . . he is loco too. 'Sam Marks! You better watch yourself,' Valerie says, patting him firmly on the rear.

A screamingly good game of Pictionary is being played at Brenda's. The tarts are beginning to brown.

We troop out of the Markses' and down the hall, drinks in hand, because the swimming pool is the best suggestion of the night. When we arrive, we are careful to be quiet as we spread around the area like druids. Melanie pops open a

226

bottle of champagne and sits, fully clothed, in the baby pool. Her gauzy skirt is transparent; her shirt has become mostly unbuttoned. I am the first to take off my clothes and dive into the deep end of the big pool. Many follow suit and we swim away a few points of alcohol. I hear a two-finger whistle from above. I look up. It's Greg and Samantha. They are spending their New Year's alone. It's their tradition, because it's their wedding anniversary. And somewhere in the back of my mind, I'm guessing there are other reasons.

'Fancy a swim?' Tim says, putting down his binoculars. Brenda lowers the volume on Frank Sinatra, miffed that the cappuccino wasn't timed properly. She straightens her taffeta skirt and puts out the tarts, crumbles and cakes. She calls Tim to come and reach the brandy snifters. She places them on the table. They have no brandy in the house, but she is not yet aware.

We see flashlights heading our way. Of course the guards have found us and all we can hope for is that it's Mr Loco. If it's Don Knotts, he won't rest until we get the caning we deserve. If it's Mr Quiff, we'll lose our pool privileges for a while. I can already see from the silhouette that it's none of the above. It's the guy who wears the worst toupee you could ever imagine. It is a carpet sample. Or maybe it's the hair-part from a giant Ken doll. Maybe it's half a coconut. Maybe he glued brush bristles on a yarmulke. Whatever, he wasn't born that way and it's got to be pretty hot under that thing during the day.

'Let's run!' I say. I don't want him shining his light in my face and identifying me. Everyone races to the sides of the pool and catapults out, grabs whatever they can find and runs in the opposite direction. I look back to see if Melanie is hustling but she is still rooted in the baby pool and now she's crying.

'Simon!' I hoarsely whisper. 'Simon!'

'I think he's vomiting in the bushes,' says Tess.

Melanie wails as if she can't believe he'd do that without her.

'I'll help you with Melanie,' Tess offers.

The bushes part and Simon comes toward us, then way to the left, then back in our direction, then way on over to the right, and in three times as long as it should take, he is there, standing above his wife saying, 'Bloody hell, you stupid git. What the hell are you doing? Mad cow, can't you see this is a pool for children?' Then he slips down next to her, pushes her back, lifts up her skirt and throws himself onto her. Melanie grabs his back and moans. Tess and I look at each other and run. We catch up with everyone in the lobby of block three. Clive is in the middle of a pile of clothes holding up a bra. 'Okay, I have one black lacy thing here, size 32 B. Do I have any takers?' Lisa shyly stretches out her hand and yanks it away. 'Has anyone seen my other shoe? Jennifer, where's my shoe?' Ward asks.

'Marks and Spencer white cotton briefs . . . anyone? Going once . . .' No one fesses up.

Brenda kisses each cheek of each guest who supped in her home and bids them a Happy New Year and a good night as she hands them a designer goody bag. She closes the door and rolls her pantyhose down, kicking them off along with her mules. She goes to the kitchen and stands in front of the counter with a knife, evening up the edges of the cake. She slivers off portions from each end, like trimming a mous-tache. It is very important. She wipes the chocolate from her face and sees her husband slipping out of the apartment with a towel over his shoulder.

'Let's go to the beach!'

'Wait, I can't find my shirt.'

228

People are still pawing through the tangle of clothes.

'Your mascara escaped down your face.'

'So what, I can see your nipples.'

'Fran, we have no money.'

'Where's Simon and Melanie?'

Ding. The elevator doors open. Twelve adults come out, carrying small, decorative bags full of festive whatnots. The last to emerge is Brenda's husband, Tim. 'Hey mates,' he says, 'guess I missed the swim but made it for the garage sale.'

Everyone heads to the beach. Tess and I hesitate, look back, and figure that as Natalie and Charlie are safe with Posie, it's okay to go. There's a party going on at the Surf Club which, when I say that, sounds a lot cooler than it really is. What it really is? A ton of Singaporeans ten years younger and ten degrees less uproarious than us, and a smattering of expats much like ourselves and therefore embarrassing to look at. There's a trifling Singaporean DJ saying things like, 'All right! Now, let's get the party started!' and playing music that acts a lot like a finger down my throat. The drinks are totally watery and this seems like a big mistake . . . until . . . I see the big, black, juicy sea. 'Come on!'

'No, Fran. Don't,' Frank says with all the conviction of Willy Wonka before Augustus Gloop drinks from the chocolate river. I pull Sam. He was just thinking the same thing. We run to the sea, singing 'She's Come Undone', leaving a trail of clothes behind us. We swim out and moon the crowd, dive about and swim some more. Frank and Valerie are dancing a slow dance.

When we see our gang leaving, we hurry on after them. Everyone goes back to Sam and Valerie's to gather their things and go home, but no one does because Sam insists on one more song and the best drink of the night. He's been saving it for this moment: an iced coffee white Russian. Mmmm, I put my bag back down. The track Sam puts on, the first great Smash Mouth song, gets everyone stomping again so naturally it's just a matter of seconds before . . . knock, knock, knock.

'Who's there?'

'A guard.'

'Agard who?'

'A guard, please . . .'

'I don't know an Agard Please, perhaps you have the wrong . . .'

'Sam Marks, it's *not* funny. Let them in!' admonishes Valerie.

'Okay, doll.' He opens the door and, this time, actually does kiss the guard, full on the mouth.

'We're terribly sorry, everyone's just leaving now. Happy New Year,' Valerie quickly says and hands over a plate of cookies.

The guard nods and says, 'Dis is de segond gomplaind, please do nod gause any more drouble.' She leaves, the lady guard, the one with the *bindi* on her forehead.

'Sam, you'll get us killed one day!' Valerie says and laughs. Simon and Melanie come in. So now we *have* to stay for the grand finale cocktail. We dance in our socks. And finally, at four, most of us head out. As I walk down the hall, I hear Tim say, 'Hey, man, let's get the party started.'

Brenda has put the latch on the door. She is propped up in bed with two large feather pillows. She picks up her book and a bag of M&Ms.

Simon and Melanie follow us as best they can to our apartment. It's slow going because of the zigzagging. We finally get there and all is quiet. I'm about to lead Melanie upstairs to her children but she and Simon go out on the balcony, put their feet up and light cigarettes.

'Frank,' I say under my breath, 'why are they out there?'

'I don't know. Why don't we bring their kids down. That should be a hint.'

'Hey!' Simon calls from outside. I stiffen. 'You have any vodka?'

'No.'

'Yes.' Frank and I contradict each other.

'I'll get the kids; you make them *one* drink,' I mutter.

I scoop Natalie up in my arms and bring her down to the sofa. She sits upright for half a second, then falls over, deep in sleep. I roll Charlie's pram into the living room. Melanie waves to her unconscious children from the other side of the window.

'I wish I had some cocaine,' Simon says. 'I'll bet you have some, Music Man.'

'Sorry, my friend, can't say that I do,' Frank responds.

'Well, you can't *say* it but you can bring it out.'

'Really, I don't have any.'

'Fuck you, you fuckin' selfish faggot.'

'Simon!' Melanie says.

'You too, bitch. Come here.'

Melanie goes over and sits on his lap, giggling away.

Simon tells a great story that almost makes me feel like staying up longer. It's about working on a cruise liner in Spain and suddenly waking up to find himself on a sofa in a casino in St Moritz.

'I *have* to go to bed.' I stand. 'I'm having the New Year's Day party here. Good night, see you around two or so tomorrow.' I leave but I have a moment of complete telepathy with Frank and I hear his mind call mine a 'traitor'. I stop and turn around. 'Frank, would you please come up, too? I'm sorry, Simon and Melanie, I just think Frank needs to help me tomorrow and I don't want to go to bed alone on New Year's, so, well, here are your two great kids and thanks

231

for making things so much fun. No one I would have wanted to ring it in with better, that's for sure. Good night, see you tomorrow.'

I pull the covers down. Oh my God, this feels so good.

'Do you think they left?' Frank asks.

'Did you actually get that impression when Simon went into the kitchen and brought the bottle outside?' I whisper.

Frank climbs into bed. 'Good night.' We both hear it: Charlie's squeaky pram is being wheeled out the door, Natalie is saying, 'Where are we?' Frank and I smile and settle in. These sheets are so chilled, so fresh, they feel, uh, so amazing. The mattress is perfect. Every muscle is relaxing, and, though I still have ghost-music in my head, it's getting fainter. Gee, that was fun, boy, I wish someone videoed me and Sam doing *Hair*. We're getting really good. Frank's in love with Valerie. I'm not in love with Sam. He can dance, that's for sure. He's fun. So's Frank. We're all a bunch of fun. These pillows are too high. I didn't eat anything . . . I am yammering away to myself and my eyes are open wider than they've been all night and there isn't a chance in hell I will ever ever ever fall asleep. Nope, not when everything's just buzzing and buzzing around in my little head and I had such a great time and, gee, I wish I knew if Frank wished he was married to Valerie. 'Frank, you up? Frank, you up?' I kick him. He is asleep. I know this because he yawns.

I must have fallen asleep because I am wishing I never woke up. I go downstairs to make some coffee and on the way see Melanie, passed out on our balcony chair.

Love Stinks

I have to get the stuff ready for the New Year's Day party. I've told everyone to come at two. I slice bagels, carve up chicken for chicken salad, roll deli meats into appealing funnels, bake some salmon, whip up two quiches and a noodle *kuggel*. At about 11 am I go out for a run, which is not nearly as bad as I thought it would be. I come home, rinse off, arrange chips and dips and olives and gherkins, and at about one, the kids and Frank are exactly as I found them five hours ago when Sadie and Huxley bounded into our room. They are on our bed, watching TV.

'Frank, did anyone eat anything yet?'

'Nah, they didn't want to.'

'Did you ask?'

'Nah, they didn't want to.' His eyes are dilated, transfixed on Cartoon Network.

'Sadie, Huxley, would you like something to eat?'

'*Yeah!*' They both scramble off the bed.

I don't make too fine a point of it. I calmly usher them out of the room and say, 'I'm so sorry, guys, Mommy was busy making 900 dishes and running 16 kilometres and Daddy was busy too, obviously, lying there, turning the channels.'

'I turned the channels, Mom!' Sadie says proudly. 'Daddy was sleeping.'

I make them cheese omelettes and cinnamon toast. I stew two apples in the microwave and add sugar, vanilla yogurt, raisins and Graham crackers. Frank comes down and takes up the sofa. He puts on the Disney channel and holds out his arms. The kids leave their breakfast and leap onto his chest. He enfolds them and tells them what they missed on *Tarzan*.

I organise chairs, put candles around, and start making a strudel. Frank is getting his appendix taken out with a plastic screwdriver by Dr Huxley and his temperature taken by Nurse Sadie.

'Frank, can you go buy some beer and ice?'

'Daddy's dead,' Huxley announces.

'Gosh, Huxley, it was just supposed to be a routine operation. Ah well, we'll get another daddy when the shops open tomorrow.'

'Fran!' Frank is horrified.

'It's a miracle! Listen, do you think maybe you came back as, hmmm, someone *useful*?'

'All right, kids, get up, Mommy needs to give orders to be happy.' Frank gets up, then sits back down. 'I forgot, I don't have a cent and I can't find my card.'

So I go out for money while Frank is assigned the task of getting vertical.

'TRANSACTION CANCELLED' comes up again on the screen. I guess the holidays are the worst times to count on a cash machine.

'Now what would be the trouble yere havin', Frahn? And, if ye don't mind, Happy New Year.' It's Irish Kell with her daughter, Ryot, which is pronounced *Kim*, of course.

'Machine's out of money.'

'Is it, now? Aw, I'll give 'er a try.'

'All yours. See you later at my house around two.'

'Hey, I'm a lucky winner!' she calls out to me, waving bills in the air. 'Come back, Frahn, I'll lend ye the money ye be needin'.'

'Thanks. I don't get it, though, why didn't my card work?'

'Temperamental bastards, that's what these devils are. Here, take a couple hundred to tide ye over. Come on, Ryot (Kim).'

'Gee, I wonder where everyone is?' I say to a plate of rolls. I am standing entirely alone, surrounded by perfectly balanced pyramids of once-tempting nosh; it's three-thirty.

Frank bounds down the stairs. 'Fran, since no one's coming . . .'

'Frank, that is so mean!'

'Hey, don't take it out on me. I didn't tell them not to come. I'm going to see if your card is working yet.'

'Well, hurry back. I'll need you to bartend.'

'No, you won't.'

'Yes, I will.'

Na na na naa na. As he opens the door, a wave of people knock Frank back inside. Everyone's come at once. They don't look terrifically fresh. If we were in a different climate, the dress code would be sweatpants; everyone seems to have messy hair or the mange. I swing way far away when Arthur comes to kiss me. He's got that white sticky stuff in the corners of his mouth. Valerie, who wins for most radiant, says she was feeling sick all morning.

'But you didn't drink.'

'I probably got high off Sam's fumes.'

Sam doesn't know it's *not* morning. He just got up.

I'm delighted to see my tennis pal Julee and her husband, Daniel, and some friends from the gym who I thought would be too shy to come. My local friends might not know what to make of me, but they seem to be enjoying the show. It's a nice, mellow party, people moving wordlessly down the table, unable to speak not so much because their mouths are full of food but because they're having trouble making complete sentences. The only sounds are from Elvis Costello, the tons of kids jumping around unattended upstairs, Greg and Samantha, who, having shared an evening in romantic sanctuary, *now* crave conversation, and intermittent sobs from Melanie in the bathroom. Simon assures us that she's always melancholy on New Year's Day, she'll get over it, not to worry. 'Let the bloody fat-arsed wombat have her cry in private, you vultures,' he says, not unkindly.

As the sun drops into the sea and brain cells multiply, the drinks stiffen, the voices escalate and Frank plays me like a marionette, putting on songs to make me go faster and faster. He and Valerie watch me from a shady corner of the room. The party starts to swing. The bunch of kids running around unattended have thrown all 500 balls from the ball tent into the living room. Barbie heads come next, followed by Barbie limbs and torsos and a heavy shower of beanie babies. Melanie comes out of the bathroom, finds Simon and they embrace and sway as their tongues lap the length of each other's neck.

Irish Kell clinks a glass. 'Can I have yere attention? Um, sorry to say, we'll be 'avin' it of you lot. We'll be movin' back to Ireland in a month's time. My Collin got the job, God love him. So, 'ere's to you.'

We're shocked and dampened. Irish Kell has been here longer than anyone. She has never gotten tanned, never learned how to swim, never gotten used to the heat and the mosquitoes, never had a kind word to say about most anyone or anything; she seemed so happy here. She just gave birth to twins two months ago – Bymthe and Gvngythe (pronounced *Eileen* and *Sue* of course) – and she has two other daughters and two maids. How can she bear the thought of leaving?

'Yere all invited to dinner at the Shangri-la on Chinese New Year's.'

I've never heard Collin say anything. I don't think he talks. I look over at him and see he's a little surprised by his generosity.

I go over to Kell. 'Are you all right?'

She says, 'I'm madder than a grubby in a Guinness.'

'That bad, huh?'

'Ah, yeah, sad as a lutinary. Sure, to be going back home isn't worse en cauliflower cake, but this life's been good to me. I'm makin' damn certain my Collin pays for this, Frahn. I'll tell ye, I don' wan' to go.'

Melanie comes over. 'We're leaving, too.'

'Oh no! Is that why you locked yourself in the bathroom?' Melanie nods.

I say, 'I thought you'd be happy to go back.' (Yeah, right, Melanie-go-lightly, who's only been depressed twice in her life – once for four years and once for 30. She told me age five was a good year for her.)

'Yeah, I'm fine. Only Charlie's so pissed off about it.'

'Melanie, you're kidding. Charlie's three months old.' I laugh.

'Just look at him.' She thrusts the baby to me. He starts to cry. 'See, he knows. Uprooted again.'

'So when are you leaving, Melanie?' I ask.

'I don't know. Could be years.'

The party breaks up at 11. Frank and I put the kids to bed in their clothes, unwashed, with promises of brushing twice as hard tomorrow. We clean up whatever might attract pernicious knids and leave the rest for Posie when she is back on duty tomorrow. As we're putting dips in Tupperware and wrapping chicken salad in cellophane, Frank tells me that everyone had fun at my house; it's all I need right now.

The next day, Frank goes to work. I need to grocery shop. I go to the bank machine with my fingers crossed. We're out of beer, cigarettes, wine, food too, I think, and, apparently, money. Again, as I request a few hundred bob, the machine has the nerve to say 'TRANSACTION CANCELLED'. I guess I'll borrow more off Irish Kell, help her in that wrong-headed effort to get back at Collin.

I call Frank. 'There's something the matter with my card. I can't get out any money.'

'I'm in a meeting now, Fran.'

'There's no money, Frank.'

'I'll call you back.'

'Did you find your satchel? You're always losing things. We can't afford those kinds of losses any more.'

'I'm sure I didn't lose it.'

'Remember when you left your brand new raincoat and laptop on the train? Those were the days, huh, when we could just buy another raincoat.'

'Fran, I'll call you back.'

Ah, yes, of course, wink-wink, nod-nod, let the office pay for the call. 'Gotcha. I'll be here.'

An hour later, I'm about to break down and call him again when the phone rings.

'Fran, the account is dry. I checked it on line. What did you do?'

'Nothing. I haven't taken anything out since we went to Phuket.'

'All right, I'm sure it's just a computer thing. I'll have more time tomorrow to go to the bank and check it out better. I'm coming home now.'

'Frank, drive carefully.'

'Aw, that's sweet to hear, Fr –'

'Don't push down on the gas if you don't have to. Drift as much as you can. We have to conserve the fuel.'

I'm trying to think of how I can disguise the chicken salad so it won't seem like the third time it's showing up at the table. I decide to mould it on the kids' plates in their favourite animal shapes.

The next day, Frank comes home early. He drops his briefcase wearily and says, 'Where's Posie?' The kids rush up to him; he pats them absently.

'Doing laundry or something, I guess. Why?'

'I got to the bank. I got a new card.'

'Yeah! Let me have some.' I hold out my palm, itching to feel some cash.

'No, the problem is someone got to our account first. They took out money all over town. How'd they know my PIN, Fran?'

'Well, I guess they figured it out.'

'Really? That's not easy.'

'Hmmm . . .' I tap my finger on my cheek, putting off my confession.

'Fran?'

'Oh, stop badgering me. Maybe they saw the Post-it.'

'The Post-it?'

'I was going to take it off as soon as I memorised your number.' I point to a sheet taped to the wall above the phone headed 'Emergency Contacts'. Attached to it is a big green sticky on which I have written 'FRANK'S PIN NUMBER 9986'. (Duh, how easy would that be to figure out, anyway . . . a tribute to *Get Smart*. Get into Frank's account.)

Of course, there's really only one very likely suspect. I open the door to Amahville. '*Posie! Can you get in here?*' I send the kids upstairs so they'll be spared her predictable breakdown and grovelling.

'Posie, please have a seat,' Frank says calmly.

'*You're a fucking idiot, Posie. Stealing our money,*' I yell at the same time.

'Um, just a moment, Posie. Would you like a cold drink?' Frank asks her, motioning for me to join him in the kitchen.

'Fran, let me handle this,' he says once we're out of earshot.

'I thought we'd do the Good Sir/Mean Ma'am thing,' I whisper eagerly.

'That's what we've been doing since October. I want to be fair but firm.'

'So now she can tell all her friends, "Sir so *firm* but good, so *hard* but soft." Jeez, aren't you in the least bit *furious* about this?'

'Does she talk about me?' Frank asks, brows arched, slight hint of a smile.

'Oy. Come on, we'll compromise: Firm Sir/Mean Ma'am. She'll still like you.'

'Okay, but I go first.'

'Fine.'

'Fine.'

We bring in three cans of tonic water. It's all we have. The kids have found it to be an acquired taste on their cereal. We sit down all civilised. Posie sips her tonic water and Frank undoes his top button.

'Posie, we have good reason to suspect you have stolen money from us. The coffee can is empty and there aren't any receipts and our checking account has been wiped out. Someone used my card while we were away. It's missing now, along with some other things, including about 600 American dollars.'

'Sir, I . . .' Her eyes are big and dark; she's pulling at a string on her shorts. Her lips part and then close as if she's changed her mind or can't screw up the courage to speak or she's willing back a sob. One thing is certain: she's making herself transform; she's getting into character. She just hasn't picked one out yet. She's still madly thumbing through her mental catalogue: 'Liver transplant could save my life, Sir. I have no insurance. I yam ashamed.' (Clutch stomach, hunch over, fall off sofa dead.) 'A man was going to steal your car if I didn't give him money. This is where he shot me.' (Shyly, awkwardly start to pull up shirt and hope Sir says to stop just before exposing chest.) 'I only took the money out to clean it. Now that it's dry, I'm putting it all back.' (Stand up efficiently and go back to the laundry.)

'You know what? *You know what?* There isn't a bank machine on the planet that doesn't have a video camera, Posie. So now you can take your fucking sorry act on the road. Let's all go and watch some home movies of Posie stealing all our money.' Um, that's what I say even though I wasn't supposed to yet.

'Posie, I'm afraid that what Fran says is fairly accurate.' (But did Firm Sir have to take her hands in his?) 'If we ask for an investigation, you will be caught by the police and not only deported but never allowed in again and maybe even thrown in jail. So, we need you to talk to us.'

'Talk!' I holler, inches from her face.

'I swear, Sir, Ma'am, it wasn't me,' she says, leaning forward and switching her meaningful focus between me and Frank.

'I believe you, Posie. So, do you know who did it then?' Frank asks.

No longer keeping up with the terms of my partnership, I say at the same time, 'What a load of crap. I'm calling the police.'

'I think it was Aruhn, my boyfriend,' she mumbles softly.

'Posie, *I can't hear you*! It really annoys me that you mumble like that. If you're old enough to lie, cheat and steal, I think you can talk like a big girl, hmmm?'

'Fran, you're scaring her.' Frank turns to Posie. His face softens, as if he's tending to a child's wounded knee. 'Posie, we can ask for it all on video and even if it is Aruhn, you are still implicated. We aren't looking to get anyone arrested. We want an explanation and we want the money back.'

'Okay.'

'And if we don't have our money back, you're gonna wish you never met me,' I scream.

'Posie,' Frank says, 'I would like to have a talk with your young man. He got you into some big trouble. Tell him to come by tomorrow at six.'

'Okay, Sir,' she says. 'I'm sorry, Ma'am,' she says, turning to me. Frank helps her off the sofa, ushers her out to her room and, who knows, probably tucks her in bed.

The next day, there is a call from Bet, Samantha's maid and Posie's good friend. She says, 'Aruhn won't meet. But he has left a sealed envelope with me.' With Bet?

When Frank gets home from work, Posie, Bet, Frank and I sit out on the balcony. Bet produces the sealed envelope. She hands it to Frank. I don't know why she doesn't give it to me. I'm affronted.

Frank opens it and pulls out a bunch of mixed bills. He says it is the exact amount that was in our cash machine account. Then he unfolds a long letter:

Dear Sir and Ma'am:
I do not suppose that returning your money is enough. I know I must explain how I can do this crime. There is only one answer. It is love. My love for Posie.

Bet sighs and brushes the back of her hand over her right eye, she sniffs. Posie sits still, with her hands in her lap. I'm dying to hear what's coming next, probably: 'We couldn't afford to remove the tumour, even with the 50 jobs I have. We were short by the exact amount you keep in your cash machine. Here, take it back. At least Posie will die an honest woman.'

Frank clears his throat and continues.

You don't know this thing called love. It has made me do what I did. My love for Posie.

Posie's head is hanging and her hair covers her face. I can't get a read on her expression. Bet is staring out over the balcony. She nods a silent 'amen'.

She is everything to me. She is the earth, the stars, the fruit. I want her with me always. She is the clouds, the sun . . .

Shut up already. What about the money? Bring it on home, Aruhn.

I will never do this again. This love has made me do a terrible thing. I wanted to get Posie in trouble with you. She will not marry me. She says her job with you is too important. I wanted her to lose her job. Then she would marry me. I am ashamed. I did not think it out. You do not know how love can make a man crazy. Yours Truly, With God, Aruhn.

That's the end. Frank folds the letter and tosses it on the table. He leans back in his chair. There's a great deal of expectancy crackling in the air but I know what's going to happen next. He's going to hold her like a baby and say how sorry he is that she had to go through this. He's on her side for some reason that probably has to do with the fact that she's 23, helpless, vulnerable and beautiful. I look down and see my revolting bunions have grown and yellowed with calluses.

Now what? I'm not one for long silences, you know, so: 'What the fuck was all that about? It'd be pretty hard to marry you once you'd been deported, huh?'

243

'It's the love, Ma'am Fran,' Bet says. 'It can make a man crazy.'

Frank looks at Bet but is talking to Posie. 'Well, now that we know how *crazy* he is . . .'

Bet interrupts, 'He is better now, Sir. I saw him just yesterday.'

'Yeah, but, gee, Bet, how do I – a man with a wife and two kids – know about this thing called love? No, I'm sorry, but Sadie and Huxley are not safe. Posie, you're not safe here either. He knows where you are.' Oh, save little Posie by all means.

'Oh, but Sir, in the last part of the letter, he said, "I will never do this again,"' Bet chimes in.

Frank now shifts his focus to Posie. 'I'm afraid that the best course of action is for you to leave. Tomorrow. I'll buy you a ticket home.'

What? I am stunned.

For all my raw anger, I have never once actually done anything that hurt someone worse than words – okay or a *little* punch and kick. There's no doubt I'm relieved and grat-ified that Frank is on my side, that he and I are thick as thieves, partners, pals, going through this crazy thing called love – but, well, part of me says, gee, I hate her, but I don't want to destroy her life. And, okay, I have to say it, though you have probably already guessed it, a tiny, tiny part of me says, gee, I'd sort of rather still have my maid, dammit . . . It won't happen again.

I motion Frank into the kitchen. He doesn't move to follow me. Instead, he stands up powerfully, *firmly*, and walks to the balcony wall. He looks out to the horizon. After a moment, he turns around and – with a voice full of tenor and a stare that would wither anything with a heartbeat, a look I've seen rarely – he begins. 'At first, I'll admit, I thought, "Poor Posie, terrified by her boyfriend. He wasn't who she thought he was. Perhaps he locked her in her room when he stormed through the house, stealing whatever he pleased, my satchel for one." But then, I don't know, something about her demeanour. Her posture was so still, but tentative.' Frank pauses and puts his hands behind his back. He paces the length of the balcony.

Frank is amazing me. This is the guy who can sit in a car silently thinking of *nothing* for hours. Actually capable of driving and *not* wandering from deep reflection to self-analysis to suicidal thoughts, like most people – or like me, at least. He is a man who drives and says to himself, 'Bird. Sky. Yellow line down the road. Tree. Cloud.' Now I'm learning that his camera catches interesting angles. (Okay, I guess I suspected there was a little more to him. I mean, I married him. And not *just* because no one else was asking.)

'Go on,' I say.

Frank continues. 'But then, I see it all. Correct me if I'm wrong – Bet? Posie? – last night, the Assembly of Filipinos of the Sacred Holy Blessed Young Heart held an emergency meeting. "What are we going to do to help Sister Posie?" they ask around. Someone says, "A bake sale?" – "We don't have the time, Sister Eugenia." – "A fashion show?" – "Sister Eugenia, we have to help her by tomorrow." – "We dig the tunnel from the Lucky Plaza to the . . ." – "Sister Faye, thank you, now we're thinking." – "Why don't we get the boyfriend to return the money?" – "Sister Beluga! Haven't you been listening?" Then, Bet, the clever sister, stands up. "I will write a letter and we now go collect the money. Everyone put in what you have. Sister Angela, can you get another diamond earring off Ma'am? Good, I'll see you at Ah Luit's pawnshop. Everyone, we meet back here at 5 am." Grumbles from the sisters. Bet shouts, "Posie would do it for you!"' Frank, legs astride, stabs his raised finger at an imaginary congregation, as he envisions Bet did last night.

His body is coursing with energy. We don't dare move. I am speechless.

'I don't know if Aruhn stole the money or not. If I'm wrong on all of this, then the fact remains that Posie is involved with a nut who might do something worse the next time. No matter what, we're left with a person of extremely poor judgement and character. Are we not, Fran?' I blink.

'Go? As in tomorrow?' I ask.

'Yes.'

'But Frank, we have a party to go to tomorrow.'

'Too bad.'

I have to grow up too fast, too soon. Okay, okay, we can miss the party. Frank's right, of course, we can't leave the kids in Posie's care no matter what the truth is, so I dejectedly nod my head and say, 'Posie, you have to leave tomorrow.' When she begins to cry, I wish I could just go back to being Mean Ma'am.

There is a knock. I am grateful for the excuse to turn my back on the people on the balcony. I open the front door.

'Pearl!' I say, seeing my stocky little friend. She stands on the threshold and peers at the balcony.

'Oh, I come at the wrong time.' She looks at me and smiles. 'Maybe right time?'

'There's a bit of a mess. What's up?'

'I have a subcontractor now. Jean. She's a grandmother. So here's her card and here's an invitation to my house for Chinese New Year. I invite all my clients.'

'Listen, I don't want this to get out, but we've just had to fire Posie. I could use someone for a couple of weeks.'

'Can can, *lah*. Jean will be here.'

'But I don't know Jean.'

'Okay, you don't want a babysitter?'

'Well, is she good?'

'Yes yes, *lah*.'

'Um, all right.'

The next day, Frank purchases Posie a ticket to Manila. He and I had gone over it again and again and had decided that she was possibly a thief, had a stalker boyfriend, lied, showed incredibly bad judgement . . . the best thing was to let her have a new start. She could return to Singapore later and pretend we never existed.

Posie breaks down when she kisses Sadie and Huxley. Bet shows up in a new party dress and full make-up. She wants to go to the airport to see Posie off. I wave to Posie as Frank puts her little birdcage of a suitcase in the taxi. Posie is wearing a sweet, pale yellow dress. I see Frank slip her a fat envelope of money. I did the same thing earlier. I think this whole affair is more costly than having our money stolen but we feel it's the right thing to do. Frank gets in and the taxi drives away.

I go back inside and open the door next to the refrigerator. I want to travel down her old hall, take a look in her room, perhaps to punish myself, I think. I need to feel for her for a moment.

I slide open her bedroom door. The television, VCR, microwave, toaster oven, cable TV box, even the rice cooker . . . gone. And it hits me. Oh! My! God! *That* was *my* sweet, pale yellow dress. And, of course, the pearls, you know, the ones I wore with it on Christmas Eve . . . gone too.

There's a Chink in the Amour

Someone, I don't know who, left the cake out in the rain. It's been sitting in the middle of the sidewalk on the corner of Marine Parade and Boonlap Road for two weeks. Every time we walk to the New Barrel, every time we make our way home from the New Barrel, I pass this cake. The other night, in a torrential downpour, the cake acted like it was perfectly normal to be there, like it was perched on the bakery shelf, fresh and dry. No one dropped it by accident (a Singaporean would never, ever mistreat food). It is an offering, a token for someone deceased who must have liked cake al fresco. Or the person who invented weatherproof cake, falling down dead before the craze really took off. The cake won't melt under the sun; it won't budge in the winds. It holds court there day after day. We pass it now as we make our way to Pearl's Chinese New Year lunch. The big dent left by my shoe when I got the urge to smoosh the cake collects a small puddle in the middle. Frank seems happy to see the cake's surviving; he's all about live and let live. The reason it was placed on that junction is a mystery but no more so than what we see every day, like finding a huge wake being held in a corner of your parking lot or a shrine erected behind a shrub off the side of a cricket field. We just assume that the location must hold meaning to someone involved here or beyond.

The fortnight of Chinese New Year celebrations has disgorged so much peculiar detritus it is improbable they can move about at all in China, hemmed in with holiday shrapnel. The red packets, *hong bao*, are strewn about the streets; ashes from joss sticks, shrivelled oranges and fake money swirl about the gutters and nestle themselves in the boughs of trees. The whole country looks red, gold and gaudy. And, there must be some passage in the Mandarin text that claims the apocalypse is near – the food-buying frenzy amounts to sheer hysteria. There isn't a parcel of land, not a sidewalk, parking lot, building site or even traffic island that hasn't remade itself into an instant convenience store. Even the quickie-marts have stopped pumping gas so they can use that area to clone themselves. The goods are all the same: sodas, nuts, dried fruit, hard candies, big cello-phaned gift platters stacked with all the above, chips, chips and chips, expensive tins of abalone and shark fin soup, floss, floss and floss (that'd be your standard pork floss, chicken floss and cuttlefish floss), instant noodles, durian and beer. 'Tell me again, what is it that no human *really* needs? Okay, I'll double my order.' I shouldn't make fun. I mean, what's so different about this to the holiday hoopla back home? Our chickens might come with their heads off, and we might serve our food to those still visible to the naked eye, but it's all about abundance . . . Ah, who am I kidding, it's totally different here: the smells, the sounds, the scurrying to buy, sell, give, eat, burn; and their junk is junkier. I *am* in a foreign land. I need to simply accept their way of doing things without analysis or criticism, rather with generosity and respect; no judgement, but embracing, absorbing, growing, learning. I'm glad I came to this decision *after* I got the pleasure of stepping down on the cake.

The holiday seems to mean the world to Pearl. Issuing an invitation to her home on the most important day of the Chinese New Year season means she considers us as family, or very important people in her life at the least. People she wants to impress. Should she happen to bounce a kid on her knee, I'm sure she'll waive her usual fee on this day. Of course, we'll all get a card. Not a holiday card, silly, the new one's she's putting out that now includes information on her seminar: 'FilipiNO, How to Fire Your Maid! (Call Pearl Now.)'

But Pearl probably wouldn't have been so eager to entertain us had she known I'd go back to the maid thing. After Frank and I had fired Posie I thought about calling Pearl but found myself calling Jessica: 'May I speak with Jessica, please?'

'Hello, Mrs Rittman. This is Jessica.'

'This is Fran Rittman. I came to you from Samantha Burns. We hired Posie.'

'Yes, Mrs Rittman. I just saw your husband the other day to prepare the paperwork for Posie's departure.'

'Posie left.'

'I know, Mrs Rittman. I helped with Posie's departure.'

'I'm not sure I understand your tone, Jessica.'

'Pardon?'

'Pardon? *Pardon?* You *helped* Posie? Like, I *didn't*? Do you even know how hard I tried to make her a member of the family?'

'Mrs Rittman, sometimes it just doesn't work out.'

'I gave her every Sunday off. And holidays, too. I gave her a workout tape.'

'Would you like to interview for another maid, Mrs Rittman?'

'One that she could do in her room. I told her that she should start off with cans, big tins of beans that I would have used in a recipe or something but instead I gave them to her . . . and I promised I'd buy her a set of weights once she mastered the beans. Oh, it is just so hard to believe. Do you know I gave her brisket lessons?'

'Yes, you did the right things. Would you like to look for another maid?'

'Yeah, right, life goes on, huh, Jessica? I remember the time she told me right away, when I came back from something or another, that Huxley had cycled down the steps. "Ma'am, Huxley rode his tricycle off the steps." Just like that, that's how she used to talk. She gave him a bandage. He rolled down 16 concrete stairs.'

'I have several girls who would be suitable for you.'

'Jessica, I just lost my Posie. Am I to settle for *suitable*?'

'I assumed you were calling me to look for another maid.'

'And replace Posie. Just like that?'

'She was special, but . . .'

'But what, Jessica? You think I forced her to steal from me? I raised her to be a good maid.'

'Yes, Mrs Rittman. You did your best. Why don't you take some time and call me next week.'

'Okay, but don't sell them all before I get back to you.'

'We don't sell them, Mrs Rittman.'

'You know what I mean. Save a good one for me. Listen, just so you know, I think I want a fatter one this time. Not sloppy, just, um, ample.'

I should've known my call to Jessica wasn't necessary. Fortune Gardens had learned of Posie's departure and all the surrounding facts about the same time we did. There's the speed of sound, the speed of light, and the speed of gossip. Frank had just arrived back upstairs from seeing Posie and Bet off and found me in the middle of Posie's old room, stupidly looking under posters and envelopes for the missing television. I wanted to find it because I did not want to get in the hot car and chase her down some steamy tarmac. I'd just showered. I didn't care any more, really. There was no one there to watch the TV now, or to microwave a small bowl of noodles and hot Milo. The necklace, well, everyone saw it on me a few times anyway.

'What are you doing, Fran?' Frank asked.

'Frank, she took *everything*, see?'

'I cannot believe this! What a . . . everything? The TV? The refrigerator?'

'We can still catch her if we hurry.'

'Um, like now?'

'Well you don't *wait* to catch someone about to board a plane.'

'Yeah, but by the time we park.'

'And pay for parking . . .'

'That's $2.50 already, we might as well just buy a new set.'

'Yeah, and we'd be rushing. Our luck we'd get into an accident or we'd get a ticket.'

'I agree. Rittman luck.'

'She doesn't have them on her, anyway. Bet probably has everything down at the church ready for some raffle.'

'And we'd get in that accident for nothing.'

'Yeah, we can always get another TV.'

'But you don't get your life back, Fran.'

Before we could continue pretending we weren't just hot and lazy, the phone rang and didn't stop. Everyone was offering condolences, which basically meant offering some maid-time. Caroline was breathless, 'Well, I told Bethy she could do your laundry on Sunday at three.' Dana said, 'Gwen isn't working two Saturdays from now so you could go out.' And Tilda said, 'I knew it was coming. You were too nice, practically ruined it for the rest of us. I was sure Carol was about to ask for a radio. *BUT*, mind you, you should

252

call Irish Kell. Two maids over there and they're leaving.'
And so I did.

'Hi Kell, Vulture here.'

'Oh, Frahn, I was just gonna call ye. I know ye'll be
thinking of having a wee word with Imogenia or Marzipan
now, won't ye?'

'Tilda mentioned . . .'

'Aye, I know. Well, we'll be taking Marzipan back with us
and Imogenia, well . . .'

'Can I talk to her?'

'Just don't be expecting much.'

'Not the brightest bulb on the tree, eh?' I whispered to
Kell, who was no longer on the extension.

'Hello, Ma'am. It's Imogenia,' she said softly.

'Oh, hi. How are you? Did you hear about Posie?'

'I didn't hear about the TV.'

'What else didn't you hear about?'

'The VCR and the fridge, Ma'am.'

'How's the church raffle going over there at Our Lady of
Overburden?'

'Ma'am?'

'Never mind, anyway, I want you to come work for me.
That way you get to stay in Fortune Gardens with
your friends and you know my kids already and they know
you . . .' I was getting excited by this now. Imogenia was a
big, soft, oleaginous thing with stringy hair and big, thumb-
nail-sized teeth. Her silhouette was decidedly missing linkish.
She had worked for Irish Kell for years, so she must be
efficient, and I recalled that kids didn't necessarily run away
the minute they saw her coming, so it'd be okay. I continued,
'You could start after –'

'Ma'am,' she broke in timidly, 'Ma'am?'

'Call me Fran. Come on over and I'll show you the room.'

'Ma'am Fran, I can't.'

'Well, I know you can't right now, but when you get a chance.'

'I yam sorry, but I yam afraid of you too much.'

'*What do you mean?*'

'You yell.'

'I do not yell.' I made my voice tiny.

'You get angry.'

'Oh, not very often.' I made my voice tinier.

'Your temper is bad, Ma'am.'

'Do you *like* television, Imogenia?'

'I yam sorry.' Click.

Just as I hung up, astonished, stung terribly by the rejection and quite shamed to know that I wasn't simply considered volatile-though-kind, the phone rang again.

'I *heard*,' said Jenny.

'Yeah, some say I was too good and some say I was too fierce.'

'Well, don't start counting the votes, just move on. Sisteema has a friend who's looking for a new job.'

'Send her over! Tell Sisteema to say something nice about me and I'll get her a cell phone.'

I vowed to be easier going, more pleasant, friendlier, caring . . . just, please God, get me a new maid.

The next day I met Sisteema's friend, Susie. She wore jeans and a wide leather belt. Her hair was styled in a soft, short bob; it looked to be an expensive cut. Her nails were done. Her shirt was a relaxed jersey that fitted her beautifully. She was not ample. She had a big mole above her lip, perfectly centred, perfectly round. It was as if she had found a place to stick her spare brown M&M. She was animated but almost skittish. Her eyes darted around when she talked. She didn't look the type to flatten a roach or scrape a toilet.

'Do you do pests and toilets?'

She was puzzled. 'Oh, Madame.'

Taking that for a yes, I said, 'Call me Fran.'

'I have a fiancé. I will be spending some nights at his place.'

She didn't seem like a maid with her strong style, forthright manner . . . is that so bad? She was someone who might say, 'Madame, I am pawning your diamond studs. But I will be back in time to babysit.' I mean, that's what matters. Trust. Babysitting.

Susie continued, 'My fiancé and I are going to a week in France for a holiday tomorrow.'

'Oh, that's why you call me Madame instead of Ma'am, getting ready for the trip.'

'Non se plus, Je yam from Francais. Mon mere birthed me der. Je mappelle is Button Lip in French you see der.'

'I'm sorry, I thought you were Asian.'

'Si si, French Filipino.'

I spied the kids. 'Oh, Sadie, there you are, and Huxley, meet Susie.'

'So cute. Cherries.' She tucked her hands into her pockets and took a step back to lean against the wall.

I heard Frank come in and called him up to meet her.

'Frank, this is Susie. I've got to get dinner started so just say goodbye on your way out, Susie.'

A few minutes later, Frank showed Susie to the door and said, 'So we'll see you in a few days. Have a nice trip.'

'Au revoir, Sir, Madame.'

'Frank, you hired her?'

'I thought you did?'

We were hot and tired and didn't want to run after her. Let her show up. It was fate. Nothing we could do. Out of our hands.

A week later, Button Lip came with her Prada tote bag. She said her other stuff was at her fiancé's. Frank had meetings in Hong Kong and a couple of dinner parties, one was a big MTV party. I was invited. I decided I really couldn't find anything to complain about with Susie – she wrote down everything I said, put Huxley's diaper on the right way, didn't burn the house down – and when the perfect dress waved at me from a window when I wasn't even shopping, well, how many signs do you need? I was meant to go to Hong Kong, to an MTV party. It had been so long since Frank and I were away together, alone. We needed to connect. We needed enough time to go through all the phases that brought us together – flirting, sex, laughing, buddies. Lately, we made time for sex *or* laughing *or* flirting *or* talking. The days of having it all seemed to have been left on our old sofa in Apartment 3D in New York City.

What can I say about Hong Kong? That it has a giant bed, 25 feet of floor-to-ceiling glass and the biggest bathroom in the world. I didn't leave the hotel room. Well, not once I got there. I went from the airport to the Regent in Kowloon. I saw traffic and fancy cars, tons of bikes, rickshaws, sky-scrapers, alleys full of signs written in Chinese. I saw a man in a great-looking suit talking on a slim cell phone and then I couldn't see him any more because another man peddled by carrying an entire, intact, dead pig with its tongue hanging out. I saw the jade centre and people of all shapes and sizes busily, madly, trying to get somewhere. I saw my lobby, my bellman, my bath, my bed. I got clean and decided to stay that way, so I got into bed, turned on the TV, called in for smoked salmon and toast and only moved to put the tray down. I kept the curtains open and had a fantastic view of the harbour and Hong Kong skyline. Our room was on one of the upper floors of the hotel and our window took up an entire wall; it felt like I could walk on the tops of the buildings. I could clearly see the men working on the new stadium that, by government decree, had to be built before the looming British–Chinese changeover. It was barely more than a foundation and a web of endless scaffolding. They were working as fast as humanly possible. When one worker dropped with fatigue and fell off the platform, another would pick up the jackhammer. That Tung Chee-hwa is good.

I had brought my laptop and thought about it now and then, but there was a good movie on and I was so, so comfortable. I couldn't bear the thought of cluttering my head. I was here for one thing, us. And Frank had made it clear that he did not want me to bring work along. He could come in any minute and find me tap tap tapping and that would spoil everything. He was finished with work after today, except for the evening events. At last, I heard a key. I brushed the crumbs off my chest and the bed, and popped in a mint. I pulled the covers down a bit so they weren't bunched up under my chin like I'd rather be cosy than sexy. I swung one leg out of the duvet entirely and lay on my side. I put my hair over my shoulder. My elbow was hurting and my neck was getting cramped. Enter Husband.

'Ah, Madame, you are finished?'

It was room service. What's with everyone calling me Madame?

Frank came in behind him as I was bunching all the covers back up. He put his briefcase down, stood still, gazed at me and smiled appreciatively nevertheless. Why do we look so much better in hotel rooms?

'Come 'ere, cowboy.' I sat up and held out my arms.

'I'm just going to take a quick shower. Stay right where you are.'

What? With the outstretched arms?

If he could take a shower . . . As soon as the bathroom door closed, I jumped over to take a tiny, teensy, little peek at my computer. I slowly unzipped the case. I very, very quietly stripped off the velcro. I turned the volume way down so the squawking wouldn't be heard. I carefully lifted the top. And screamed. I slammed it back down. Frank flew out of the bathroom, half soapy, as I flung myself over on it, hiding it, hating it, protecting it, mourning it, rolling and flailing on the bed.

'What! What?'

'Oh, God . . . Oh God . . . OhmyfuckingGod . . .' I started chanting, hyperventilating, slapping my forehead like a nutcase. 'I brought my fucking computer. You told me not to. Why the fuck didn't I listen to you? I broke the screen when I dropped it at the airport. It fell off my shoulder. I should have put it down but I thought it'd stay on while I bent over. We have to get it fixed! Now! I mean, it's just the glass part, right? Anyone would have a little piece of glass to put back in. What's that face about? Do you have any idea how many emails I miss every day I don't turn it on? They just keep piling up and piling up and piling up and piling up and piling up, until by the time I get home, I'll have 500 and you'll never see me. I had to bring it. I wasn't going to let anything get to me, you know, like ruin my mood.' (And I did tell myself: no dives into mortal dread, no plummeting like a meteor, keep it in perspective, keep it in perspective, they are 10,000 miles away. Even if you make a mistake or get fired again or told to call at 3 am – 'IT'S URGENT' like a book gets a heart attack – for a conference meeting about motion picture rights to a three-page manuscript about a cow . . . or *anything*.)

'But now, *this*. I have to do something. What can we do? What will I do? What will become of me? We have to call the bellhop.'

'I'll be out in a minute, Fran. Calm down. I just have to get the shampoo out of my eyes.' Frank retreated. 'Bellhop?' I heard him say.

'*Hurry up!*'

I paced the room, naked, because everyone knows you can see them, but they can't see you. Though my mom would disagree. One of her gifts, along with knowing when a hair fell out of my head and into the sink, whereupon she'd make me actually stop racing around getting ready for the biggest date of my life and march right in there and *find that hair* and *remove it*, was knowing when I was changing in front of an open curtain. She would bang into my room and snap the shade down, saying, 'Mr Levin is looking at you.'

The busy bees on the stadium site stopped working. Then they started pointing. I waved and threw myself on the bed again.

Frank came out and slid into the bed. He held his arms out to me.

'We'll deal with it tomorrow.'

'It has to be *now*. Emails are coming in all the time, every minute. I have to do it now. I can't let it wait! I'll jump out this window. Shit! Tonight *and* tomorrow won't be good with your plan,' I said, jumping up and getting my jacket on.

So we got dressed. Yes, I did leave the hotel after all. I lied before. I was hoping to change history by writing it all wrong. But it's true that I didn't observe anything of Hong Kong. My eyes were trained on locating anything remotely like a computer store.

'Here's a shop, Frank.'

'It sells watches.'

'Which are primitive computers.'

At last we got to a mall that had floors of computer servicing, selling and parts stores. I went into one that fixed things. Two young men with limited English stood before me as I opened up and turned on the computer to display the shattered screen. I felt very hopeful. I mean, Hong Kong is like where computers are from – Fujitsu, that's Hong Kong, right? Sony. Toshiba. And this is just a little piece of glass-like substance. Get me one the same size, screw it in, I'm back in business. But they shook their heads and told me that the part would take days and it'd cost as much as a new computer. Goddamned hustlers. Putting up a 'We Can Fix It' sign and then trying to sell you a whole new system. The next five places had the same reaction and then Frank squared my shoulders and turned me to face him. 'I tried to tell you. The screen is the most expensive part of the whole laptop. You have a four-year-old machine. We'll get you a new one when we get home.'

'Oh God, and then I have to get the data switched and get online again. It's going to take weeks. I'm going to be up all night forever. Everyone's going to think I ignored their messages. Oh, how could this happen to me? I cannot believe it. What will become of me?'

'I'll do it. It won't take long. A couple of days to get you set up. You can't keep worrying about *everything*. Things happen. You'll be fine.'

He was there for me again. There for me again. I'd be fine. I had a great dress to wear and if I stopped crying now, my eyes wouldn't still be puffy and we'd be meeting some really cool people. Frank hugged me, tightly, putting the pieces back together. And, if we hurried, we'd still have time for a romp at the Regent with the curtains wide open.

But instead, Frank spent the next hour reconfiguring his laptop so that it was mine now.

When we got home, the kids looked fine and Susie's French had improved. Dishes were in the sink and toys were all over the place but since Susie was up to her elbows in papier-mâché, the kids and I cleaned up.

Now I'm feeling guilty that Susie is working out and I'm

wondering what to say if the whole maid issue comes up today at Pearl's. 'Oh, her? She's not a maid. She's French! She's Button Lip!'

We're following Pearl's detailed map of how to get to her apartment. I've driven past the fields of public housing, known as HDB, but never really through them. And certainly not hunting for a friend's house. HDBs are projects – clean and graffiti-free, of course. They'd be more attractive without the garish colour scheme but tastes run that way over here. Despite the festive paint job, a haunting aura is emitted. Always situated in a nothin'-to-do part of town, clothes hanging off bamboo poles, eight kajillion units per block. Old men smoking to the filters over cups of tea and Tiger Beer in the eating houses below. Aunties in *sanfoos* and short, tight perms energetically tugging on grandsons' arms in the playground.

Looking for Pearl's apartment, 3886, #99–125, in a ghetto of orange and sky-blue sameness where every balcony whispers 'Jump', I am thrown off balance. On one hand, I recognise, with intensified appreciation, the miracle of there being such peace and harmony in Singapore. The complete distinction in this small, small country between the haves and have-nots has not stoked consuming fires of discontent. Indeed, Singaporeans, one and all, feel some measure of fortune, shelter and relative safety from the strife of most of the world, and of course, lots and lots of food wherever you look. So what if the rich eat sambal prawns in a restaurant for $45 – the poor get six more, minus the radish rose, in the hawker centre for $3. On the other hand, my industrious, ambitious, dogged, determined, laborious and crafty Pearl has nothing to show for all of that industriousness, ambition, doggedness, etc, but this: these monoliths, these cubbies, these pods keeping humans in storage. They scream for graffiti, some passion, some outrage. Something quelling the seductive cries to *jump*.

And less orange.

We arrive with our candy and 'red packet'. Pearl is in her very best go-meetin' clothes, jewellery and lipstick, grey roots tended to, clearly nervous to impress her client–guests. Her flat is two bedrooms, but only because she has hung a batik tapestry in the middle of a room. There is the room we entered, the family room, and if you keep walking a few steps, there is a kitchen. The family room is short and narrow and full of old, mismatched furniture. There are pictures on the wall of Pearl's daughter, Emma, alongside gift-shop art. Pearl's ruddy, cheerful but itinerant Portuguese husband, Bert, jumps up, knocks over his beer and pumps our hands. Pearl ushers me proudly to her sombre, disengaged Emmy for an introduction that frustrates her view of the TV.

There are some aunts and uncles and sisters and cousins chatting, laughing, breaking peanut shells. I'd like to be part of the real celebration. I'd like to share life stories. But Pearl wants to show us the red carpet. We're scuttled off to the kitchen where the other clients are already seated. They include Anastasia's mom, Anna, who is Russian with perfect, lustrous skin (no one has ever seen her husband but there is one), and a dissipated vampire family from Poland – the Something-skis – who chain smoke and sit miles away from the table, legs splayed, absently looking at the food with the same interest they behold the floor, their cuticles and their son, who has a heat rash and a gold chain around his neck that is making his skin turn green. Bert seems to be the only one, besides Pearl herself, allowed into the kitchen with us. She ignores her crowded living room full of loyal family and devoted friends, and hops from Frank to me, serving food onto plates before we've even had a chance to settle in. I feel so terrible. I can't let her know that I hired a maid just as she's dolloping out some dish she won't even let her family have because the abalone is for clients only. Bert puts down cans of cold Carlsberg for the men. I give Frank a naggy look so he'll remember we have a big party tonight. Irish Kell! Shangri-la! Dancing after! He thanks Bert.

When all of our plates are loaded and her pots are empty, Pearl drags a stool over to the far door and sits down, smiling a broad grin that doesn't belie the anxiousness in her eyes. She nods for us to go on, enjoy.

The Polish couple light cigarettes for each other and spank and swat at their spotty child. I have a party to go to. At the Shangri-la! Dancing after! There are dozens of different dishes – beef rendang, ribs, fish cakes, spring rolls, vegetables, all of them warm, fragrant and filling. I can't eat this. I'll be stuffed and beached. The Polish couple, cigarettes still smouldering in one hand, taste the smallest morsel of rendang. Man-ski, exaggeratedly chewing, says to Woman-ski, 'I expect there is a dog or two missing from the neighbourhood.' He puts his butt out in a carrot.

I say to Pearl, 'You have no idea how fantastic this smells. I'm starved.'

Frank, Anna and I clean our plates. The kids have been sitting on Bert's knee and he hands them all red packets. We give ours to Pearl, kiss her and thank her. She smiles but it quickly falls off her face, bowing her head and bowing her head, she says her goodbyes and thanks for comings hurriedly, shifting from foot to foot, patting our backs and showing us the way to the main road. I can practically hear her falling into her spot on the sofa between her husband and daughter, surrounded by her friends. But tomorrow? What will become of her?

When we get home, there are just a few hours before we have to be at the Shangri-la! For Irish Kell's farewell dinner! Dancing after! She's invited over 50 people for a buffet. They are known for their buffets over at the Shangri-la.

I don't want to go. After eating at Pearl's, I think I'd rather just lie flat on the cool kitchen floor and wait until the noises in my stomach stop, but that might take years. I should make myself vomit, but that would remind Frank of his first girlfriend. What can I wear under these bloatsome circumstances that will be festive and fun, sexy and sharp but won't push down on Pearl's gift to my system? A nightshirt. I don't want to go out. I want some quality sofa time. I want to cuddle my family. Come to me, children.

'What's the dress for tonight?' Frank asks. 'Why are you on the floor?'

'Because it feels good. I don't know, wear what still fits after this afternoon.'

'Madame. Madame.' I hear Susie's voice and am pulled from a strange sleep, the type you have on a floor at dusk on Chinese New Year.

'Hi, oh, sorry, am I in the way here?' I slide over closer to the pantry so she can get her soufflé out of the oven. I close my eyes again. I want to get back to my recurring dream. The one where I'm in a home, my home, but usually not the real place I live, and I've just discovered, or rediscovered, that there is a whole other wing of rooms. At first, I'm like, 'Oh, this is fantastic, so much room, such a big house!' And then I start to worry about furnishing it and how to make good use of it and reminding myself not to forget to have everyone spend lots of time in these rooms. I want to finally get to the part where I am flinging doors open and saying, 'This is the pinochle room and this is where we keep things that are pink.' More likely, the sequel is that we now live in this wing and I forget all about the old one until one day . . . and it never ends in this crazy cycle of wonder and worry and burdensome gifts.

I turn on Jethro Tull. I think 'Locomotive Breath' has lyrics to get you dressed, feeling like a tiger again. I'll have to hear the song a few times before I can meow. Frank is trying to get the kids in the bath but they're not interested.

'Forget it,' I tell him. 'We have to get dressed, anyway.'

'Do we have to go?' he asks. 'I'm not sure I feel good.'

'Get over it. Yes, we have to go. It will be fun if you just put some effort into it. It's the fucking Shangri-la. God!'

'I feel sick too, Mommy.'

'Great. Where, sweetie?'

She points to her shoulder.

'Ah, boy, we better stay home. Sadie has strep shoulder.' I get into the tub and turn on the shower. Frank flushes the toilet and I hear muttering.

'Frank,' I cajole, 'we just had a long day, that's all. Come on. I'm sorry. We don't want to miss the look on Collin's face when he pays for all of this.'

Frank gets into the shower with me. Sadie and Huxley follow. Good as this sounds, I mean, who really wants to get nudged out of their shower? Why should I wait for my turn at the hot water just because everyone liked my idea? Get out! I'll see you on the other side!

'Susie,' I ask as we're leaving, 'did the kids like the soufflé?'

'Madame?'

'Their dinner. Did they like it?'

'What dinner, Madame?'

'That.' I point to the soufflé.

'My crêpe? It is for moi and Francis.'

I nuke up some leftovers and we leave.

'So, how do I look, Frank?'

'Fine.'

'What did you say?'

'I said you look fine.'

'Oh, okay, it's just that, you know, you so rarely dust off superlatives like that unless I'm asking you if I made out the cheque correctly or put your computer away properly or if the coffee is too hot. Then you sometimes bring yourself to those scary adjectival heights and pluck from the clouds the word "*fine*".'

'Oh jeez, Fran. What you're wearing is *nice*.'

'Like, we'll make it through the evening without much snickering? Like, I should have you turn the car around so I can change? Or like, at least my outfit isn't mean?'

'God, will you stop this?' He yanks the car to the side of the road and stops. 'What is your problem?'

'I'm *fine*, Frank. Just drive. We're late.'

'You know what?' he snaps.

'No. What?'

'You look stupid in that.'

'Who the fuck asked you, anyway? I do not.'

We arrive at the imposing Shangri-la only 20 minutes late. The lobby is one of my ideas of heaven. Several cosy bars, light piano show-tune music and a singer of so little distinction you forget about her, ceilings high enough to fortress a tower, people dressed well, sipping happily, men in formal service wear bowing before you with cocktail napkins. I do have other ideas of the beyond. I love nature, the mountains, creeks, wild flowers and dewy grass, redneck bars with trivia games, cold beers sitting out on tables, playing pool. But opulence, wealth, ease, enjoyment, *regality*, well, they're up there too. Unfortunately, there's no time this evening to sit back and be dead and gone to heaven. I squeeze Frank's hand, hoping we're pals again. He lets me. I have a way to go, I guess. I adjust my scarf and look around; there is no whispering from the balconies here. I put my arm around Frank's waist. He lets me. His arms hang at his sides. It doesn't matter. It's small stuff. This minute, the next minute and all the rest of our lives, we need to remember we're lucky. Look where we are, think of where we could be. I stop and turn, expecting a kiss . . .

'What, Fran?'

And get that instead . . . so what else can I do but . . .

'Frank, your hair looks flat.'

I walk ahead, downstairs to the restaurant. Fairy lights surround the pool, all the terrace doors are open on the restaurant. I see the long, long table where our friends are seated. I go around gripping shoulders, planting kisses, waving to people far down the line. Everyone's commenting on my outfit, wondering where I got it, telling me it's amazing. Ha ha, flathead!

I hold Irish Kell's face and we hug for a while, cheek to cheek. It's not as if we've known each other all our lives. It's that we're like passengers on a plane together. We've been able to reveal so very much. And, all the while, knowing it's perfectly safe because we'll be getting off and going to separate destinations. The reason for the sadness, the deep loss, I feel is that there is never an end to what I want to divulge to someone like Kell, someone who laughs in the face of your gaffes and pounds them down to a wee little size under the weight of her much mightier mistakes. One day, we were hanging around the playground and I said, 'I am the worst mother.'

'Aye, it's hard, isn't it?'

'I threw Sadie on the bed.'

'I kicked the chair out from under Bymthe [Eileen], Frahn.'

'I watched Huxley gag on vegetables and still made him finish.'

'Can you imagine what poor Ryot [Kim] suffered when she didn't take to the potato, Frahn?'

I swore I wouldn't tell.

Vibba points at me from across the room. She mouths,

'You're wearing it.' And gives the thumbs up. See, Frank was wrong. Everyone has their eyes on me. It was good luck that I went hunting through my closet for something swishy. I found the perfect thing.

I had totally forgotten about my *shalwar*. I bought it on Serangoon Road in Little India with Vibba. It's made of a floaty sort of fabric that changes hues as you move. Though the material is light, it weighs thousands of pounds because of all the intricate beading. I look like I should be singing 'Viva Bombaygas' except for the scarf-bedspread that is part of every Indian dress. It's green or red, depending on the angle, and has a plunging V-neck. The pants are flared below the calf and every inch or so, on both the top and the pants, are clusters of pearls, sequins, rhinestones and other flashy baubles. I meant to get my *shalwar* tailored but haven't yet so I'm full of hidden pins and duct tape. All the *sarees*, all the *lenhas*, all the *shalwars*, come in just one size and that size is *plenty*. You might not know this but ghee is tremendously fattening. Makes butter look like Diet Coke. So next time you think you're eating smart with that vegetable jalfrezi (cauliflower, chickpeas, stringbeans . . . that's two Weight Watcher points, we can get dessert!) or with that saag paneer (I'll just have the spinach, Ravi), remember that the folds of skin so proudly displayed by the Indian women in their little tube tops and swaddling clothes are not the result of a malfunctioning thyroid. I don't know what the *National Geographic* wastrels are dining on, but that's not the point. The point is that I'll have to give up half the outfit when I get it taken in. That aside, now that I really let myself absorb before I react, I've come to absolutely adore all things Indian. They're the Italians of Asia – passionate, sensual, loud, lively. I've taken a great interest in all things Indian. I'm getting to *be* a little bit Indian. I have some CDs from movie soundtracks that I dance to; I hennaed my hands; Sadie and I wear *bindis*. And, now, I look Indian, especially over the phone: 'Vhad are you dolking aboud? I am nod from New Yorg.'

I met Vibba and Lindsey a few months ago in the playground. She's a beautiful, glamorous Indian woman. I think her name – *Vibba* – suits her incandescence. She's a major league banker in Singapore, extremely kind and lavishing, never without a compliment. Lindsey, a brilliant, oft-quoted macroeconomist from Australia, is six- or eight-feet tall and practises being geeky in front of a mirror. I would like for all of you to see him rollerblade. You'll never love someone so much. He wears a big white helmet from outer space, hand pads, elbow pads, knee pads, shoulder pads and he goes through the parking lot, sailing over the speed bumps, lurching forward, ready to come crashing down with hands outstretched. But his cover's blown with me. I've caught him looking off, in thought, face relaxed or breaking into a smile, and I think he could wear any style he chose.

Frank and I take a seat. It appears that every couple gets a bottle of champagne. That should last about a minute between the Rittmans, except, I have to admit, this night, I'm feeling odd. Which is exactly why I should drink and get better. I go up to the buffet, which is 1.5 miles long. I come back with two rolls. Frank comes back with one. 'Oh, you got one already,' I say. 'I got this one for you.' I hand him his favourite German bread – hard and black. I feel badly that he didn't think of me. I am missing his friendship in this loud, chaotic room with its fourth of July chandeliers cascading down upon gargantuan flowers.

I pour out more champagne for us. The waitress comes over and places new bottles up and down the table.

'Compliments of Mr O'Maley,' she says. We cheer and clap and clink our glasses.

'This is going to cost Collin a fortune,' I say to Frank. He nods. I try to count that as coming into my corner.

'This is going to cost Collin a fortune!' I say to Lisa.

'Collin lost a fortune!' Lisa says to Roy.

'Collin lost his future,' Caroline says to Phil.

'Collin's lost the furniture,' is what Tilda hears from Dana.

I take some more champagne and cheer Frank. He picks his up and drinks. Ah, forget it, I'm through trying. We'll have one of those nights where we float through the same evening as if we never met. We'll talk tomorrow as if nothing went astray and by evening we'll hash it all out until I'm right.

Time to shmooze.

I stop at each person, pull up a chair and talk to them while they eat, or travel with them while they get seconds, thirds, fourths. I'm completely annoying but I can't stop because I don't have my friend Frank to just be with and I want him to see how popular I am. I'm completely not tempted to try the garlic prawn Valerie is offering and we're talking away – well, I am – when suddenly, we hear a chair sharply, forcefully scraping back over the floor. Collin is standing, fork in the air, beet-red. Moving away from the table, he stabs his fork in the direction of his plate. He swings it to his left and uses it to direct a waitress over. He jabs his fork again and again, backing up, an invisible duel on hand. He speaks rapidly, excitedly, to the waitress, eyes wild and fearful.

'What happened? What happened?' we are all asking each other. I have never seen Collin's mouth move at all and here it is, up and down and up and down. Valerie and I give each other a 'whatthefuck?' shrug. The news spreads downwind. Finally, it reaches me. 'There's an earwig in Collin's lobster bisque!'

The 50 dinners at the Shangri-la, famous for its glorious buffets, the 40 bottles of Moët, some unopened, the odd beer, various juices, Diet Cokes and sodas are all on the house, picked up by management. And now we're off. Dancing!

Collin's pockets are intact, save for an earwig.

We go to a bar in the basement level of a shopping centre. All the stores are closed and dark. I'm slightly drunk, wearing non-mall clothes at a non-mall hour in a shut-down mall. No sounds at all except for the forceful buzz of electricity and a few hollow giggles. It's as if we decided to do lines in Dad's office at night instead of going to some more perfect place, like a car. It knocks the adrenaline down a few pegs, makes you stop and think about what you're doing; it reprimands and inhibits. I swing my scarf-bedspread around my neck and brace myself for the uphill hike to having a good time.

'Does it look better over my head and around my neck or just hanging loose over my shoulders?' I ask Samantha, who doesn't hear. 'Samantha! Samantha! Does it . . .' But she doesn't turn around. Caroline has everyone's attention. She's prepping us on the Johnny Cash Pub, telling us how much fun this place is, how much we'll love it. They screw a railing on the bar and let people dance and swing once they're good and smashed. They only play classic rock. I raise my hand. 'Yes, you in the back?' Caroline addresses me.

'And they play Johnny Cash, right?' I say.

'I don't think so, but they have a bust of him by the cash register.'

I look across to the Young Gurl Cutz beauty salon and then over to The Bra Bazaar. Rock? I don't hear a note, not a chord, not the thrum of a bass. I only hear a pop. It is from Sam, who's sitting on a marble bench, next to a fake fir tree, a bottle of nicked champagne to his lips. I go over, adjusting my scarf, wrapping it around my neck twice, weaving it through my arms, taking it slightly off the shoulders and casually tying the ends behind my back.

'Ah, come to share?' he asks.

'Just the bench,' I answer, tucking up my trousers, admiring how the threading goes from green to crimson depending on the light. I take out my own nicked bottle. 'Well, there were so many just left there,' I say.

'Lucky for us we kept our wits about us,' Sam says and points out his second bottle behind a fake tree branch.

'Yeah, while everyone else ran through the halls screaming, "An earwig! An earwig!"' I laugh.

Caroline finishes her introduction and leads us in. The minute we cross the threshold, we forget the morgueishness of the sanitary mall and catch a wave of floor-beer stink and cigarette fumes. The bartenders speed-walk from end to end, multitasking like they invented the word. The music tries to get you to do something brainless and wild on the dance floor, the stage or even on the bar, which is now being set up with the steel rails, just like Caroline said.

I hide my bottle behind me and give a one-armed *namaste* to the door guy. Sam and I take a seat in the corner and put the bottles in a dark nook under the table. Valerie, Frank, Dana and regular Collin, Tess and Clive, Simon and Melanie, and even Jennifer and Ward, who have left their kids for the first time, come to join us. I tell Jennifer that I like her new GAP skirt as I take my scarf off and whoosh it around my neck. 'Thanks. Ward said I could get it the day he got his second set of spare golf clubs. Well. That's quite an outfit you have on, Fran.' Jennifer is always so sweet.

Irish Kell beckons us to the dance floor. I'm really not entirely in the mood but I feel it's my duty . . . to the Irish. I tug at Frank but he begs off; Sam tags Valerie, but she says, 'Next song, doll.' So, I dance with Sam. Not long after, the floor gets crowded; Frank starts dancing with Valerie. Then Jennifer, Melanie, Pam and Dana get up while their husbands hope this next lager will make them better dancers.

At 'Tequila Sunrise' Sam and I go back to our table. A waitress in pink hot pants comes over. 'I'm sorry, you can't bring in from the outside.' She motions to his bottle.

'No worries,' Sam shouts over the music. The waitress leans in and he orders us each a vodka. 'Thanks love.' He pats her on the rear. She returns with four drinks for us.

I'm looking at that bar and looking at that bar and now I just have to hop on that bar. Kell is leaving, goddammit, and she wants us to make some noise. Sam's got his hands all over Valerie, turning right and left to tell whoever is near, 'This is my wife. Isn't she gorgeous?' Valerie smiles, rolls her eyes and slithers out to go sit down. I've got my place on the bar and I'm taking myself seriously, I'm bringing cultures of the world together in just one outfit and all I know is I'm just a shootin' star and all the world will love me just because, because I am . . . Frank grabs my ankle. He squeezes it. I'm supposed to stop. Shit, what a bad place to stop. I look at Frank and see an urgency; he is clearly disturbed. I unlock arms with Sam and Jonelle and unsteadily bend over to him. 'What?'

'We have to go. The kids are sick. Susie called on my cell phone.'

I feel so entirely foolish and criminal. There I was peeling away, abandoning all responsibility, about to walk the length of the bar swinging my enormous scarf and shining my *bindi*. Now, I'm exposed and facing demons because I am a bad mother and sooner or later we all get caught. My kids are sick and I'm here, pulling my heel out of some poor sod's drink, apologising to a young girl for stepping on her pocket-book, taking Frank's hand and jumping off a bar in a dead mall. My flared pants get caught on the beer tap and I flatten out over the railing like a crashing plane, ripping the pants and landing face down. When I get up, the pants stay down. The tape did not hold up as well as I had hoped. My ankle hurts and my knee is ripped and bleeding. As Frank helps me to the door, Valerie comes over and asks if she can have a ride back to Fortune Gardens with us. She's feeling a little tired, she says.

When we get on the expressway, Valerie's phone goes off. 'Sam, doll, I told you I was just feeling poorly because, you know . . . I can't understand you. Sam? Sam! *Sam!*

'His phone just went,' she says, punching buttons on her phone.

'Sam! Sam?' she shouts. We all can hear Sam's phone clattering onto the floor, his distant voice sounding unreal as he says, 'Look, it wasn't like that love . . . don't do that, mate . . . [thud]' and the Beach Boys sing, 'Wouldn't it be nice . . .'

'We'll go back, Valerie,' Frank states.

'Just stop the car.'

'No, Valerie, we'll take you back,' Frank insists.

She pukes on my *shalwar*. 'Oh, too late, sorry Fran, all over your new outfit.'

'Don't worry, Valerie. We're here with you. You're fine,' Frank comforts.

'It's all right, I can clean it, I think,' I say.

When we get back to the Johnny Cash Pub, no one is there. We take Valerie home and Sam isn't there either. Frank offers to sit with her while I return to our house to tend to the kids.

'You don't think I've been through this with Sam Marks before?' She vomits again.

'I don't know, Valerie, you're not well,' I say.

'Comes with the territory, mate,' she says with an unconvincing smile. 'I'll be right.' She leads us out the door and adds, 'I'm just pregnant.'

By about four in the morning, me, Frank, Huxley and Sadie are all sweating out our fever and taking Panadol. We watch some late, late movies and take turns adjusting the aircon and blankets. By seven in the morning, we're still camped out on the living-room floor, eating toast with lime marmalade.

Susie is delivering soufflé to Francis.

Irish Kell is calling for her final taxi.

Valerie is 12 weeks pregnant.

And Sam is in jail for 'outraging the modesty of a woman'. 'Thanks love.' (Pat pat.)

What will become of us?

Father's Day

A sobering silence fell upon the land and the whirl of social activity halted for many moons. Two masters of discipline were sent to me by the gods so that I might follow in their path – the path to a clean heart, healthy lungs and a damned good liver.

One day, I was minding my own business down at the pool, trying to get through some work, when I heard Samantha cry out, 'There she is! Eating raisins!' Well, actually, I was reading more than raisining, but what of it? Would I look up to find a few grapes after me? People for the Protection of Produce? Was she narking on me to the gendarmes? No, of course not. She was simply pointing me out to a couple of aliens. They were tall creatures with alabaster skin that shone as if it were made of marble; highways of finely developed muscles covered their whole bodies, including their glistening, shaven pates. 'Hmmm, so this is what Man will look like in 10,000 years, eh Darwin?' I think.

They stride over sinew-fully in their bathing suits. With an apparent understanding of English, they extend their hands, as we do, and introduce themselves. They are Marge and Tom.

'Okay,' I say, 'but I'm gonna have to rename you for the book. You'll be Majestic and you'll be Magnus.'

'Fine,' they say.

Samantha met them at the pool the other day. Well, actually, she two-finger-whistled down from her balcony to them and then shouted, 'You averaged 35 seconds a lap! That's incredible. Wait there. I'm coming down.' A few minutes later, she appeared before them in her swimsuit, clutching her goggles. And humbly, standing in the shadow of their large greatness, she implored, 'Teach me.'

Maj and Mag are professional triathletes and after a small matter of paying a fee and undergoing a test of our commitment, which amounted to proffering said fee, we were taken under their tutelage. We were told to rise and shine with the bullfrogs at 0400 for time trials at the track.

A week later, I heard Samantha say, 'Let's have a clambake' and I said, 'Sure, why not?' Except what she really said was, 'I'm signing you up for the Singapore marathon.' See, she did that thing you can do to a puppy – use the exciting 'I got a treat for you' voice when you're actually telling him 'You're going to the vet'. Either way, you get the same doggy jig. Samantha made it sound like fun. Time trials! 0400!

Apparently, according to our track times, we were likely to do very well in the race. Maj waved a hand at me dismissively when I questioned how twice around a track could possibly tell the whole story of a 26-mile race. She said, 'If you follow my workouts exactly and eat Biospliven bars, it will happen. And, here, take this carton to sell to other athletes in your neighbourhood.' The side of the box read: 'Liven it up with Biospliven. Yeah!' and showed Maj striking a Mr Universe pose. That's where I'd seen her before, on the Biospliven commercials. Yeah! 'By my calculations, you will complete the race in under 3:30,' she said.

Maj and Mag began emailing workouts to us. Every

night, I'd see what new torture tomorrow would bring. Each day seemed to start at five, except for our day off, which was marked with 'DON'T FORGET THIS IS YOUR DAY OFF – ☺ HAVE FUN!' Oh my gosh, I forgot it was my day off and I just ran nine million miles in the blazing sun. Silly me.

I am not sure why I'm doing this. I don't have time to answer the question, except when I'm already running.

Yeah! My alarm goes off. I generally don't need it because my dreams are all about not forgetting to wake up. Big dream hands roughly shake me all night long. ('All. Night. Long' is grossly inaccurate. I should say 'a very small portion of a very short night'.) Except on this night, I slept soundly for four hours. In fact, the same thing happened yesterday and a few times last week.

I have two minutes and 15 seconds before the coffee is ready so I climb back into bed to be with Frank. He isn't there. And then I realise that this is why I slept for four hours straight. We didn't have the ritual. Every night at about 2 am, for some reason, I get hot and he gets lonely. I am not horny hot; I am stuffy hot. Even if I were cold, I'd be frigid, because when you are giving yourself four hours of sleep and you're at the midsection, you don't want to use any up for sex or cuddles or human contact of any kind, not even 10 to 12.4 minutes of it. I sleep without a pillow and without covers. I don't want to get too comfortable. Invariably, Frank will extend his quilted claw, hook it around my waist and reel me in to snuggle. Every night, I find myself whizzing backwards in bed until I thump against him. I pry the arm off and slither back to my side but as soon as I'm drifting off, I'm travelling over the prairie of our bed once again. Happens about four times in a row before I finally shove him as hard as I can and beg him to let me sleep. He flips around so his back is to me and calls me a bitch but it's all in his sleep so I don't get mad. Maybe he thinks he's calling some other bitch a bitch. But, now that I think about it, several nights have passed undisturbed.

I look in the kids' room and there he is, sleeping on Huxley's trundle bed. They're holding hands. It's a scene I will never want to forget but I know that in a moment, I'll think too much about it, understand it, and it will hurt me.

I go downstairs. Everything is so dark and quiet. I take my coffee and smokes outside and pray that Maj and Mag can't see me. I flip through a three-month-old *Variety* that only arrived yesterday and read about the potentially bank-rupting delays in releasing a movie I just rented. See, it all worked out, Mr Eisner, this is Hollywood. I read about a few exciting mavens-on-the-move. They all seem to be going from large companies to dot.com thingies that sound as alike as the taste of yellow, green and pink Fruit Loops, except there's more of them. I'm just out of it, I suppose, but it seems so improbable to me. Then again, what doesn't? I use one-tenth of my brain, one-tenth of my VCR, one-tenth of my watch (I make it light up and I read the time) and one-tenth of my computer and I don't surf much. I mean, sheesh, who has the time? I stub a second cigarette and head out for a three-and-a-half-hour run.

I check Samantha's balcony. No white sheet, so she's decided not to go. She had said she wasn't feeling great. Oh well, just me and my thoughts. When I get home, I'll have just enough time to shower, check faxes, play with Huxley, pick up Sadie from pre-school, do the groceries. I think I'll take them to story hour, get new running shoes and then meet Samantha, Maj and Mag at the gym to lift weights and swim laps after. Hmmm, what should I think about now? Reviewing my schedule took up, oh, roughly two minutes . . . just 207 left. Just do it! Yeah! Oh, I forgot, I also have an appointment with Dr Soondartisradnoosvishnuam this afternoon. I have to go. The other day I had a spell of temper so now I have to see this man. I tried to punch out the booking office guy. He said we hadn't signed in for our reserved tennis court the night before. I said, 'Yeah, 'cause the courts were wet.' He said we still needed to sign in. I said it was pouring rain so we went to a movie. He said that we should have cancelled three hours before. I said that it wasn't raining three hours before, just 40 minutes before. He said, 'You did not cancel three hours before time. You can*not* use your card for two weeks. No tennis for two weeks.' I said, oh, I don't know, something like 'You're a dead man' and reared my arm back. Sadie and Huxley, who were with me at the time, can verify that I did not connect with his face. He sat behind his Plexiglas window and I swung my fist through the speaking hole, but he wheeled back in his swivel chair to avoid the blow. A flier about a ping-pong match fluttered down to his feet. He grabbed the phone and dialled. When the police arrived, I was already cooling off in the baby pool with the kids.

'Mrs Rittman?' It was a cop.

'Yes?' I got up and held Huxley against my chest and Sadie to my leg, trying to look like the last person in the world who'd become violent – l'il bit of a thing like me, a mother, just like your mother . . .

'You've been accused of vandalising.'

'*What?*' I was insulted, outraged. I don't wreck stuff. 'I didn't *vandalise*. A piece of paper came off when I went to *punch* the stupid idiot.'

'Oh, I see. So you didn't vandalise?'

'That's right, officer. No graffiti, no gum, no smashed glass. Absolutely no damage to property.'

'I'm sorry then, Mrs Rittman. Thank you for your time.'

And that would have been that except for the fact that everyone at the pool started cheering for me and the story swept through every playground and playgroup, down the shop line and over to the beer garden at Fattys. Fran almost punched the booking-office man. Within hours, I was a legend. Fran of Arc. Fran Ali. Rebel with a cause.

I can't blame Sadie. She thought her dad would share the wild adoration of the teeming crowd shouting 'Fran! Fran! Fran!' whenever I passed by. That night, before he even had a chance to put down the old briefcase, she flew over to him and said, 'Mommy almost punched Mr Quiff. Isn't she great?'

'Fran!' Frank gasped. 'Do you have any idea what this could do? Look at poor Sam. Two days in jail and hundreds of thousands of dollars later . . .'

'Daddy, don't worry, the police were very nice to us.'

'*Police?*' Frank turned to me.

'Just one guy . . . little guy . . . barely a cop at all . . . smallish fellow . . . yes, very, very tiny,' I explained.

'When did this happen?'

'Um, about three. Okay, okay, don't say anything.'

I knew Frank was going to say a whole lot of parental-sounding things to me about getting us all in a lot of trouble and not being able to control myself and 'in front of the kids!' and if I didn't learn how to calm down . . . I don't know the end of that one, actually, the one that starts with 'if'.

I went over to Samantha's with the kids to get away from Frank's self-righteous, disappointed, master-of-the-family swagger, hoping to hear the echoes of my day in the sun. Samantha had heard the story and she smiled, but it faded. Squinting, she said, 'Ya need to calm down, Frannie. You're scaring me.'

'Oh, God, I'd never do anything to you!' My eyes welled up.

'Not what I mean. I see you getting a head full of steam

and worry that one day, I don't know ... look what happened to Sam. Listen, go see my doctor. I'll bet it's just a nutritional imbalance.'

Disturbed at being considered imbalanced, I left as I came, disturbed and imbalanced, but with an appointment to see the master of medicine, Dr Soondartisradnoosvishnuam, and that appointment is at three today. He better not keep me waiting. Ha ha!

I see the usual cast of characters in East Coast Park. I wave to some who have come to know me as the white thing that trots by at 5.25 am. I get some nice, big 'hellos' out of a few now.

When you turn the bend around the fish pond, the landscape opens. Until then, you are between trees and the NTUC villas, which are government-run chalets on the beach costing practically nothing to stay in except for the price of the phone call to reserve them. I am always inspired by the expanse of water, the various patches of trees and flowers, and on the way back, I'll catch the red sun just coming up.

Today, as I turn the bend, I am stopped in my tracks. I stand before the most enormous and amazing moon I have ever seen and would never have imagined possible. This moon is here with me, so close to earth that, in a minute, I'll be running through it, shattering it in a million pieces. It is the size of a stadium, bright white with sharp edges, perfectly round. I have never been so awed by any natural wonder in my life. I've seen glaciers and geysers, alps and orcas, and have thought each a glorious miracle, but this contains magic. This is simply incredible, improbable and shocking. This moon has defied its place in the solar system entirely. It has come down to deliver a message to the people: 'Has the sun ever done this for you? Vote for moon!'

Oh, how I wish my friend Frank were here to see this.

And then I hear a baseline, a subtle, steady whoosh. It's sort of like wind through the trees but more organised and powerful, almost like the sound you hear inside a plane. (That'd be a *roar*, Fran.) Yes, yes, I hear a roar. Where's that coming from? I am not left pondering for long because 20 metres ahead of me, the water has begun to advance. It stealthily creeps over the sandy border and marches through the grass. It spreads around the trees, the granite picnic tables and telephone booths and topples over rakes, brooms and garbage cans. I am heading into the water's conquest; as I run toward it, it runs toward me. I reckon it's not wise to become a part of this natural disturbance, but I can no sooner turn my back on these forces than they will heed my cries. I let the black water flow across my feet, and up my ankles and shins, and soon I am stumbling through it like a mindless hyena, except for the fact that I feel glorious.

The rains begin, spoiling the moon's moment of glory, and soon it is hard to see. It's as if Mother Nature is scolding, 'Get back in here, ya loony, Mr Levin is watching you.'

The moon resists and continues to navigate the advancing waters, culling up more gravitational force than he has ever attempted in all his billions of years. The sea has now extended to the rest stops and swells into the jungles beyond. In mere moments, the streets are flooded.

I note the signs along the path that say, 'Warning: Beware of falling coconuts during storms.' I've run in many a mighty rain and been lucky so far on the coconut–noggin encounter. I will take the gamble once again. After a few more kilometres, the winds are summoned and I might as well be on a treadmill for all the ground I'm covering. My shoes are buckets, my contact lenses have popped out, but I persevere. I can't turn back. I can't miss this. And, I can't face not having done my workout. Two very different emotional responses, but each compelling nonetheless.

Puddles turn to lakes and lakes become bays as the sea defiantly conquers the plains, and I'm feeling like a foolish Pharaoh at the Red Sea. I am very far from home and now so uncomfortable, so alone, for everyone has left the park, and perhaps not exactly *not* in a great deal of danger and I have to pee. So I just do it, adding my signature to the end of the world.

I must always remember how marvellous this is, how lucky I am to be awake to witness the grave and quiet strength, the mysterious and powerful forces, that truly govern life. I try not to think of my bed at home that smells like us and the loving arm I never endure with patience. I try not to think about how I haven't seen my kids appear at my side of the bed, rubbing their eyes, pyjamas all twisted, because I am never, ever there in the morning. I try to stop asking myself: Why am I doing this?

I can't not. That's all. If I don't, I will hold little conversations in my head all day long: Oh, it's okay. It's okay. It's okay to be a quitter.

I decide that tonight, I won't work. I'll sit out with Frank and we'll talk. And then I'll have a tuna sandwich – no, no, I'll *make* us *all* something – and I'll have a husband to hold on to for dear life and we'll all, the four of us, sleep on Sadie's queen-sized bed and giggle and tell stories around and around and I'll make up some songs and everyone will say 'I love you' to each other a second time in one miraculous night.

I cut out of the park and run a few miles inland and circle back for home. The moon's demonstration of gravitational sovereignty rages on without me.

But I did it. I ran for three-and-a-half hours. I barrel in and shout, 'I'm home! Hey, guys, let's get in the car and check this out. You won't believe what's going on out there. Hello? Hello?' I can't believe they're not up. Where's Susie?

And, gee, can't Frank do anything? I walk upstairs. 'Frank! Sadie! Huxley!' I shout as I pull off my shoes. 'Get up!'

Susie is tucking her hair into a beret and carrying out a baggie full of snails.

'Frank took the juenefilles out for petite dejuenes. 'Ere es a note from 'im. My Francis wants escargot so I deliver.'

I pick up the note.

Looked like a cool storm coming in so we went to the lighthouse. Kids begged to come to work with me, so, why not? Now that we're out of the way, you can get stuff done. Love Frank.

I crumple the note. That's not it at all. I wanted to show you the moon. I don't want time. I fall to the floor and pound the wall, hot tears rolling down. That's not it at *all*. *I don't want time*. I don't know what to do with *time*, you asshole. I use it for all the wrong things, over and over. I thought there would be picking Sadie up at pre-school and story time and another hellish trip to the supermarket that starts out great with all of us traipsing around looking for familiar foods and then winds up with everyone getting screamed at judiciously, from the clerk to the kids. Even the parking attendant pisses me off, the way he stands there, holding out a ticket, making change. But I always know that next time, it'll go better and I'll laugh and be easy and won't sweat when Sadie opens her drink and spills it and I won't let Huxley wander away so that I have to go out into the mall and call for him, finding him in the men's department playing with ties, or at the information desk charming the assistants. I had promised myself that today we'd see things together, at the same eye level, and my lap would hold two small children and my hands would squeeze two small hands. And I'd kiss the children good night and they would feel safe and cherished instead of sometimes, quite frequently, like obstacles in my way, barriers to the next irrelevant thing I conjure up and am driven to do. Now, I have time to waste all of these promises and instead fill my day with, what? At least I have my appointment with Dr Soondartisradnoosvishnuam.

I feel the silence in the house pool around my feet much as the sea did earlier. I take a shower – more water streaming over my head – and have a most revelatory idea. I shall join the family for lunch! Yes, I think I can sit down for lunch. I'll call Frank now. It's not something I do, you know, take an hour out of the day and sit inside somewhere and lunch. But I can. It's a normal sort of a thing and I can and I will. I put in a new pair of contacts and from the corner of my eye, I see the possible rip in the plan – pages of faxes piled in the tray. I bravely walk to them, praying they all say the same thing, 'Great job! Thanks!' or 'Name your price!' Sure.

The first one makes me sit down. It announces a conference call at 1 am my time with a guy in Los Angeles. That means I get no sleep at all. The next one makes me reach for the bucket. The most annoying client on my roster chirps that she will be in Singapore for a week. Can she stay? I write back in magic marker 'NO, GO AWAY' but I don't send it. This client wrote one book and then wrote it again with a different title and some new names attached to the same old 'dashing' nobleman and 'raven-haired' broad and has proceeded to do this again and again unbeknownst, apparently, to the publisher and public. Okay, that's not at all fair of me to say. I never read anything after the first one. Don't need to. Hate the stuff. All sounds alike.

Here's one from Melanie reminding me that we're all meeting for her girls' night out farewell party at Vie. I told her I'd attend even though this is a dress rehearsal. She isn't going anywhere.

And here's the one I was expecting. Not always from the

same client but I get something like it once a month. It attacks me for failing to notice that the contract I accepted on said client's behalf was actually a document designed to destroy his/her life. Ah, but what they never pick up on is that if you read the contract backwards, it says, 'The publisher has the right to pretend he wrote your boring book and send you on a negative publicity tour and rip you off in every possible way he can think of because that's why he really wanted to be a publisher in the first place.' It's understood that I'm in cahoots with Lucifer.

I get on the computer and do the old damage control and swear that Client Zip is welcome in my home and we'll have all sorts of fun (even though I know that she'll be asking dumb questions like, 'Did you like my last book?' and 'Can you get me more money?' and 'But what do you really know about this market?') and just as I sign off, it's time to go to Dr Soondartisradnoosvishnuam's.

His office smells of jasmine. Crystals of amethyst and quartzite the size of my leg are planted in the centre of the waiting-room floor. Sitar music wafts overhead and a bookshelf solely housing titles by Dr S himself stands directly in front of all the chairs so it is impossible to miss. Quite a spectrum of subjects the good doctor writes on – from parenting to hair analysis. I fill out the general information questionnaire – happy for any opportunity to talk about myself – with startling lies. I 'on occasion' smoke; consider myself a 'light drinker'; exercise 'consistently and moderately'; 'eat three meals a day'; 'do not have more than two cups of coffee'; have 'never' suffered bouts of depression. I think if they have to ask this sort of thing, then they can't be real doctors. I'm going to make Dr S figure it out. If someone admitted they drink lots, eat lots, smoke lots, never sleep, don't get off the sofa, etc – well, I guess any idiot could give a fairly correct diagnosis.

Dr Soondartisradnoosvishnuam appears and ushers me in. He's a short man with thick, unstyled hair. In his small examining room, a computer screen sits on a side desk. It displays an enlarged human eye on the screen. I say, 'I don't know, Doc, I feel sort of watched all the time.' He laughs warmly and explains, in a voice that sounds trapped in a bubble, that he can ascertain almost anything about your health by looking at your eyes, more specifically, your retinas.

'I see,' I say.

Dr S gives a little snort and wags his head. As much voodoo as there is around the room, I find myself liking him. I do believe he has a gift, a sixth sense. I trust him. Perhaps it is because he chuckles again as he reads through my report.

He asks me to lift up my right leg. He pushes it down and chortles again.

'What's funny?' I ask.

He says that I made a lot of jokes on my record.

'I did not.'

He turns red trying to swallow his laugh and magnifies my eyeball. Which really gets him going. I've never seen a doctor enjoy his work so much.

'What? What?'

He asks me if I ever have bouts of rage.

I say I'm not telling. He writes something down and looks at the sheet again. He smiles.

He flips my ear with his index finger. 'So you're a literary agent,' he says.

'Yeah.'

'I have a book.'

'Yes, I saw them out in the waiting room.'

He asks me if I'd be interested in his novel, a murder mystery set in Santa Fe.

'Listen, Doc, I'm barely in the business any more but I'll see what I can do,' I say as I lift the other leg up and he pushes it back down. He giggles.

He asks me if I stay up late, if I like salt, if I have dreams of being Indian, and what I eat during the day.

'I don't know. You tell me.'

'Why, I bet you have crackers and drink a bottle of wine.'

'Sometimes I have chips and beer,' I say.

He tells me I need chromium, vitamin B and 'Dr Soon-better' powder.

'You have a blood sugar problem,' he says.

I give him a couple of pieces of my hair for a $400 analysis and pay $300 for the vitamins and a box of 'Dr Soon-better' powder. I lug it all home and put it on top of my Biospliven carton.

There is a note from Frank: 'Took the kids out to dinner. Have a nice bath and relax.'

I work until they come home.

'Hey, kidlings!' I say and hug and kiss them. They smell like fries and clutch Happy Meal junk. They laugh about something the evening presented. I tell them about the moon. They tell me about the lighthouse. Frank goes out for beer. Susie returns from Francis's and I head for Melanie's party, leaving a note for Frank.

The minute I walk into Vie, I see something's horribly amiss. What are Samantha and Louise doing at the same event? The same table? Sitting next to each other. It was at Melanie's farewell lunch, six months ago, that they had a spat and they haven't spoken since. They look extremely uncomfortable so I sit between them and it works out fine. I have two people to share a bottle of wine with and the tension in the room sort of makes us all a little thirsty, then a little bawdy, which turns to bawling as we rehearse our 'goodbye and good luck' speeches for Melanie.

And then I see that I have to race home to make the 1 am conference call.

I'm sure it's rather impressive when I fall asleep in the middle of it. I wake up, acutely startled, when the producer asks, 'What do you think, Fran?' If I were a tad smarter I would stay quiet, pretend the phone's dead. If I were not so sublimely dumb, I would choose not to say, 'Huh? Wha . . . ? Are we still on the phone?' And, when they answer 'Yes', I most certainly would not say, 'Oh, good, I thought there was something wrong with the TV.' And, indeed, it is most unfortunate that I fall asleep again.

At four in the morning, Frank is not in our bed. He is not in Huxley's room or Sadie's room. He is out on the balcony. My morning has become his wee hours. He sits with a glass of beer and stares out at the sea, occasionally jotting down something on a notepad.

I bring my coffee out. 'At last, we meet again!' I say. 'We're like the cartoon sheepdogs. Fran and Frank doing our shifts. Remember that cartoon?'

'Yep.'

'You okay?'

'Yep.'

'What's wrong?'

'Nothing.'

'Why are you still up?'

'Working.'

'Big project?'

'No.'

'So why are you up?'

'I have work to do.'

'I didn't think you were that busy.'

'Yep.'

'Boy, you're in a bad mood.'

'Wasn't a minute ago. I'm working, okay?'

I want to tell him this is *my* balcony but then I realise it actually isn't. Still, I resent him sitting there making his mood fill up all the open spaces.

'Well, guess I'll go for my run.'

'Guess so. See ya.'

Inspiration is like dandelion fluff; you can't catch it in the air, it has to land on you. I never know when these moments are going to come but just as I'm thinking about how much I miss doughnuts, it hits me: Frank needs a party. I need a party. Same thing. Melanie's doesn't count; I had to pace myself so I'd be fresh for the conference call. Plus, no men.

When I get home, I call Safra Resort and book the beach-front canopy, table for 20, for Father's Day. My girlfriends say they have to ask their husbands but think it sounds like a plan and eventually I hear that everyone can come, except for Caroline's crew, who already bought tickets to the American Club barbecue and bowling tourney.

At Safra, the kids can play on the beach, run around the playground and throw coins into the video machines while the adults drink beer, watch the planes take off and the sun set. Most of us like to ride our bikes there and generally leave wobbly and full. It's always a good time.

'Look, Frank, I know tomorrow is Father's Day,' I say to him while we get dressed to go over to Pam and Jacque's new house (17,000 square feet and probably no yard for that poor Appaloosa they just bought, what with the three other horses they're raising . . . anyway, not my problem), 'but can we start it – you know, doing all the things you want to do

– *after* I get back from my ride? Maj and Mag have me doing a four-hour but I'll go really early so I can be back.'

'Fran, that's fine. I don't even want to acknowledge Father's Day. Commercial holidays are for lemmings.'

I come out of the bathroom holding my mascara wand. 'Frank! You have to celebrate things in life. You can't just plod, plod, plod. Father's Day is the day you can design to be your perfect day. Whatever you want.'

Frank looks at me like I am a talking booger.

I continue, 'All right, I didn't want to tell you because I thought it'd be a fun surprise, but . . .'

'So don't tell me.' He tucks in his shirt, walks out to the computer and begins emailing.

I follow. 'Well, I think it will make you happy, so . . .'

'Can't get much happier, Fran.'

'What's *wrong*, Frank?'

'Nothing, *nothing* and NOTHING. I don't want a Father's Day, but obviously that doesn't matter. You just won't let things well enough alone. You'll just keep doing whatever *you* want.' He turns off the computer and goes downstairs.

He's right about one thing . . . I run to the top of the steps half naked, half mascaraed, and scream, 'AM I SUPPOSED TO APOLOGISE FOR THINKING OF YOU? FOR WORRYING ABOUT YOU?'

'You're a real piece of work, you know that?' He leaves the apartment and slams the door.

I follow.

'Go back inside, Fran, and take a fucking pill. And by the way, I'm not going to Pam and Jacque's.'

'How can you do that to me? To her? She made dinner!'

'I. Don't. Care.' The elevator door closes behind him.

I go to Pam and Jacque's house alone. There are three other couples besides Pam and Jacque and the widow Fran. Frank is dead to me.

'Frank is sick,' I say.

After a glass of wine, I tell someone else, 'Frank is away. In Hong Kong. Big project.'

After two glasses of wine, I tell everyone, 'Frank is a bastard', and I go over the whole entire thing just like it happened and I get everyone to hate him as much as I do.

Over coffee, I tell them there's probably a bigger context I should mention which might be important in our judgement of Frank, and perhaps I should enumerate his strengths, out of a sense of honesty and fairness. Unfortunately, at this point in my analysis, everyone has to leave, as happily married people do on a Saturday night, so we plan to continue the discussion at Safra the following evening, amidst assurances that everything will work out fine.

'Oh, I know. This happens to us all the time. I mean, not *all* the time, then it would be a really bad marriage. But we have so much fun together. And, I push. I do have to blame myself here . . .' I wave as the taxis pull out and return my gaze to the Appaloosa's pleasant nostrils. She nuzzles my cheek, nodding her big head 'yes'.

Sunday morning, when I get back from my ride, Frank has tidied up the house, made fresh coffee, and put flowers in a vase, toasted bagels and smoked salmon on a plate and a grapefruit in a bowl. The kids are shiny clean, wearing clothes that fit and match. The toys are in their places except for the game of Memory they're all playing. Van Morrison is in the CD player. I've got a lot of road dirt on me and my helmet is dripping with sweat; my hair is foul and my toes hurt. I promise them I'll be down in a minute, don't get near me, I stink. The shower feels so good. I shave, dry off and do a little pampering.

I go downstairs and Van Morrison has been replaced by the TV; Memory is but a memory. Frank gets off the sofa and pulls out a chair for me at the dining-room table. He pours out some coffee with sweetener and milk and hands it to me.

'Dank ew,' I say because I can't open my mouth very wide until my face mask comes off. I take little pebbles of bagel and put them on the tip of my tongue. The coffee's steam melts my cucumber peel. Frank sits back and gives me a soulful smile and fixes his gigantic blue eyes on mine. (NB: When I say 'gigantic', I do mean it. Most people say, of eyes, 'big' or 'bright' or 'almond-shaped' or maybe even 'brooding' and what have you. Frank takes ten minutes to blink. Beat that, Yoda.)

'I'm sorry,' he says, shaking his head, 'for last night. Forgive me?'

'Ew k.'

'Here,' he hands me a piece of notepaper, 'I even wrote out a list of things I want to do on Father's Day.'

I take another pebble of bagel and read the list: *Go hiking, biking, kayaking, swimming, rollerblading, bowling, picnicking, drinking* . . .

'Frank,' I let my mask crack, 'you gave me the wrong list. Yours says *take nap, read paper*. I think this is my Mother's Day Boot Camp one.'

He comes over and hugs me. 'You deserve it. You have good ideas, Fran, and I love you.'

'But I push.'

'Sometimes over the edge.'

'But you love me.'

I remember the time a mentally handicapped person in the halls of the Jewish Community Center came up to me and showed me a picture she drew. It was a vibrantly sketched flower and vase, not bad at all, by any standard. Except she scribbled with black crayon all over the picture, bearing down and ripping it in places. Perhaps she was only handicapped when it came to leaving the picture well enough alone.

'But you love me,' I repeat.

'*Yeeeessss.*'

'Frank, what's been wrong with you lately?'

'Look, I'm sorry. I don't know how to explain . . . I . . . It's, I don't know, it's . . .'

'You're having an affair!' I shout. Now I get it. The list. My 'good ideas' . . . favourite breakfast . . . make everything look like my fault . . . right . . . I knew it all along.

'No. I am not.'

I didn't think so. Too much effort. 'So, what? Are you going to lose your job or something?' I wish the panic didn't come out so loud and clear. Why didn't I think to ask him about his health? I guess even that has something to do with me, me, me, me.

'No, no . . . I guess I'm sick of some of the shit . . .'

'Well! Join the club. I haven't told you what I got emailed today! I cringe when I think about it. God! Anyway, listen, now I know I did the right thing.'

'I don't follow.'

'I was going to tell you last night but, you know . . . Anyway, you need a party and we're having one tonight, a big get-together at Safra.' Frank glowers and gets up.

I stand. 'Frank, not big-big, just big-fun big. It's only our good friends. Remember, you just said I always have good ideas? Well, I think you need a party.'

Frank doesn't have much fight in him after last night. He sits down and sullenly opens the paper. He puts it back down. 'Okay, Fran, you know best.'

'And why don't we get there early and rent kayaks?' I suggest, warming up to the whole wonderful day ahead.

'I guess you'll insist on riding the bikes?' Frank smiles.

'It's the best way to get there.'

I try to do some work but Frank and the kids are playing hide and go seek and Huxley wants to be sure you 'don't look in the closet' and 'don't look under the bed' so it's hard to concentrate. I close the door but they're laughing so loud, the best I can manage for viperous language in paragraph two of my email is *Ha ha ha*. At three, we put Sadie and Huxley in the bike cart and cycle the 12 kilometres to Safra Resort. We rent kayaks, paddle to our secret beach and ignore the flotsam – discarded clothing, bricks, ottomans and other unbeachy things – that have washed up. We bob up and down in our life jackets, find some good shells and sea glass and then get back in the kayaks. I've almost forgotten the party. 'Hey, we have to go and get changed. Let's shove off.'

The kids complain, but they'll cheer up when they see their gang of friends and go off to the playground or the beach or the parking lot or the highway while the adults totally lose track of them. They have a club, a brotherhood, with these kids. Such memories of Halloween and Christmas and New Year's and umpteen barbecues and Sunday happy hours at our place, not to mention the many times we've all found ourselves together at Safra.

After Sadie and I have a lovely shower in the clubhouse, I organise the seating so we're under the cabana on the beach with two big tables – adults here, kids over yonder. I get a pitcher of guava-lime juice and three jugs of beer. Sadie and Huxley are already in the playground. Frank and I sit side by side, admiring the view. We are so close to the airport here that you can see a passenger's tie; you can't hear your husband point out, 'This is the last 747 they made using tsongtung in the fustlegrade.'

'Isn't this fantastic?' I say.

'*What?*' Frank says.

'Yes,' I say.

I feel wonderful, from the bike rides, the kayaking, the walk on the beach, the shower, the sun, and here's some nice, chilled, lovely Tiger Beer and a yummy bowl of *ikan bilis* (fried anchovies and Spanish nuts – yum, yum, *not*). I push aside the snacks and pour another mug; tomorrow is my day off, say Maj and Mag. Yeah!

'Happy Father's Day, Frank.' I raise my glass. The plane has passed and all is calm and easy.

'Happy Father's Day,' comes a chorus of voices. Kiss kiss. 'Sorry we're late.' – 'Just got back from a soccer match.' – 'Is that new?' – 'How's your day been so far?' – 'Did anyone order another jug?' – 'Where are the kids?' – 'Oh, you're so tanned.' – 'I just got up.' It's Tilda and Hugh, Dana and Regular Collin, Jenny and Steven, Lisa and Roy, Simon and Melanie all at once. Frank and I don't clink.

My favourite waitperson arrives with more *ikan bilis* and I bring out my cheesy crackers to share, remembering Dr S's words: 'crackers and wine'. But this is crackers and beer. We always ask for this waitperson who loves the kids, knows our peculiar way of doing things (like wanting all the dinners brought out together so we're all eating at the same time) and makes sure we never gaze upon an empty jug. But we also ask for this waitperson because we're dying to know if it's a she or a he. The name is Trace (long e).

After two hours, we order food. Burgers and chips for the kids, some fried rice and curries. Sadie wants plain white rice. Frank looks at me for approval on devil's beef. ('Go ahead, it's Father's Day!') I get egg foo young, fried calamari and dry vegetarian *kway teow*. Two seconds later, it all arrives except for the burgers and the plain white rice. Ten, 15, 20 minutes later, after many reminders, there is still no sign of burgers and white rice. This is appalling. The kids have nothing to eat and our dinners are cold. I get up. 'No, Fran, don't,' they all implore. I walk. 'Please, Fran. Let Frank handle it.' No one can stop me. I'm running on steam. Someone has to save the day. I'm damn glad I didn't take Dr Soon-feel-fucking-better powder; I want to be mean and I want to be scary and someone is going to pay for this.

I plough over to Trace and shout, 'What is so, incredibly, fucking hard about giving a kid a bowl of white rice?! And the hamburgers? We all *came* together, capiche? We want to *eat* together. Get your pitiful act together!'

'Sorry, sorry. So sorry, Ma'am. Busy kitchen. New staff. Food's on the house, okay? Very sorry. Okay?'

They always do this over here: douse me with patience and kindness. No one ever gets mad. It makes me mad. It makes me ashamed.

'Oh, yeah, that's good, thanks. Hey, I'm sorry too.' We hug and I feel bosoms. I can't wait to tell everyone.

Eventually, we have our feast and continue our lively chatter. The kids disappear again off into the dark and we swoop down on their leftover French fries, pour out more beer, wave cigarettes around and circulate. By nine, we've had enough. Frank locates the kids and straps them in and I ride like the wicked witch, pedalling furiously, berating anyone walking on the cycle track or riding stupidly.

Frank and I are brushing our teeth.

'Have fun?' I ask.

'Yeah, it was nice.'

'So much fun.' I sigh, getting under the covers. 'Frank?'

'What?'

'You had a great time, didn't you?'

'Sure.'

'Really?'

'Sure.'

'Good. Me too.'

'Yup,' Frank says and turns the lights out.

I turn them back on. 'Are you being sarcastic?'

'Let's not fight. It was great.' He closes his eyes.

I sit up. 'Did you or did you not have fun tonight?'

'I did. It was great. I just said it.'

'But what?'

'But nothing.'

'Really?'

'Fuck! Fuck! Fuck!' He bolts out of bed. 'Shut up already.' He takes his pillow.

'Frank, don't go. I'm sorry. It's Father's Day. Please stay.' I crawl across the bed.

He pauses by the door. 'Yeah.' He grabs a pen and writes on the wall, 'FATHERS DAY'. 'See, lots of fathers. No apostrophe there, no singular possessive, not in your little world. Your complicated, scheming, ever-expanding . . .'

'Screw you. Go to hell!'

'I was just about to!' He slams the bedroom door and I hear him taking a blanket from the closet; he stomps downstairs.

My alarm goes off. How could I have forgotten today was my day off? But when my hand reaches the clock, I'm aware that it's the phone ringing. I know it's just some client calling to tell me how much he hates me, not realising of course that he's waking me up but delighted when he finds out that he ruined my day after I ruined his life.

'Hello?' I say warily.

'Fran.' It's Frank's brother, Walt. My face gets hot and my stomach drops. 'Bad news,' he says, 'Dad died.'

'I'll get Frank.'

I find Frank working on his computer out on the balcony. I hand him the phone and sit on the sofa he made up for himself when he's ready to sleep. I will be here when he's ready to come to me.

The Long Run

Dear Samantha,

Thanks for your note. Can't believe we've been in New York this long. Good news is we leave in a week! Here's the lowdown:

Not many people attended the service. In fact, it was four Rittmans – me, Frank, Walter and Pat – and one Bybell, Anne Bybell, mother-in-law of the deceased. The last funeral I attended with these people was for her husband, Frank's grandfather, Pat's father. I was pregnant with Sadie, and Anne thought I shouldn't view the body, bad for the baby or something. The way I remember it, I didn't need to make a special trip to view the body. He was perched way up on a pedestal, the walls were mirrored and the casket was spinning round and round like the prize car on the showroom floor. I could clearly see the entire head reflected to infinity around me. After that initial excitement, I mostly thought about getting a slice of pizza across the road. Anne seemed in a rush, burdened in a very busy-person way, someone who simply didn't plan for this glitch in the day. Frank's grandfather was a lovely man. He was the sort to don a hat and tie

301

every day of his life. He took Frank and Walt to see fire engines and feed ducks. He loved Pro Wrestling, knew every character on the circuit and was either a very good actor or one of the few clean souls in the world who, with all his heart, believed it was a real sport. We'd egg him on and try to get him to admit the stuff was staged but he'd become glossy-eyed and recount wonderful rounds he'd seen on the television between Buster Butt and Wild Man Marvin. I bought him linen handkerchiefs every Christmas. When he was very old and very feeble, one day I saw him patiently, with true self-acceptance but not without great effort, get out of an easy chair. Uuuuuup he heaved with shaky limbs, slowly, thump, thump, dragging his old and feeble body down the hall. At last, he almost reached the bathroom door. He paused, took a breath, and suddenly a blur confronted him, a whirling dervish, who swung open the bathroom door, slipped in and slammed it shut, locking it for good measure. It was his wife on her battery wheelchair. I don't know why Anne couldn't have used one of the other four bathrooms on the ground floor. She's like that. Every time I ask Pat to babysit, Anne shouts, 'Pat, you promised to take me to the hairdressers.' Hey, it's important to look your best when you're a 94-year-old widow who never goes anywhere. But I do admire her. The day I saw her thwart her husband, a prostate cancer victim, on his way to the loo, I also saw her reading the stock pages while watching the Bloomberg report while phoning her broker.

As for Frank's father's service, it was fine, and while I could smell the bubbling cheese and sauce from the pizzeria across the road, I was able to meditate on the man who was my father-in-law. He took the place of my own father for a few years. He listened to my tales of woe and offered considered advice. He wanted to know his boys as they grew to men and was saddled with regret that he travelled so much while they were young. He could take a joke, make a joke, get a joke. He was intolerant of democrats but he didn't know his family was infiltrated with 'em. He thought we should move to Australia because 'America is turning into a third-world country'. He didn't like to show affection but became tearful easily. Whereas my parents planted us in a nice safe pot on the windowsill and pruned us and watered us and cooed to us, he and Pat tossed their seeds out in the yard and let them grow, viewing them from the window and delighting in their wildness, their freedom and their thorns. He liked scotch, he liked my cooking, he liked the nice, long birthday cards I wrote, and he liked our kids but was scared to hold them. He liked Super Market Sweep and Rush Limbaugh. He collected exotic foods that would sit on the kitchen shelves until we were around and then he'd pull some jar out and say, 'Fran! Frank! Come in here. Get a spoon, Fran. Here. Have you ever had stuffed gerbil brain? You don't know what you're missing.' He had rules: you don't touch your sons past the age of three; you don't meet people from three destinations at a restaurant; you don't ask for a raise. He vented about his mother-in-law, who stole his wife and his chair every chance she got, coming along for the ride some 50 years ago when Anne clearly said, 'We do.' But he never complained to her.

The minister closed the service with the prayer for the living, 'In life, in death, oh Lord, abide with me.'

'Amen,' we said.

'I win,' Anne said.

We hung close, surrounded by a brown, warm, tucked-in calm, straightforward emotions, the lack of ambiguity in bereavement, the slight sweetness of missing someone who was loved. Frank and Walt and Pat sat in the kitchen until two in the morning reminiscing.

Bill would have been embarrassed if he heard Walt remembering that last hug, 37 years ago, as if it were yesterday.

A day or so later, Frank checked in at his New York office. I checked in at my New York office and the kids went to daycare. Frank stayed late for a conference on new top-secret business (I'll tell you more when he tells me), I picked up the kids. Next day, I stayed late to meet with people and Frank picked up the kids. The only thing that isn't back to the way it was – besides Frank not having a father – is that we're just visiting. It's a vacation from my vacation. 'Enjoy an exacerbating two-week holiday! Renew your tension! Reactivate your ulcer!' I'm getting lots of stares, too. I don't know if it's because I look like a negative with all this fake blonde hair and charred skin or maybe it's the jogging shorts and platform shoes, but I catch people looking. I think they're trying to figure me out, work out where I fit. New Yorker? Tourist? Tannist? I seem busy and heading somewhere without being dulled by routine or strung out on anxiety or wowed by the fact that I am in New York City, hot damn!

The other day, we went to visit our house. I guess we should have called but we just took a chance. I mean, if we had said, 'Hey, we're in town, not more than 500 yards away, thought we'd stop by', they would have had a chance to screw in some bulbs, take out the trash, weed the garden, sweep the deck, fix the wallpaper, rinse out the toilet, make a bed or two . . . But we just pulled on up the drive.

'Hi, sorry to intrude. The kids wanted to see the old place. If it's not a good time?' I gave her a chance. She could have said, 'No, but in 48 hours I'll be happy to let you come in.' Instead, she smiled warmly and hugged us and offered us drinks and told us how much they love the house and asked us how we were doing. I couldn't answer because I was busy being bewildered at the state of the place. As I took Sadie upstairs to her old room, I passed a hole in the wall. 'What happened here?' I called down the stairs.

She came bounding up.

'Ya, the paint chipped.'

'Paint is not eight inches thick. We are missing pieces of the house here. I can see its innards, for God's sake.'

'Oooh, maybe you're right,' she said, moving her hair from her face and tilting forward to get a better glimpse of the panoply of exposed pipes and wires that you could not fail to notice even if you just had both your eyes poked out. 'Does look like a little of the wall came off.'

Tell Maj and Mag that I am receiving the workouts and doing them under much cooler conditions than you are. The weather's good, actually. I will miss Diet Snapple – I wish they could come back with me. And I wish Frank's mom would, too, for a visit but if I dare suggest it, who knows what Anne might do to me. There she was taking a shower when . . . Seriously, Pat is sad, so deep-down sad.

I've been thinking, life just isn't long enough to be sure you got all of it sucked down. When you lose someone, it seems you wonder why you didn't just sit in a room and stare at each other because one day you won't be able to ever, ever again. Frank was lucky to have had a great last conversation with his father but he wasn't lucky enough to have had it sooner. It was six months ago.

I'll save the rest of the sermon for our next long run.

See you soon.

Love, Fran.

'Jet lag means one day off! Drink Biospliven and meet us tomorrow at 0500 at the track. Time trials! Condolences! Yeah!' reads the message on my email.

I have three weeks to acclimatise before the marathon. I train hard and only see Frank as he lumbers up to bed and I heft myself down to coffee.

'Hiya Frank.'

'Hiya Fran.'

'Everything okay?' Big yawn.

'Not really.'

'That's good.'

'Have a nice run, Fran.'

'You too, Frank.'

But at last, the marathon.

Frank and I go to an early dinner the night before at a nice, boring place offering 'red' and 'white' wine. I have something simple and forgettable, just like Maj and Mag told me to. I wake up the next morning at three, drink two cups of coffee, smoke two cigarettes, feel nervous and sick and want to be dead, but somehow I rally when Maj and Mag get on the boom horn and call up to my balcony: 'We are waiting in the cab. I repeat, we are waiting in the cab.' Columns of lights go up around Fortune Gardens but it's ever so brief a disturbance.

I have sewn my number on wrong so I have to wear my shirt backwards. I wait at a portaloo, in the middle of the line, for ten minutes but someone obviously moved in there, and, looking at my watch, I have to abandon the ablution.

The runners are called to the line-up and I humbly take my mark way in the back of the line to make it clear to all that I am casual. As I look around at the eager faces, the ready loins, as I feel the ruckus of pent-up energy, I take a moment to berate myself lavishly. Why in the world didn't I just do the right thing for once in my life? Why didn't

I work out smarter, stop smoking, stop drinking? The gun goes off. Got me?

It is still dark but the humidity, though a mere fraction of what we can expect by the time the sun comes out, is thick. I am dabbing and dabbing with my wristbands. I need a bathroom. I spot a Mobil station and veer in. My luck, the bathroom is being cleaned. Double happiness: the attendant is a deaf, toothless guy from China who hadn't noticed the 1500 people running by and doesn't understand why I am doing some monkey dance. I yank him out of the bathroom, forcefully pee on his scrubbing bubbles and thank him as I join the ranks again.

I feel much better, much springier, and sprint a few clicks, trying to make up for lost time. I almost lose my footing leaping over a pig's head in the middle of the road. Yes, that is correct: a pig's head. Middle of the road. Just the head. I might like to read the entrails for wisdom but they're not about. No doubt I'll trip on the large intestine later.

The course takes us past thousands of eating houses, coffee shops, hawker centres and food carts. The smells can make you hungry or sick, depending on a number of variables, like: do you want to eat fish-head soup at 7 am? Do you like the odour of last night's chilli crab? I am assaulted every block with noxious fumes until I hit Serangoon Road, Singapore's Little India. There is the scent of curry, cinnamon, tandoori – now *that's* aromatherapy But it's a short road and I am now on Balestier and shop house after shop house is festooned with shellacked dead ducks, row upon row of them, waving to and fro like gamey wind chimes.

I slip on a mound of rice and am totally blinded by the gold outside a Buddhist arts and crafts shop. People are passing me left and right.

Okay, I get it now. This is karma. See, when Frank and

I were in our early 20s, on New York City marathon day, we'd sit outside our apartment. We were positioned on the course at what is known as 'the wall' for most runners – the three-quarter mark just before entering the park. It's not unusual for people to stand on the sidelines and cheer, but that's not what we did. We sat on folding chairs with our feet up, drinking from a pitcher of Bloody Marys set on a card table like a lemonade stand. We taunted the runners as they passed, telling them to give it up, get a life, have a cocktail. It was sick fun.

I had forgotten until now that I thought running a marathon was a ridiculous way to spend a Sunday afternoon.

I have a bottle of Gatorade with me in a pouch, along with enough money to convince someone to bring me back to life. At the three-quarter mark, I chuck the bumbag. I can't stand the way it's bouncing. It is the most annoying bumbag in the world. I hate this bumbag. I see it bobbing in the river. Drown, bumbag! Oh, shit, I forgot to take out the money. That's one rich, dead bumbag.

Well, well, well, now I meet 'the wall' and it is laughing at me with Bloody Mary breath. I think I might fall over. I need a cool sponge. Instead, a bus almost swipes me and I have to wait at a red light. Where are the officials? I should not have to wait at lights or worry about traffic. The good news is: I'm angry. So, adrenaline, a lucky break after all.

With two kilometres to go and early onset rage, I find my stride. I'm gonna be looking good for any photo ops. I have no idea where the finish line is and stop to ask someone. I learn that it's on the track in the stadium. I sprint though I'm sure it looks more like a geriatric jog.

As I cross the finish line, Samantha is already there and dry. She hugs me and I cry. I don't know why, really, just because I am so drained I guess and because I am glad to see her. I thought I had killed her for getting me into this thing.

Thank goodness it was just a daydream . . . but it seemed so real. I loudly proclaim that doing this makes about as much sense as pushing an orange across town with my nose. Some finishers find that offensive. Sadie and Huxley jump up and down, pumping the air, and Frank, now hoarse from screaming out '*Run, Fran, run*', brings me a cold drink.

Maj and Mag trot over. Immediately I'm feeling guilty. I didn't run it in 3:20! That's not what they came over for, though. They give Samantha and me each a big hug and deliver the news. It isn't official, they say, but it seems Samantha came in third and I came in fourth. They hand us something they've been saving for a special occasion . . . a Biosplighten, yes, same low polyoxen-free, but now in a bar. Yeah!

I go to the awards banquet that night with Samantha and Priscilla, our friend, who came in fifth. By the time we get there, I feel strong and proud. I walk up on stage to receive my prize money and consider maybe the heels weren't such a terrific idea just this one night; my feet are throbbing.

Later, they give us our food. Sweet and sour cuttlefish, *char swee*, *yam ring* – nauseating stuff, not for consuming. Frank calls me on my cell phone to tell me the evening paper has the results: seems a Flan Littman came in fourth, not me. I miss Frank terribly. He tells me to come home, he's rented a movie. Indeed, what am I doing here? I look around at this goofy gaggle of health nuts and tell the only two normal people in the room, Samantha and Priscilla, that I'm going to split. The others at my table are aghast: '*And miss the lucky draw?*'

I'm smiling in the cab. I feel a bit special. I'm wrecked and my feet are killing me but can't seem to finish the job. I did a marathon and now, *never again*, I say to myself in the taxi as I chug wine all the way home. I pass out before the movie starts.

≡

'Clambake?'

'You bet!'

Samantha and I are having a light run. It seems I have just agreed to do the Borneo Challenge in Malaysia. This is not a marathon. It's a triathlon held near Mt Kinabalu, where they also hold an annual run up and down the mountain. Maj and Mag just came back from that and were positively outraged, militant even, because a local sherpa won the race. I mean, it's not fair, is it? This guy gets to practise every day. With luggage on his head!

We have about six weeks to train. I can't say I have any bike-racing experience at all, except for one time when I was taking a bike and camping trip with my old boyfriend, a British schoolteacher called Mark. We were going to Scotland from his folks' house in Goldhanger. (Goldhanger is a small town in England that is about two blocks long on one straight road. If you write a letter to someone in Gold-hanger, England, you have to write a lengthy note to the postman saying, 'Yes, it does exist. It's near Maldon. Take the M10 and stop at the farm stand, lovely strawberries this time of year, and ask them to point out the Dog and Sparrow Pub. When you get to the Dog and Sparrow Pub, ask for a man named Pete. If Pete's not in, ask for Darcy. If Darcy's not in, look for Ebin; but, fair warning, he is, on occasion, demented. Any one of them will pull you an honest pint and, if they're of a mind, let you know how to get to Goldhanger. If they aren't, they'll pretend they are and you'll wind up in Festershire and there's no way out until the following Tuesday. Good luck and Godspeed.')

Mark and I rode four or five hours a day and found bed and breakfasts and fields to sleep in. I had beautiful new panniers on my bike and four pairs of running shorts, several jerseys, sweaters, heels for nights out. Mark had some shopping bags looped on his handles containing a change of clothes, a washcloth and toiletries. He carried the tents and camp stove, bits of groceries, wine, some books and maps, and a Scrabble game in a backpack. Most of the time, we rode at a nice pace, facing daunting hills and gusty winds, and would stop at a pub when it opened for a sunny farmer's lunch and cider, or Guinness, or cider and Guinness, or lager, or whatever-you-have-that's-cold-on-tap. We'd stay until the pub closed for the afternoon, get back on the bikes and pick a reasonable destination, say, a mile from the pub we just lunched in, set up camp, cycle back to the pub with our Scrabble board and wait for it to open. You wouldn't have known it, but Mark was actually job-hunting at the time, undercover. One day, he called his answering machine, otherwise known as his mom, and found out that he was wanted for an interview at a school in Leicestershire the next day at two. His mom – worried to a frazzle that he wouldn't ever find a job and more worried still that he would marry me and what with all my fancy notions, I'd never live in a council house and he'd have to have a proper job – informed the school board that he'd be there with bells on. She didn't mention bicycle bells. Leicestershire was miles away and that was if you took the highway. Which we did, on our bikes, and which pissed off a lorry or two. We had to get there an hour early so Mark could buy shoes, a shirt and tie, and some trousers and nice socks. That was my race. We made it, and Mark not only found the necessary clothes but also got the job.

Point is, I'm not a real cyclist. I don't have a speed bike so I borrow Priscilla's 18-year-old son's ten-speed. It predates Schwinn.

Maj and Mag continue to email our workouts. On Wednesdays, we practise the entire race – swimming, climbing out of the pool, scuttling over to our bikes, donning the helmet and shoes, jumping on our bikes and riding for 40 kilometres, ditching the bikes and running for ten kilometres. Susie has to wait for me in the parking lot to receive my bike and put it safely upstairs so I can run. 'Deux minutes faster this time, Madame,' she sometimes says. More often, she looks at me like she cannot believe this is how I spend my time.

Running immediately after riding is difficult. It's hard to be in one position – arms locked, legs spinning – and then tell your body you changed your mind and now you'd like to lurch forward and pound your knees. It's awkward. I feel like Clara, toppling off her wheelchair, Heidi taunting, 'Last one in sits with Grandfather.' I really don't move well.

On Thursdays, we ride out on the airport road, challenging head winds, dump trucks and frisky monitor lizards the size of stegasauruses. We peddle through the army base at Changi and then up a steep hill ten times, all the while captivating the young army lads as they sneak a cigarette or check to see if their socks are dry. Samantha once threw herself onto the sidewalk to avoid being flattened by the Number 9 bus. The foreign workers who were weed-whacking that particular stretch of grass looked up to heaven and gave thanks for the woman who landeth on their turf. In their wonder, they didn't turn off their machines and Samantha, bloody and sweaty, became quite verdantly hirsute.

'Fran, can you get that? I'm in the shower,' Frank calls as the telephone rings. I roll my eyes, put upon. I pause the *Swim Perfect* tape, just at the good part about double-sided breathing.

'Frannie!' It's my mom. 'I only have a minute because Joe is picking me up. Trudy is still at the dentist so he's getting me and then we'll go there to get her. We have reservations at Chips and you know how they are on a Friday night. We can't go on Saturday because Viola is there and she talks and talks and drives me crazy. How are the kids? How is Frank? I called Pat but her mother answered and said "Pat is busy with me" and hung up. The reason I'm calling is I want you to take a look at my jewellery. I don't want any fights. I'm sick about the idea that you girls might bicker over this jewellery. It's what happens. Are you ever coming home again? Listen, I'm thinking about coming in three weeks or so. Dorothy says she can get a good deal for me and Cathy'll be out of town so I won't have my hair appointment. They say there's nothing to do in Singapore and the real Far East is Bangkok and Bali. Eileen and Stan came back from a Tauk Tour and didn't bother because her butcher said that they say there's nothing to do in Singapore. I can't wait to eat those kids up. You never tell me anything about what they're doing. Oh, there's Joe. I love you. Can't wait to see you!'

'*Mom!*' I shout.

'Oh, honey, what? Let me just flick the light so Joe knows I see him . . . Okay.'

'Mom, I won't be around that week. See, I came in fourth in the marathon and now I'm going to do a triathlon in Borneo.'

'Frannie!' She says it with her 'another hair-brained scheme' tone. 'You're a mother!'

She hangs up, perturbed.

If you look up 'You're a mother' in the Lebowitzionary, it means: Don't do anything that might (a) make you die young; (b) cause your husband to leave you; (c) keep you from being home when the kids get off the bus; (d) interfere with a good dinner; and (e) be different to what your own mother did.

I figure I better make this next hideous call now and get it over with. I dial the phone.

'[Client Zip?] Hi, Fran here, when did you say you were coming?' I ask.

'Three weeks from today,' she says.

'Great! Can't wait! Don't forget to bring me that new book you're writing!'

'I sent it to you four weeks ago. It's already been reviewed,' she says.

'Duh! So, what, now you're retired? I mean the *next* next one, you nut.' She is silent. I clear my throat and go for inconsolably disappointed. 'Did you say three weeks from today? Oh shit, I was sure you said five weeks. Well, I won't be here when you come.'

'Fran,' she pauses, 'is it because you don't know the romance market?'

'Oh, [Zip], that again? No, I'm doing a triathlon in Borneo and that's the same week.'

'Can we have a phone date on Friday after you talk with my publisher and find out what she plans to do to get me on the bestseller list?'

'Done. Call me any time.'

How am I going to prepare for this race with Client Zip harassing me, obsessing about everything? Can't she just talk to her husband or that little bunny she dedicates all her books to?

'Frank, what are you doing home so early?' I ask as I lace up my shoes.

He drops his briefcase and gives me a puzzled look.

'I'm heading out for a masters swim class,' I say and grab the car keys.

'It's Wednesday, Fran.'

Tennis night.

'Oh.' I swing the keys.

'Yeah, oh,' he grimaces. 'I put off an important call to get here on time. Where are the kids?'

'Sadie! Huxley!' There is no answer. 'I guess they're outside with Susie.'

'That's a good game, Fran. Do all the moms play? Guess where the children are.'

'Don't be mad. Tennis tomorrow?'

'Yeah, sure. I'll walk out with you and find the kids. Maybe the trail's still warm.'

The following night at the New Barrel, we look into Frank's daily planner and read our future. He has marked out Monday and Tuesday for Borneo and then he flips a few pages and asks me if I'd like to go with him on a business trip to Sydney. Just us. Sneak up to the Blue Mountains after.

'Oh, God, what a treat that will be after all this hard work. You have gone and saved me again. I love you so much.' I kiss him, but public displays of affection are generally unwelcomed by him (though he would not consider sex in an alley to fall in that category).

'We'll just lay around and sleep in and take naps,' I muse.

'And hiking, right? And probably river swims, mountain sprints and boulder rolling, knowing you.' He pops a few peanuts, kerrrunch, chomp, chomp, chomp.

'Frank, I will be so ready to relax. I've earned it. This will not be a boot camp vacation. This will be about *the love*.' I go to kiss him and he lets me. With my eyes closed, I am picturing a meadow of soft grass and swaying wheat, lilies and buttercups. We are in the middle of a big white spread, the lovely picnic's been eaten, everything is peaceful, because I am sleeping, for a while maybe even. There are no ants in Australia for me right now, no snakes that can kill you in one one-billionth of a second, no spiders that can kill you in half a billionth of a second, no completely missing ozone that

315

can kill you real slow and painful-like. Just that clean sheet and gentle breeze and a couple of empty bottles of that chardonnay they rave about. We'll wake up, trudge home and go to bed . . .

'Done,' he says. He's just written us in there, in pen. 'Fran and Frank, Australia.' Fate sealed.

'I miss you, Frank. This will be a good chance to really focus on each other.'

'Definitely. It's about *the love*.'

We kiss again.

'Are you doing okay?' I ask meaningfully.

'There's a lot going on. Like this last meeting in Manila . . .'

'Frank? Let's save it so we have something to talk about in Australia. I really have to get to bed. My workout's at 2 am tomorrow.'

Singapore airport is packed with people going to Borneo for the race. Old friends gather in clusters and confess how slack they've been this year: 'This is just the third race I've done since June.' – 'I've been partying every fifth Friday night!' – 'I totally didn't buy any Biospliven.' And lots of talk about bike components. Most people have special suitcases for their bikes. I have an old box covered in electric tape. I know they talk like this so they have an excuse for losing: 'Well, if I had done four races this year, partied *never* and ate every last bit of Biospliven . . .'

The Rittmans and the Burnses will travel together and stay in Borneo an extra day. The kids are so excited to be together, sharing activity books and swapping snacks. The plane ride is about four hours' long. Samantha is ebullient, relaxed, truly looking forward to the race.

'Fran, what are you doing?' Frank asks me, amused.

I didn't realise anyone could see me. I was trying to read Samantha's mind. How does she do this upbeat thing time and time again? It must be Canadian. I have been imitating her, saying things into the window like 'Oh, it's in the baig' and 'It'll be a lark, ey' and 'You're gonna do great!'

'I'm getting psyched,' I answer truthfully.

'Why are you saying "baig", though?'

'Oh, you heard that?'

'Yeah.'

'If you didn't know me, would you think I'm Canadian?'

'You mean if I didn't know you were secretly Indian?'

I get my own room for the night so that I can get to sleep early and wake up early. Frank and the kids are in adjoining rooms on the fancy floor that has great views and complimentary drinks. Tomorrow, I will shift over.

I decide to join Frank for a wee bit of courage, two glasses of wine. We go downstairs to meet the Burnses for dinner. I order a 'whatever she's having' and point to Samantha.

Back in the room, I read and pray tomorrow I wake up with a raging fever so I can get out of this race. I turn off the lights, comforted to know that Mecca is 90 degrees southeast, at least according to the neon arrow on the ceiling.

The next morning, I am faced with crippling doubts. I can barely make it through my breakfast of champions, ie, two cups of coffee and two cigarettes (well, at some point Samantha ends and I begin, right?). I think I'm not going to do this after all. I so so so so so don't want to. I am so so so so soo nervous. I'm going to throw up. My heart is racing. What have I got myself into? How can I get out of it?

I have brought the whole family along for this. The kids

are looking forward to watching. Well, even if they aren't, how would they feel if Toby and Heidi's mom ran the race and I didn't? *I need to know what Samantha is thinking now!*

I take my gear to the starting camp. You have never seen such women: long-legged, broad-shouldered, made of rock, the shape of things to come. The bikes are sleek. Some still have their price tags on – $15,000. I tell Priscilla's son's bike not to look. Triathlon suits? Who knew? Protein gel packs, shoes that click into the pedals, heart-rate monitors, water bottles? I don't even have a water bottle. Here I am with my friend's son's old bike, a hand towel that says 'Hyatt' and some flat Coke in a sippee cup. I am the Ellie Mae of the race.

'Oh, wave all you want, you jerks,' I think as I smoke.

This event, this one I am participating in, qualifies you for the Olympics. So, it's packed . . . with people from all nationalities . . . people who apparently have a problem with second-hand smoke.

We're led to the beach for the start. Samantha's chatting away, making new friends. I hang back again in a great show of deference. The gun goes off and we run into the water. I am ready to quit in five minutes. This isn't swimming; this is underwater wrestling. Bodies are covering me, arms are tugging at my legs, elbows are conking me in the head, someone is most definitely trying to drown me every time I get near. I would avoid her but I can't see my hand in front of my face. The water is a muddy, oily, churning death pool. I know that I am the last person in the swim. I tell myself that it doesn't matter, the family will love me anyway and we'll have a good vacation.

When I get out of the water and do the little run on the beach to my bike there are, like, four people left to cheer me on and they seem either bored or hired. I lope dejectedly over to my bike, towel off, pick sand from between my toes, swig a sippee of soda, put on my socks, tie up my runners and get into the saddle. 'Have a good ride!' says some jolly fuckwit.

I ride like a madwoman because I am competitive. I do not want to be last. I can be not first, but I will not be last. The locals laugh and shout every time I pass. I am sure I have something hanging out of my bathing suit but, fuck it, I'm not wasting a second to adjust. I won't even grab the water for fear it will slow me down. I will pedal until my legs turn to fucking ghee. I see Samantha on the other side of the loop. 'Lookin' good, Fran!' she shouts, fresh as a daisy. Behind her are Vilja, Christine, Tamami. Everyone is a lap ahead of me.

And then, I'm on my fifth lap and I am despairing. I have five more to go. The temperature must be 200 degrees and we're riding – and soon to be running – on bubbling tarmac.

Here we are on this gorgeous, exotic island surrounded by sea, covered with mountains and jungle, but the race is four laps on a stretch of highway that offers nothing to look at except for one big, gaudy mosque. We might as well do laps around the Miami K-Mart parking lot in August. They are so damned proud of their new road and that neat yellow line. And why is a country so full of poverty giving out entire bottles of water to riders who take one swallow and throw it away? What's wrong with a Dixie cup?

I finish the bike, jump off and do my Clara step for ten minutes. My friends ride by me on their bikes and cheer, 'Run, Frannie.' – 'Looking Great.' – 'It's in the baig.'

'Omigosh,' I think, 'I'm actually ahead. They're still riding.' Now it starts to matter. I have a chance here. I'm totally not last. I run in earnest. I don't care if I collapse. I pass tons of people. At about the six-kilometre mark, I get the chills and feel woozy. I shake it off when someone over-takes me. I grab some water and catch up to the bitch who dared. I high-step it to the finish line, hearing Frank's hoarse voice shouting, 'Yeah, Fran! Go Fran!'

Sadie fingers my medal and Huxley hands me water. I have finished in the top quarter. People come up and tell me what a wonderful run I had and say, 'Boy, you're some runner', and suddenly hick is chic. I have qualified for an Ironman and am offered a spot on a relay team. As I'm basking in the glory of it all, I say a sad farewell to my bad habits. *Smoking, I'll miss you most of all.* My innocence is gone. This might never be fun again.

Frank and I have hired a babysitter for the night and plan to have a romantic evening. But so far, I've been sitting alone for 20 minutes in the lounge while Frank talks to New York. I don't mind, though. I have some lovely cold champagne and all the feel-good endorphins galloping around in my head.

'Hey, I thought you were going to quit?' Frank enters, nods at the cigarette I'm lighting.

'New plan,' I say, through a plume of smoke. 'I'm going to ask Marlboro to sponsor me. We'll have the warning changed to "Smoking might take two minutes off your time. Have a nice run!"' I pour a glass of champagne for Frank.

'Better yet, I'll have my podiatrist sponsor me. I can wear a T-shirt that says "Ask me about my bunions!"' I pour myself another glass.

'You could design triangular-shaped running shoes. You know, for people with enormous bunions like you,' Frank adds.

'Thanks, Frank.'

'Sorry, I thought we were kidding. Well, here's to you. That was pretty amazing.'

'Wasn't it!' My hands keep running over my shoulder

muscles. I can't help it. It's late in the evening . . . I've put on my make-up and brushed my long, blonde hair and . . . oh . . . I look wonderful tonight.

I continue, 'You know, in all seriousness, Frank, I'm serious about this racing now. Seriously.' I flash the bartender a bicep as I motion for another bottle. 'I'm going to do that Ironman.'

'Are you serious?' asks Frank.

'Do I look like I'm joking, Frank?' I light another cigarette.

'You should know, sweetie, you haven't taken your eyes off yourself since I got here,' Frank quips. It's true; the wall in front of me is mirrored.

'I'm looking at the bottles,' I say, gazing ahead, thinking, 'This is what I look like when I say, "I'm looking at the bottles."' I turn to Frank. 'Okay, yeah, you're right. I can't help it.' The laughter suddenly goes out of me and I tamp down my cigarette. 'I just feel good . . . like from the inside out, like the search is over. For once . . . oh, this is hard to say . . . I don't know, Frank . . . I don't really know . . . It's everything, everything's good . . . for once, I feel like a winner. I really do. I tried something and, for once, it worked.' I tear up at the sad truth of that.

'You are always so hard on yourself, Fran. Look, do the Ironman if you think it's what you want to do but it won't define you to me or the kids. In fact, I'm not sure what it really means. You really want to go through it? You really have the time? I think it's crazy. But if it will make you happy, do it.' Frank looks into my eyes.

'Frank,' I say, 'I'm serious.'

'Of course you are.' He hands me a cocktail napkin and lights my cigarette.

The next day, Greg's lined up a speedboat to take us to a small, uninhabited island. I call down for a picnic basket and Frank and Samantha get snorkelling gear for everyone. The kids have a wild time, bumping across the South China Sea. The captain looks for every chance to help them fly overboard into the roiling water. I'm trying to sit on both kids to keep them down but I'm bouncing around the vessel randomly, suddenly, violently. Finally, we stop at a lush little beach and it appears we're the only people on the island. The boat drops us off and makes a quick u-turn and disappears.

'Greg,' I say, 'how can we be sure he'll be back?'

'Calm down, Frannie.'

Uh, these Canadians! Not a care in the fucking world, eh?

'So,' I whisper to Samantha, 'where should we run?'

'No!' everyone shouts, including Samantha.

'Frannie, one day off. It's not gonna kill ya,' Greg, Mr Mellower-than-thou, says like he knows.

And maybe he does. Despite my anxiety – knowing as I do that a body at rest stays at rest and tomorrow it's going to be that much harder to get off the sofa and just do it – the day unspools gloriously. It is a day where thousands of moments seem blessings. Two families playing, enjoying our children. The kids exploring their strengths, investing energy in running up and down the white, soft beach. We snap wonderful pictures of them in their snorkelling gear and we all flipper through the water, swimming up to each other and tapping a shoulder, pointing to a clownfish or a sea anemone. Greg tries out his new underwater camera and tracks down a huge turtle, which we all spend about an hour following and losing. We picnic on rolls and butter because I guess when I asked the hotel for sandwiches, they decided to give me their national favourite. We hike, draw messages in the sand and, just as we're growing tired of being sticky and salty and even weary of feeling grateful, our man with the boat returns, grinning like a hellhound.

The following day we return to Singapore and Frank immediately goes into the office for a few hours. He must have felt buried with work. On the plane he alternated between flipping through sheaves of paper and playing with his calculator. For lunch, he had fingernails.

I check my emails: 35 from work, which I'll ignore for now, especially the one that has 'YOU DIDN'T CALL ME FRIDAY' for a subject. Maj and Mag wrote: 'Good work! Ironman is serious. We need to upgrade your Biospliven. Bring a sample of sweat. Visit our website www.fitness-isallthatmatters.com. Yeah!' Every nut has a website now.

'Susie?' I call.

'Yes, Madame.'

'Can you hold this cup under my chin while I run in place here?'

'Of course, Madame.'

Plink, plink, plink.

'Okay, will you take this over to Maj and Mag?'

'Right away, Madame.'

Hmmm, I think, this is what I have to put up with, a maid with attitude. It's just a cup of sweat. She didn't have to be so sullen. She could have made it more fun if she tried a little. I go into the kitchen and see she baked a torte. 'Sadie! Huxley! Want some?' There's a sign sticking up: 'Congratulations, Ma'am'.

I line up friends to pop in and check on Sadie and Huxley for every day that we'll be in Australia. I hire two more baby-sitters for day and night shifts so that I have constant, vigilant supervision of the kids. The kids have playdates every day.

Susie tells me not to worry, she'll call if there is any problem.

Frank pulls some string or another and manages to book us into a penthouse at the ANA with quintessential panoramic views of Sydney Harbour. The minute I'm there I see no need to leave the room to have a satisfying vacation, but I want to walk around before it gets dark.

'But this is about *the love*,' Frank says, coming toward me.

'You'll be working tomorrow. Don't you want to have a quick look at the place?' I say. 'And, then, *the love*.' I wink.

The weather is chilly and I'm happy to wear my motorcycle jacket and black jeans as we cruise through this ancient section of town. The Tildons were named after the sandstone bluffs where the first convicts cut bricks for gutters and buildings in the 1700s. It was also where prisoners were piled up in dosshouses run by drunken marines. Now, it's just full of drunken investment bankers and thick-necked yobbos and the odd maritime folk, depending on the bar.

We wander through the warren of streets and go into every pub that looks interesting. One has two lovely big old stone fireplaces. A dog is sleeping on a woven Aboriginal rug and an old sailor sits propped at the bar. Behind the bar is a bosomy girl in her mid-30s and an ancient man, probably the bartender's dad. I get the feeling that, even though they have plenty of vacant seats and probably need the money, they don't want our type. American. My Australian and British (and German and Irish . . . and Singaporean . . . and Indian) friends always say, '. . . *oh, but you and Frank are different*' whenever they've just finished saying 'Of course they were *American*' or 'leave it to an *American*' or 'bloody fucking wankers, those *Americans*'. Anyway, I'm rather indifferent to the snub.

We go to a few more pubs and walk down to Woolloomoolooo. We take a ferry to Watsons Bay and have dinner on the wharf. The afternoon had been like a New York early fall day. The city is quite nice, but it's the weather and the Australian way of life – a passion for pleasure and ease – that makes me say, 'Frank, Australia has got to be your next gig. Let's start scheming.'

'What *next* gig?'

'Well, wouldn't it be great to get a job in a new place in a few years? I mean, I'm not ready to leave Singapore, but when we are, then, Australia! That would be so fantastic. The weather is awesome here and they're like us even though they hate us. Then we'll do Europe . . . but I can't learn a new language . . .' I take a bite of my lobster. Why hadn't we thought of this before? We're on to something here; we have discovered the wonderful worldwide expat scene. We are part of a whole secret society that knows how good it can be. Frank doesn't say anything more. He is looking off into the ocean, pensively. I have planted a seed. Or, it is entirely possible, he is thinking 'Ocean'.

When we return to the ANA, we undress for *the love*. Is it a sign that they really care when they make a bed so tight it's shrink-wrapped? As I use every ounce of strength I have to get a small corner of sheet down I see the message light on the phone.

'Frank, we have a message.'

'Can't we ignore it?'

'I don't think so. It could be the kids.'

'They don't make phone calls.'

'I mean, it could be *about* them.'

Frank dials in for the message. He sits down heavily on the bed as he listens. He hangs up slowly.

'Fran, I'm sorry. I don't think we can make it to the Blue Mountains. Ken's here. He wants to see me tomorrow. He's invited us to dinner after.'

'Ken? Your boss? From New York?'

'Yeah. It's a big meeting. I told you there might be a chance he'd show up.'

'No, see, because if you *did*, I would have brought a dinner-with-Ken outfit and I didn't.' I jump up and swing open the closet door to display my all-blacks. 'And why can't we still go away?' I huff back into bed and make no headway on dislodging the sheet, scratching and pawing at it.

'Fran, my boss doesn't come around the world so that we can piss off on a vacation we're only taking because he was on the other side of the world.'

'Ahhhh. See, you *never* said that.' I find a way to slither in. 'Okay, don't worry. I mean, now that we know how easy it is to get here, we'll do it another time. We'll bring the kids. And then when you get a job here . . . just kidding . . . good night. I love you. I'll find something to wear, don't worry.'

And I fall asleep.

Had we asked someone, we might have learned that St Leonards is to Sydney as Brooklyn is to Manhattan. We could have done it in a taxi ride. But we didn't ask. So, instead, because Frank's meeting is in St Leonards, we move into a dank, drippy little motor lodge in the heart of a suburb.

'What am I going to do here?' I complain.

'Didn't you bring your laptop?'

'Actually, no.' And it occurs to me that I didn't even bring a manuscript or a contract. I have completely forgotten about work.

'I gotta go. Just take a bath and get your nails done. Go shopping. I'll be back soon.'

The minute he leaves, the walls start coming toward me. I'm making them do that because I'm bored. I could lie on the bed and pretend I'm a junkie. I'm going crazy. Why?

What do other people do when they are on vacation? Relax, read . . . but the walls . . . it's for real this time . . . ahhh!!! I cave. Much as I wish I could deviate from my routine, it seems I can't. There simply is one thing to do. I put on some shorts and tie up my shoes and go out for a run.

In front of the motor lodge I spot a guy, about 60, tying up his shoes, a fellow jogger.

'Hey,' I call out, 'you know a good route around here?'

He says, 'Yeah, come with me.'

I don't really want to. I mean, I'm training for an Ironman for God's sake and this man is, well, *not*. But I can't be rude, that'd be so American, so I run with him. And, actually, he keeps up fine. Our conversation is crackling. He's a doctor and a writer and a very interesting man. He takes me on a wonderful path through Aboriginal caves and cliffs and bushland and into exclusive neighbourhoods. He asks about my kids and I ask about his. One is an actress.

'Oh, that's tough,' I say.

'Yeah, she lives in the US but she comes to visit.'

'Is she getting work?' I ask as we round a cliff wall.

'Oh, she and Tom do pretty well.'

Nicole Kidman's dad and I had a great run together. Next time, I'll get the vacation that includes tea with Elle's mum.

I get a book and take a walk, come back in time for a shower, and lay out all my clothes. Frank returns. 'Frank! You'll never believe who I ran with today.'

'Fran, Ken and Jill are waiting downstairs. I told you six.'

'Frank, there's no downstairs here. It's a motor lodge. I'll be ready in a second.'

While I'm putting on my make-up, I call out to Frank, 'We have to play this carefully, you know.'

'What are you talking about?'

'Well, someone's going to ask, "How are you, Fran?" and I don't want to seem too happy or else Ken'll be, like,

327

"Hmmm, they have it too good", but then we have to get him to know we'd love to be here four years, five years, forever . . . Okay, how do I look? Like I can wrap him around my pinky?'

Frank doesn't take in the gauzy shirt and black jeans, he looks at my face. 'Fran, you've had a long run.'

'I usually have good colour after a long run.'

Frank pulls me close for a moment, tightly. 'That's not what I mean. Listen, let's go. The boss is waiting.'

Dots All, Folks

I kiss Jill and now probably have more make-up on one side of my face. She tends to apply a little extra, maybe in case you forgot to wear your own. Same thing with the perfume, because, who knows, the whole town might smell bad. She wears a lot of jewellery; they don't like to be separated. She and I have matching hair.

I like her and I like Ken. Sure, they're the boss and his wife and a generation older and rich, rich, rich – from what he's accomplished and by virtue of her birth – but she makes me feel like a girlfriend and Ken always laughs at my jokes. It doesn't matter if she never calls me the next day to keep on being my girlfriend or if Ken was only laughing at my jokes because I am. It's a form of kindness, no? Ken's a *guy*, a guy's guy. If he married a different girl, he might've been racing cars, or fixing them wearing a jumpsuit and a name patch, 'Ken'. He's a man of action and decision. He makes people quake and he makes things happen.

We pile into the limo waiting at our motel and, ten minutes later, arrive at the ANA where Jill has made dinner reservations. I say hello to the concierge who recognises me from last night and wave to the bellhop who helped us with our bags and nod to the reservations assistant and oh, there's the housekeeper – 'Nice chocolates!' I say. 'I used to live here,' I explain to Jill and Ken.

We go up to the 20th-somethingth floor for dinner. It's one of those 360-degree-view restaurants where murmurs and jazz seem to be the only appropriate noises. I excuse myself to go to the ladies room while Frank orders cocktails. I fix myself up and practise what I'll say when Ken asks me, 'How do you like Singapore so far?'

It's tricky. I want to sound like a good soldier, like he's not doing us any favours: 'We don't think about our own happiness, Sir! We go where we are needed most, Sir!' I can't say, for example, 'I want to live abroad and be an expat forever. Thank you! Thank you! Thank you!' and bend down and kiss his ring. That wouldn't be good. First, he'd hear the 'I want' and get all suspicious.

Suddenly, the door opens and Jill comes in. Girlfriend or not, I can't rehearse this with her. I'll have to hope the words come out just fine back at the table. Jill spritzes and points the bottle at me. 'Sure, thanks,' I say and close my eyes for the spray.

'Fran, you look terrific. I love your hair.'

'Thanks. I love that top necklace.' She fingers it like a pet.

'How's it been, living in Singapore?' she asks.

What? Not *now*. We don't have this conversation *now*, in the ladies room, where Ken, the boss, isn't. I pretend to be distracted by the instructions on the automatic hand dryer. I open the door for her and tell her I love the fifth bracelet on her right hand.

Frank and Ken are heavily engaged in a discussion and haven't touched their drinks. Frank is nodding and Ken is gesticulating. I plunk down noisily so they know to wind down on the shop talk.

'Oh, I'm sorry, Jill. Did you ask me something back there?' I say, settling in.

'I don't recall. Let me think.' She opens her menu. 'Oh, this is a big menu. Ken, isn't this a big menu?'

Ken is tapping around the table looking for his big menu.

'That's right, you asked me something about Singapore . . . Ah, yes, you asked me how it's been, living in Singapore,' I say.

'We did have an early lunch. Ken, do you think you'll get a starter?'

'Sure. Sure. Where's my menu at?' Ken looks puzzled.

'I'm going to get a starter,' I say. 'I always do in Singapore.'

Ken finds his big menu and starts talking to Frank again. I hear 'any day now' and 'light up the sky . . .'

Frank nods and finishes half his beer. Jill turns to me. 'What sort of starter are you getting, Fran? I hear the yabbies are wonderful.'

'Probably something Asian for me. I love Asian food. I think I'm a little Asian on my mother's side.' No sounds except for the mellow notes from the fusion jazz band.

I take a sip of water. Brainwave! 'Ken! Jill! All this talk and I haven't even asked. How are *you*?' I practically scream.

'Fine, fine,' Ken says. He picks up a roll and hands Jill the basket. 'You?'

I'll take it . . . okay . . . okay . . . what to say . . . what to say? Hurry before Jill starts talking about fucking dessert.

'It's been wonderful so far.' I smile hugely. 'Though, of course, it's very difficult sometimes.' I frown morosely.

'Sure. Sure.' He opens the big menu.

'I mean, being so far from family,' I say meaningfully to the menu.

'Sure. Sure. Far from family, not good, not good.' He puts his glasses on and picks the menu up again.

Oh, shit, I'm losing him. Gave him the wrong message. 'Yeah, but now that they're all dying, it's a lot easier!'

I start and finish my drink in one strong gulp and motion the waiter over for a double. Frank's face is red and he's straightening the silverware. Ken turns a page of the big menu. Jill says, 'Oh, look, Ken, I don't have that sheet. What's that?' He yanks it off and hands it to her.

'Today's specials? Now I have to start all over again.'

After completing the task of ordering, Jill turns into a delightful flibbertigibbet, pouring out all her news about kids, grandkids, boats, vacation homes. Ken chimes in, animated, proudly embroidering missing details, like the exact size of the boats. The table is happy. I find myself travelling to their inner circle. They even ask if Frank and I would like to come over for Easter dinner.

Ken orders champagne. He raises his glass. I drain my double. Raise my glass and smile at Frank with pride and adoration. At long last, Frank's hard work will be exalted. He deserves this; we deserve this. A toast, some recognition.

'To Hitforhits.com!' Ken declares.

Oh, man, would it be so hard to say thanks to Frank? A simple 'Good job, Frank!' It's like cheering the jockey and never the horse.

'What's Hitforhits? Some dot.com pirates? Did you bust them, Frank?' I'm going to see him get some acknowledgement.

Frank turns to Ken. 'Ah, Ken, I haven't seen Fran all day. She doesn't know any of this.'

And, forgetting to be pissed off for a minute, I chirrup, 'Oh, yeah, omigod. You'll never believe who I ran with.' I look wide-eyed at everyone. 'Nicole Kidman's dad!'

Jill and I squeal and clink glasses.

'Wow . . . her dad . . .' she says.

'Oh, yeah, and he was charming . . .'

Ken interrupts, 'Of course, of course, no one knew but tomorrow it's official, in all the trade papers.' I look at

Frank. This is getting good again. Frank's hands are beside his plate. His head is slightly bowed and he is looking at the stem of his champagne flute. He's so understated, it's sexy. He's a modest man and avoids the spotlight. How like him to keep this to himself. I can see the headline, my maven-on-the-move:

Frank Rittman named President of Overseas Operations. After agreeing to his big bonus, company penthouse . . . travel all over the world . . . 'We'll need him to do a lot in Australia,' said the only other person more important than Mr Rittman . . .

'So? More?' I ask.

Ken says, 'Sure, sure. New company I started, Hit-forhits.com. Need Frank to run the International. Have to move fast on these things. Big investors. Gonna make millions! Millions! Need you back in New York, home by Easter. Have it at our house. It's good, family, friends. Frank, you get someone else to wind down the Singapore office soon as possible. This is gonna make millions.' He raises his glass.

I look from Ken to Jill. No, no, no, no, no. I heard this wrong. I have to make him turn it around the right way. Home? New York? They're not serious. This can't be happening. I stand up. I need to get some air. They think I'm standing to toast them back. Ken directs his glass to me.

'Nooooo!' I shout, slamming my drink down. 'Frank can do anything from Singapore! I do everything from there! International can be from *there*! He can use the computer. He can do it all on the computer! On your *internet*! We can't go now. You said three years. We're not finished. We're not finished!' And, heaving great sobs, I run to the ladies room.

After the cigarette and cold water, I don't know how I can come back. I've behaved like a teenager, embarrassed my husband and of course myself, and didn't for a moment think about Ken's great joy for his new million-dollar concept. All I know is that it's fucking winter, dead and grey, in New York City and I'm not going. I'm not going back. I can't go back. So help me God, all at once, the clock struck midnight and everything turned to pumpkins and mice and uncomfortable clothing, to working my fingers to the bone: 'Do the contracts!', 'Do the laundry!', 'Hurry. Hurry. Hurry.' Going around in circles, and still they holler, keep a-busy, that's what's there for me. Singapore was never real, a chimera, all of it – the friends, the fun, the tennis, the tan, the strappy clothes and sensuous evenings, the Ironman training. A wave of the wand, gone, nothing. What will become of me?

'Fran, can I come in?' It's Frank.

I open the door and turn away from him, leaning on the sink. I don't hate him. I could never hate him. He didn't know that I actually thought those glass slippers were mine to keep.

'Frank?' I ask after we stare at the floor for a while, after he tells me he really didn't know this was happening so soon, that we'll have to talk about it later. 'How do we get back to the table?'

'I don't know,' he says.

'Why don't we say I'm pregnant?'

'Why don't we just apologise?'

After what Ken did? Never!

I assure Ken and Jill that I was just like this before I had Sadie. I down the wine and smoke 15 cigarettes for dinner. After dinner, saved by Ken's undaunted enthusiasm, we say good night. They are staying at the ANA, in our old room.

We're staying in St Leonards, at the motor lodge. The sheets are sticky and thin. I climb in with a family-sized chocolate bar.

Frank sits on the side of the bed. 'Look, I'm sorry. I have to take the promotion.' He smiles, imitating Ken, 'It'll make millions! Millions!'

'Frank, we're not get-rich-quick people. It's not going to happen.' I feel nothing but the chocolate melting on my tongue.

'I can't turn the job down. And you don't know anything about the deal Ken's striking. This is exciting for me. I don't want to turn down a big promotion to stay in Fortune Gardens. Singapore – all of Asia – is in a huge recession. Did you know that, Fran? Have you heard? It's been a nightmare for me. It's been like looking for a needle in a haystack and when I find it, someone grabs it and sticks me and tells me to mind my own business. No one wants a fat American telling them what they can and can't do.'

'You're not fat. Anyway, how would I know? You don't tell me,' I say.

'I try, honey, but it's hard sometimes. I don't always know how to start and you aren't around a lot. You'll be fine. I'm sorry we have to leave early but you'll be fine.' He takes my chocolate and puts it back in the mini-bar. I wasn't finished.

'I wonder if there's still an office for me.'

'Fran, just quit that job already.'

'I make a lot of money, Frank. And no one quits their job when they come back. Everyone I know in New York works. It's what you do because it's too cold to play outside.'

'Fine, but stop figuring it all out tonight. Everything's going to be okay. Maybe it'll even be great.'

≡

'Mommy, how come I'm still in my pyjamas?'

I am clipping something from the paper. I leave it on top of Frank's briefcase.

'Mommy . . .'

'Shhh, I'm busy. In a minute.' Oh, here's another. Snip, snip.

Sadie turns the volume up to high. 'Turn it down, Sadie. It's rattling the walls.'

Why did I wait so long to do this? They're everywhere. The newspaper looks like a doily now. Frank has a short stack of small printed squares on his briefcase.

He comes down the stairs and stops. 'What's all this?'

'Just fyi, that's all, nothing . . .'

'Wanted,' Frank reads, 'account executive for securities. Fran, I'm a copyright lawyer.' He picks up another one. 'Drivers needed.'

'You love driving,' I say. 'Look at the benefits!'

'Talent search for software analyst. Fran, what do I know about this? I'm a copyright lawyer.'

'It may be analysing the legal parts of software, Frank. You could give them a call instead of –'

'Experienced drummer. Fran, I play the bass.'

'You are so inflexible!'

'Mommy, how come I'm still in my pyjamas?'

I am holding a bowl of cereal and don't know if I was heading to the table or the sink. I'm wearing a housedress. The kids are watching television and I am holding a bowl of cereal. Susie is leaving tomorrow. She and Francis are getting married, in France. I'm happy for good old Button Lip. Frank comes downstairs.

'Tennis tonight?'

I drop the bowl in the sink and wheel around. 'Why?'

'Because you like it?'

'So?'

'All right, Fran. Whatever. See you, kids.'

I am in a housedress when the doorbell rings. I am not holding a bowl of cereal. It's Priscilla.

'Are you ever bloody going to take off that bloody housedress?'

'I feel like the living dead. Like nothing matters any more. What's the point of having this conversation? Why not just say that a month ago we had our last conversation?'

'Shut up, Frannie. Get dressed. I want to see you down at the pool tonight at six sharp.'

'Why?'

'Just be there.'

At six, I go to the pool. Frank has insisted on joining me. He says he's sorry about getting irritated with me. He's got to try harder to understand. He's whistling *Goodbye Yellow Brick Road* – not the song, the album. As we go down the steps, I see lanterns and tables set up on the lawn. A small crowd has gathered and when they see me, they cheer. The men are dressed in skirts or bike shorts and heels. It's a dress-up-like-Fran surprise party.

I come back to life.

'Mommy, why am I still in my pyjamas?'

'Because, sweetheart, Mommy has blepharitis. Okay?'

For two weeks, we have found reasons to make people go out and stay up late with us. We had a dancing party and a Safra party, a beach party, a cocktail party and a party in the function room where we gave stuff away – books, liquor, kids' toys – like a rite of passage. Frank loved every minute of it. If I heard him say dot.com one more time, I would kill.

And then Frank hired his Singapore replacement and unless this guy dies suddenly, there is nothing more to do.

I put my housedress back on and sit on the balcony. Frank goes from room to room with a clipboard in his hand, noting what is to be shipped, what is to be mailed, what is to come on the plane. He asks me questions from time to time. 'Do you want to take the chopsticks?' he asks. 'What about the spices?' he asks. 'What about all *this*?' he asks, pointing to a stack of cartons: Biospliven, Super-Biospliven, Dr Soonbetter mix, vitamin B and chromium.

The doorbell rings.

'Pearl! How are you?'

'I am fine. Too bad you leave. I thought it was three years. Never mind, *lah*. I get it wrong sometimes, eh? How much you want for that?' Pearl points to the cartons.

'Why?'

She hands me a card: 'Pearl's Vitamin and Flower Shop, Expat Services, Babysitting in rear of store.'

'Biospliven good, *lah*!'

'Please take it. My gift. How wonderful, your own shop.'

After she hauls out the fourth box, she stands in the doorway. I go to hug her. She gives me a quick pat. 'Seventy dollars for you today,' she says.

'No no, you can have it all. I'm glad to give you a start.'

'I charge for removal.'

'Oh, right.' I hand her the money and she smiles.

She laughs nervously and hands me a shopping bag. 'For you and the kids, to remember me.' Inside are bracelets with all our names in Chinese.

'Thank you, but we'll never forget you, gifts or no gifts.' I step forward and give her a long hug until it is returned. 'Good luck,' I call as Pearl walks away.

═══════

The movers are here. It is our last day. I am in my house-dress. Priscilla and Samantha, Valerie and Tess have come over with a few gifts and cards and favourite recipes. I hand them a stack of menus from all the parties I had, complete with how-to's and anecdotes.

'How's the packing going, mate?' Priscilla asks.

'I haven't done it.'

'Bloody hell, get off your stupid arse and get moving. Don't give me any crap.'

We laugh. She's raised three big, wild boys all in their 20s. This is her being soft and gentle. I go upstairs and sit on the bed. She grabs suitcases and starts organising. The girls all join in. I answer questions but mostly I watch them, their hands, holding and packing my things.

'Time to go, Fran.' Frank ushers me out of the apartment. The kids are wild and clamorous because they're up late and going on a trip and life is different, exciting, promising. It's 10.30 at night. We get out of the elevator and a crowd is waiting for us, a last goodbye. There's crying and picture-taking. All the kids have been kept up late for this one final ceremony.

We get into the taxi and wave goodbye.

We live (lived) so near the airport.

There's no traffic.

Frank gets the kids out of the car and has them stand with the luggage carts near the airport entrance. Frank and the cab driver hoist out suitcase after suitcase. We have 15. The kids want to ride on the cart. Frank is perspiring from all of this effort. He pays the driver. He reaches his hand in to help me out. I stare at it. The kids have climbed up the suitcases and the tower is about to tumble. Frank rushes over to them. He turns to me and yells out, over car engines, planes, announcements, 'Come on, Fran, please.'

I sit, breathing heavily. The driver, after depositing the final suitcase, returns to the car.

Frank shouts over, 'Why are you making this so hard, Fran?'

The finality hurts so badly. I'm no longer numb. I can't control my sobbing. I would give anything, anything, to have it all back. I swear, I'll do it right this time. Let me stay.

'Jesus, Fran, please, you knew it wasn't going to last forever.'

I cry harder still. That's exactly right. 'IF I HAD KNOWN THAT . . . I WOULD HAVE APPRECIATED IT MORE!' I scream, louder than I have ever screamed before, back at him, at the world. My throat is raw and I'm shaking. I hear my words over and over again, they are ricocheting off the walls of the taxi. Things end. You don't expect them to. People drop dead, cars crash, fires wreck villages . . . The driver looks in at me, 'Miss, Miss, please.' He wants me to leave. I get out and stand in the centre lane.

I look at my frightened children across the road. Sadie's pants are above her ankles. She's buttoned herself wrong and her socks droop. Her flat bear is swinging on the ground. Huxley wears Toby's old sweater; he's made wide, uneven cuffs. I don't even know the name of the stuffed rabbit he holds. Frank's face is full of anguish, saturated with sweat and tears. He is struggling to help us all. He wishes to God that he didn't have to fail me.

I would have appreciated it more if I knew it wasn't going to last forever.

And I know I am standing on the wrong side of the road.

I didn't grow from living abroad. I wasn't close to accomplishing the 'simpler life with time to focus'. I used my freedom like fuel. I ran so fast and hard. I ran from the clients berating me and demanding 'more, faster, better'. I ran from success taunting me, 'You cannot catch me'. I ran from the vast, open space that holds life's questions and I kept running blindly and would never have stopped. I would have kept stirring those waters, never seeing the man and children who stood behind me, waiting to be reflected in the pond of my life, waiting to run with me instead of always on the sidelines.

And I make the best run of all. I run to them and hug them. I hug them and hug them and tell them I want to go home. If that's where they're going, I want to go, too. Look at these people, this man, these children. I feel like I'm seeing them for the first time, not in a perfect setting, not in a perfect world, not ready for a picture. I love my family. I've been so selfish. It's your turn now, Frank, Sadie, Huxley. I am so sorry. It should always have been your turn, babies.

I feel such a sense of peace after a while. The search is over. It's time to be still and strong and that will be the hardest thing I've ever had to do but it's clear and it's right. And, well, it'll have to be in New York.

After we cry for our losses, our troubles, our blessings, after we start to wind down, we remember we're still stupidly huddled on a curb.

'Jeez, you really do need me. I mean, who else is any fun?' I say. 'Happy hour, anyone?'

'I hear they even have that sort of thing in New York City,' Frank says.

My champagne spills over and the kids are running up and down the aisles. I pull out my party menus and recipes and decide that I won't go back to work. I'll take my time and find something else to do – something that brings families together.

Epilogue

FROM: *flebowitz@barryfix.com*
TO: *blebowitz@harriet.com; hlebowitz@snowfarm.com*
SENT: *10 September 2001*

Greetings from Singapore, Bonnie. Yes we made it. I got off the plane and I swear I could hear 'em singing 'Hello Dolly' (or maybe it was 'Hello Flanny', whatever). Anyway, it looks like I've been forgiven my Father's Day tantrum, my New Year's Eve naked dance, my assault on the guard, my flipping the bird to the bus driver, my forgetting to flush . . .

Met up with lots of friends for a boozy Safra evening. The kids all played well together in the sand, the adults ordered jugs of Tiger and bottles of expensive shitty wine. Yeah, I was back. The only difference was the sound of Frank's voice. He took centre stage from me, talking all about his new job. I was happy for him, though. It's an exciting opportunity and a whole different organisation. That whole dot.com thing, what a joke. Who knew? (ME!)

We unpacked our bags almost immediately. We stashed some Veuve in every suitcase. The only bottles that didn't make it out alive were the two in my 'better dresses' bag. They exploded. Tiny shards of glass everywhere, two-day-old champagne smell on everything.

I'll miss those bottles . . . never mind.

And now everyone's seen me in my two still-okay outfits.

So here we are in our serviced apartment until we find a place to live. We don't have many toys. Frank's gone out and gotten a boom box; it came with either a free watch or a director's chair (is it more important for you to know how long you've been listening to the music or to be able to direct it?). Frank got the watch. The kids have lots of flat, quiet things meant to keep them occupied during travel. I managed to bring my bike, of course, and two sets of weights, a few workout tapes, my yoga books, tennis racket, three pairs of running shoes, flippers, kick board, two kinds of goggles, a wet suit, oh, and my stepper.

Even though these serviced apartments (regular apartments kitted out by the management, with daily maid service and maintenance) are meant for overseas families, there was not a thought given to the obvious fact that many – maybe all? – of them would NOT be Chinese. To a westerner, the cupboard is bare. We have no coffee maker, no mugs either, no sharp knives, no icemaker, no hot water in the kitchen, one small pan and no microwavable dishes . . . or microwave, for that matter. We have thousands of chopsticks, a rice cooker, a wok and tea cups galore. We have towels with the absorbency of, I dunno, cling wrap? We have a housekeeper who doesn't speak any English. We got four bumpy oranges on a plate to welcome us . . . to our Breezy New Lifestyle. What's worse is, we have no cable! The kids look dolefully at the dark screen while rooting around in their bag o' flat toys.

I've already organised two kids' classes – drama and cooking. I have 20 students so far. I have a publisher, too, for the Expat Cookbook. *Now what?*

Well, the glass is half full, I suppose, but I did order a double . . .

So enough about me.

Love, Fran.

Acknowledgements

Nine months of pregnancy, 24 hours of labour, four hours of pushing, and out comes a seven-pound version of my mother-in-law. Not the sort of tribute to me that I had in mind, but my daughter has shown more gratitude than I deserve. Her younger brother and I are even; he was no problem delivering and he doesn't remember a thing about that first flight . . .

Thanks to old and new friends in the business – Amy Berkower and Dorrie Simmonds – and to my friends in Singapore.

Family counts too – Eunice, Bonnie and Harris Lebowitz and Patricia Rittman.